Shaw's
Directory of Courts
in the United Kingdom

2014/15

D1610256

SWEET & M   'HOMSON REUTERS

347. 4202

Published in 2014 by Thomson Reuters (Professional) UK Limited
trading as Sweet & Maxwell, Friars House, 160 Blackfriars Road, London SE1 8EZ

(Registered in England & Wales, Company No 1679046.
Registered Office and address for service:
Aldgate House, 33 Aldgate High Street, London EC3N 1DL)

For further information on our products and services, visit
www.sweetandmaxwell.co.uk

Typeset by
Letterpart Limited, Caterham on the Hill, Surrey CR3 5XL
Printed and bound in Great Britain by
Ashford Colour Press, Gosport, Hants.

No natural forests were destroyed to make this product;
only farmed timber was used and re-planted.

A CIP catalogue record for this book
is available from the British Library

ISBN 978-0-414-03465-5

Part I

APPELLATE COURTS, SENIOR COURTS, HMCTS REGIONS, CROWN COURTS

APPELLATE COURTS

THE JUDICIAL COMMITTEE OF THE PRIVY COUNCIL

Parliament Square, London SW1P 3BD
Tel: 020 7960 1500
Website: www.jcpc.uk
Email: registry@jcpc.uk
Registrar of the Privy Council: Louise di Mambro. Tel: 020 7960 1985
Chief Clerk: Jackie Lindsay. Tel: 020 7960 1510. Email: jackie.lindsay@jcpc.uk

THE SUPREME COURT OF THE UNITED KINGDOM

Westminster, London SW1P 3BD
Tel: 020 7960 1900
Fax: 020 7960 1901
Website: www.supremecourt.uk
President of the United Kingdom Supreme Court: The Rt Hon. the Lord Neuberger of Abbotsbury
Deputy President of the United Kingdom Supreme Court: The Right Hon. the Baroness Hale of Richmond
Justices of the United Kingdom Supreme Court:

The Rt Hon. the Lord Mance
The Rt Hon. the Lord Kerr of Tonaghmore
The Rt Hon. the Lord Clarke of Stone-cum-Ebony
The Rt Hon. Lord Wilson of Culworth
The Rt Hon. Lord Sumption
The Rt Hon. Lord Reed
The Rt Hon. Lord Carnwath of Notting Hill
The Rt Hon. Lord Hughes of Ombersley
The Rt Hon. Lord Toulson
The Rt Hon. Lord Hodge
Head of Judicial Support: Ayo Onatade. Tel: 020 7960 1980. Email: ayo.onatade@supremecourt.uk

SENIOR COURTS

ENGLAND AND WALES

Website: www.judiciary.gov.uk

COURT OF APPEAL
Royal Courts of Justice, Strand, London WC2A 2LL
DX: 44450 STRAND
The Lord High Chancellor and Secretary of State for Justice: The Rt Hon. Chris Grayling MP
The Heads of Division:

The Lord Chief Justice of England and Wales, Head of Criminal Justice: The Rt Hon. Sir (Roger) John Laugharne Thomas
The Master of the Rolls and Head of Civil Justice: The Rt Hon. Lord Dyson
The President of the Queen's Bench Division: The Rt Hon. Sir Brian Henry Leveson
The President of the Family Division and Head of Family Justice: The Rt Hon. Sir James Lawrence Munby
The Chancellor of the High Court: The Rt Hon. Sir Terence Michael Elkan Barnet Etherton
The Master of the Rolls: The Right Hon. Lord Dyson

Secretary: Ms Noella Roberts Tel: 0207 947 6002
Clerk: Jessica Lear Tel: 0207 947 6371
Lord and Lady Justices of Appeal:

The Rt Hon. Sir John Grant McKenzie Laws
The Rt Hon. Dame Mary Howarth Arden DBE
The Rt Hon. Sir Andrew Centlivres Longmore
The Rt Hon. Sir Martin James Moore-Bick
The Rt Hon. Sir Stephen Price Richards
The Rt Hon. Dame Heather Carol Hallett DBE
The Rt Hon. Sir Colin Percy Farquharson Rimer
The Rt Hon. Sir Rupert Matthew Jackson
The Rt Hon. Sir John Bernard Goldring
The Rt Hon. Sir Richard John Pearson Aikens
The Rt Hon. Sir Jeremy Mirth Sullivan
The Rt Hon. Sir Patrick Elias
The Rt Hon. Sir Nicholas John Patten
The Rt Hon. Sir Christopher John Pitchford
The Rt Hon. Dame Jill Margaret Black DBE
The Rt Hon. Sir Stephen Miles Tomlinson
The Rt Hon. Sir Peter Henry Gross
The Rt Hon. Dame Anne Judith Rafferty DBE
The Rt Hon. Sir Andrew Ewart McFarlane

The Rt Hon. Sir Nigel Anthony Lamert Davis
The Rt Hon. Sir Kim Martin Jordan Lewison
The Rt Hon. Sir David James Tyson Kitchin
The Rt Hon. Sir David Lloyd Jones
The Rt Hon. Sir Colman Maurice Treacy
The Rt Hon. Sir Richard George Bramwell McCombe
The Rt Hon. Sir Jack Beatson
The Rt Hon. Dame Elizabeth Gloster DBE
The Rt Hon. Sir Ernest Nigel Ryder
The Rt Hon. Sir Nicholas Edward Underhill
The Rt Hon. Sir Michael Townley Featherstone Briggs
The Rt Hon. Sir Christopher David Floyd
The Rt Hon. Sir Adrian Bruce Fulford
The Hon. Dame Julia Wendy Macur DBE
The Hon. Christopher Clarke Sharp DBE
The Rt Hon. Geoff Charles Vos

Civil Appeal Office: *Office Manager:* Tel: 0207 947 6916. Fax: 0207 947 6740
Criminal Appeal Office: Registry Enquiries: Tel: 0207 947 6011. Fax: 0207 947 6900
Office Manager: Tel: 0207 947 6011. DX: 44450 Strand

HIGH COURT OF JUSTICE, QUEEN'S BENCH DIVISION
Royal Courts of Justice, Strand, London WC2A 2LL
Tel: 0207 947 6000
DX: 44450 STRAND
The Lord Chief Justice of England and Wales: The Rt Hon. The Lord Thomas
Secretary: Miss Michèle Souris. Tel: 0207 947 6776
Clerk: Mrs Jean Curtin. Tel: 020 7947 6399
President of the Queen's Bench Division: The Rt Hon. Sir Nigel Davies
Judges:

The Hon. Sir Andrew David Collins
The Hon. Sir Arthur William Hessin Charles
The Hon. Sir Michael John Burton
The Hon. Sir Andrew Charles Smith
The Hon. Sir Duncan Brian Walter Ouseley
The Hon. Sir Robert Michael Owen
The Hon. Sir John Edward Mitting

The Hon. Sir Jeremy Lionel Cooke
The Hon. Sir Peregrine Charles Hugo Simon
The Hon. Dame Laura Mary Cox DBE
The Hon. Sir David Michael Bean
The Hon. Sir Alan Fraser Wilkie
The Hon. Sir Paul James Walker
The Hon. Sir Charles Peter Lawford Openshaw

The Hon. Dame Caroline Jane Swift DBE
The Hon. Sir Brian Frederick James Langstaff
The Hon. Sir Vivian Arthur Ramsey
The Hon. Sir Stephen John Irwin
The Hon. Sir Nigel John Martin Teare
The Hon. Sir John Griffith-Williams
The Hon. Sir Wyn Lewis Williams
The Hon. Sir Timothy Roger Alan King
The Hon. Sir John Henry Boulton Saunders
The Hon. Sir Julian Martin Flaux
The Hon. Sir David Robert Foskett
The Hon. Sir Robert Akenhead
The Hon. Sir Nicholas John Gorrod Blake
The Hon. Sir Ross Frederick Cranston
The Hon. Sir Peter David William Coulson
The Hon. Sir William James Lynton Blair
The Hon. Sir Alistair Geoffrey MacDuff
The Hon. Sir Ian Duncan Burnett
The Hon. Sir Nigel Hamilton Sweeney
The Hon. Dame Elizabeth Ann Slade DBE
The Hon. Sir Nicholas Archibald Hamblen
The Hon. Sir Gary Robert Hickinbottom
The Hon. Sir Timothy Victor Holroyde
The Hon. Sir Andrew George Lindsay Nicol
The Hon. Sir Kenneth Blades Parker
The Hon. Sir Antony James Cobham
  Edwards-Stuart
The Rt Hon. Dame Nicola Velfor Davies DBE

The Rt Hon. Dame Kathryn Mary Thirlwall DBE
The Hon. Sir Michael Alan Supperstone
The Hon. Sir Robin Godfrey Spencer
The Hon. Sir Keith John Lindblom
The Hon. Sir Henry Bernard Eder
The Hon. Sir Henry Brian Globe
The Hon. Sir Andrew John Popplewell
The Hon. Sir Rabinder Singh
The Hon. Dame Beverley Ann Mcnaughtan Lang
The Hon. Sir Charles Anthony Haddon-Cave
The Hon. Sir Stephen Martin Males
The Hon. Sir Jeremy Hugh Stuart-Smith
The Hon. Sir George Andrew Midsomer Leggatt
The Hon. Sir Mark George Turner
The Hon. Sir Jeremy Russell Baker
The Hon. Sir Stephen Paul Stewart
The Hon. Sir Robert Maurice Jay
The Hon. Sir James Michael Dingemans
The Hon. Sir Clive Buckland Lewis
The Hon. Dame Sue Lascelles Carr DBE
The Hon. Sir Stephen Edmund Phillips
The Hon. Dame Geraldine Mary Andrews DBE
The Hon. Dame Frances Silvia Patterson DBE
The Hon. Sir Nicholas Nigel Green
The Hon. Dame Ingrid Ann Simler DBE
The Hon. Dame Elisabeth Mary Caroline Laing
The Hon. Sir William Easthope Davis

Chief Clerk to QB Judges in Chambers: Tel: 0207 947 6511
Clerk of the Lists Office: Tel: 0207 947 6021
Commercial Listing: Tel: 0207 947 6826
TECHNOLOGY & CONSTRUCTION COURT
7 Rolls Building, Fetter Lane, London EC4A 1NL
Tel: 0207 947 6022
DX: 160040 STRAND 4
Office Manager: Tel: 0207 947 7427. Fax: 0870 761 7725
Judges:

Mr Justice Edwards-Stuart (Presiding Judge)
Mr Justice Ramsay
Mr Justice Field (commercial)
Mr Justice Simon (commercial)

Mr Justice Coulson
Mr Justice Akenhead
Mr Justice Stuart-Smith

HIGH COURT OF JUSTICE, FAMILY DIVISION
Royal Courts of Justice, Strand, London WC2A 2LL
Tel: 0207 947 6543
Fax: 0207 947 7304
President: The Rt Hon. Sir James Lawrence Munby
Secretary: Mrs Sarah Leung. Tel: 0207 947 7216
Clerk: George Pitchley. Tel: 0207 947 6576
Judges:

The Hon. Sir Edward James Holman
The Hon. Dame Mary Claire Hogg DBE
The Hon. Sir David Roderick Lessiter Bodey
The Hon. Dame Anna Evelyn Hamilton Pauffley
  DBE
The Hon. Sir Roderic Lionel James Wood
The Hon. Sir Andrew John Gregory Moylan
The Hon. Dame Eleanor Warwick King DBE
The Hon. Dame Judith Mary Frances Parker
  DBE
The Hon. Sir Jonathan Leslie Baker

The Hon. Sir Nicholas Anthony Joseph Ghislain
  Mostyn
The Hon. Sir Peter Arthur Brian Jackson
The Hon. Dame Lucy Morgan Theis DBE
The Hon. Sir Philip Drury Moor
The Hon. Sir Stephen William Scott Cobb
The Hon. Sir Michael Joseph Keehan
The Hon. Sir Anthony Paul Hayden
The Hon. Dame Alison Hunter Russell
The Hon. Sir Roderick Brian Newton
The Hon. Dame Jennifer Mary Roberts

The Hon. Sir Mark David John Warby

Clerk of the Rules: Tel: 0207 947 6543

HIGH COURT OF JUSTICE, CHANCERY DIVISION
7 Rolls Building, Fetter Lane, London EC4A 1NL
Tel: 0207 947 6000
Fax: 0207 947 7345
DX: 160040 STRAND 4
President: The Lord High Chancellor and Secretary of State for Justice, The Rt Hon. Chris Grayling MP)
The Chancellor of the High Court: The Rt Hon. Sir Terence Michael Elkan Barnet Etherton
Clerk: Mrs Amanda Collins. Tel: 0207 947 6412
Secretary: Miss Elaine Harbert. Tel: 0207 947 7477
Judges:

The Hon. Sir Peter Winston Smith
The Hon. Sir David Anthony Stewart Richards
The Hon. Sir George Anthony Mann
The Hon. Sir Nicholas Roger Warren
The Hon. Sir Launcelot Dinadin James
    Henderson
The Hon. Sir Paul Hyacinth Morgan
The Hon. Sir Alastair Hubert Norris
The Hon. Sir Gerald Edward Barling
The Hon. Sir Phillip James Sales

The Hon. Dame Sonia Rosemary Susan
    Proudman DBE
The Hon. Sir Richard David Arnold
The Hon. Sir Peter Marcel Roth
The Hon. Sir Guy Richard Newey
The Hon. Sir Robert Henry Thuroton Hildyard
The Hon. Dame Sarah Jane Asplin DBE
The Hon. Sir Colin Ian Birss
The Hon. Dame Vivien Judith Rose DBE
The Hon, Sir Christopher George Nugee

High Court Bankruptcy Department: Tel: 0207 947 7472
County Court Bankruptcy Department: Tel: 0207 947 6812
CHANCERY CHAMBERS
Tel: 0207 947 6754; 0207 947 7717 (Chancery Listing)
Chief Master: Marsh
Masters

P. Teverson
N.W. Bragge
T.J. Bowles

N. Price
M. Marsh

Court Manager: Tel: 0207 073 1784

CENTRAL OFFICE OF THE SENIOR COURTS
Royal Courts of Justice, Strand, London WC2A 2LL
Tel: 0207 947 6000 (Central Switchboard)
DX: 44450 STRAND
Senior Master (QBD) and Queen's Remembrancer: TBA
Temporary Senior Master: H.J. Leslie
QBD Masters: TBA

B. Yoxall
B.J.F. Fontaine
R.R. Roberts
R. Eastman

J.K. Kay QC
V. McCloud
J.D. Cook

Clerk to Interim Applications Judge: Tel: 0207 947 6508

ADMINISTRATIVE COURT
Royal Courts of Justice, Strand, London WC2A 2LL
Tel: 0207 947 6655; 0121 250 6319 (Birmingham Regional Office); 029 2037 6460 (Cardiff Regional Office); 0113 306 2578 (Leeds Regional Office); 0161 240 5313 (Manchester Regional Office). Fax: 0207 947 6802
DX: 44450 STRAND
Registrar of Criminal Appeals, Master of the Crown Office, and Queen's Coroner and Attorney: M. Egan QC
Judge in Charge of the Administrative Court: The Hon. Mr Justice Ouseley

SENIOR COURT COSTS OFFICE
Royal Courts of Justice, Strand, London WC2A 2LL
Tel: 0207 947 6423
DX: 44454 STRAND.
Senior Cost Judge: P. T. Hurst

ADMIRALTY COURT
7 Rolls Building, Fetter Lane, London EC4A 1NL
Tel: 0207 947 7357
DX: 160040 STRAND 4
Admiralty Registrar and Queen's Bench Master: J. Kay
Admiralty Marshal: Michael Parker. Tel: 0207 947 7111

COURT OF PROTECTION
PO Box 70185, First Avenue House, 42–49 High Holborn, London WC1A 9JA
Tel: 0300 456 4600
DX: 160013 Kingsway 7

OFFICE OF THE PUBLIC GUARDIAN
PO Box 16185, Birmingham B2 2WH
Tel: 0300 456 0300
Fax: 0870 739 5780
DX: 744240 BIRMINGHAM 79
Website: www.gov.uk/powerofattorney
Email: customerservices@publicguardian.gsi.gov.uk

OFFICIAL SOLICITOR AND PUBLIC TRUSTEE
Victory House, 30–34 Kingsway, London WC2B 6EX
Tel: 020 3681 2752
Fax: 020 3681 2762

OFFICIAL RECEIVER'S OFFICE
Head Office
The Insolvency Service, London Official Receivers, 4 Abbey Orchard Street, London SW1P 2HT
Tel: 020 7637 1110
Estate Accounts and Insolvency Practitioner Unit (IPU)
The Insolvency Service, 3rd Floor, Cannon House, 18 Priory Queensway, Birmingham B4 6FD
Tel: 0121 698 4000

NORTHERN IRELAND

THE ROYAL COURTS OF JUSTICE
Chichester Street, Belfast BT1 3JF
Tel: 030 0200 7812
Fax: 028 9072 4799
Lord Chief Justice of Northern Ireland: The Rt Hon. Sir Declan Morgan
Judges:

The Rt Hon. Lord Justice Girvan
The Rt Hon. Lord Justice Coghlin
Vacant
The Hon. Mr Justice Gillen
The Hon. Mr Justice Weatherup
The Hon. Mr Justice Weir
The Hon. Mr Justice Deeny

The Hon. Mr Justice Stephens
The Hon. Mr Justice Treacy
The Hon. Mr Justice McCloskey
The Hon. Mr Justice Maguire
The Hon. Mr Justice Horner
The Hon. Mr Justice O'Hara

THE NORTHERN IRELAND COURTS AND TRIBUNALS SERVICE
Laganside House, 23–27 Oxford Street, Belfast BT1 3LA
Tel: 030 0200 7812
Fax: 028 9072 8945
The Northern Ireland Courts and Tribunals Service (NICTS) is an agency of the Department of Justice for Northern Ireland. The NICTS is responsible for the operation of 19 courthouses and a number of tribunal centres across Northern Ireland.
Chief Executive: Jacqui Durkin
The Chief Executive of the NICTS is the head of the Agency. She is responsible for the day-to-day operation of the Agency and the leadership and management of its staff. The NICTS Board (the Board) oversees the work of the NICTS and consists of:
Chief Executive: Jacqui Durkin (who chairs the Board)
Head of Court Operations: Peter Luney
Responsible for providing administrative support for criminal, civil and family court business and the coroners service.
Head of Tribunal, Enforcement and Parole Commissioners Secretariat: Mandy Morrison
Responsible for providing administrative support for the majority of tribunals, the Enforcement of Judgments Office (EJO) and Parole Commissioners Secretariat (PCS).
Head of Business Support: Elaine Topping
Head of Finance and Estates: Sharon Hetherington

NON-EXECUTIVE BOARD MEMBERS
P.J. Fitzpatrick (Chair of Agency Audit and Risk Committee)
Colm McKenna (member of Finance Committee)
Four members of the judiciary, nominated by the Lord Chief Justice, also attend the Board meetings.

JUDICIAL REPRESENTATIVES
The Hon. Mr Justice Deeny
His Hon. Judge McFarland, Recorder of Belfast
District Judge Bagnall, Presiding District Judge (Magistrates' Courts)
Mr Conall MacLynn, President of the Appeals Tribunal

SCOTLAND

COURT OF SESSION
Supreme Courts, Parliament House, 11 Parliament Square, Edinburgh EH1 1RQ
Tel: 0131 225 2595
Fax: 0131 240 6755
DX: 549306 EDINBURGH 36
Legal Post: LP1
Website: www.scotcourts.gov.uk

HIGH COURT OF JUSTICIARY
Supreme Courts, Parliament House, 11 Parliament Square, Edinburgh EH1 1RQ
Tel: 0131 225 2595
Fax: 0131 240 6915
DX: 549307 EDINBURGH 36
Legal Post: LP1
The Lord President and Lord Justice General: The Rt Hon. Lord Gill
INNER HOUSE
First Division

The Lord President (The Rt Hon. Lord Gill)
The Rt Hon. Lord Eassie
The Rt Hon. Lord Menzies
The Rt Hon. Lady Smith
The Rt Hon. Lord Brodie
The Rt Hon. Lady Clark of Calton
Second Division

The Lord Justice Clerk (The Rt Hon. Lord Carloway)
The Rt Hon. Lady Paton
The Rt Hon. Lady Dorrian
The Rt. Hon. Lord Bracadale
The Rt Hon. Lord Drummond Young
OUTER HOUSE

The Hon. Lord Glennie
The Hon. Lord Kinclaven
The Hon. Lord Turnbull
The Hon. Lord Brailsford
The Hon. Lord Uist
The Hon. Lord Malcolm
The Hon. Lord Matthews
The Hon. Lord Woolman
The Hon. Lord Pentland
The Hon. Lord Bannatyne
The Hon. Lady Stacey

The Hon. Lord Tyre
The Hon. Lord Doherty
The Hon. Lord Stewart
The Rt Hon. the Lord Boyd of Duncansby
The Hon. Lord Jones
The Hon. Lord Burns
The Hon. Lady Scott
The Hon. Lady Wise
The Hon. Lord Armstrong
The Hon. Lady Rae
The Hon. Lady Wolffe

SCOTTISH COURT SERVICE
Saughton House, Broomhouse Drive, Edinburgh EH11 3XD
Tel: 0131 444 3300
Fax: 0131 443 2610
DX: 545309
Website: www.scotcourts.gov.uk
Chief Executive: Eric McQueen
Chief Operations Officer: Cliff Binning
Chief Finance Officer: Richard Maconachie
Executive Director Judicial Office for Scotland: Steve Humphreys

HMCTS REGIONS

ENGLAND AND WALES

LONDON REGION

PRESIDING JUDGES

The Rt Hon. Lord Justice Gross, Senior Presiding Judge
The Hon. Mr Justice Nicol
The Hon. Mr Justice Sweeney
The Hon. Mr Justice Singh
The Hon. Mt Justice Spencer

FAMILY DIVISION LIAISON JUDGE

The Hon. Mrs Justice Pauffley DBE

CHANCERY SUPERVISING JUDGE

Chancellor of the High Court, Sir Terence Michael Elkan Barnet Etherton

CIRCUIT JUDGES

Crown Court

His Hon. Judge Ader
His Hon. Judge Ainley
His Hon. Judge Anderson
His Hon. Judge Arran
His Hon. Judge Barker QC
His Hon. Judge Barklem
Her Hon. Judge Barnes
Her Hon. Judge Baucher
His Hon. Judge Beddoe
His Hon. Judge Birts QC
His Hon. Judge Bishop
His Hon. Judge Blacklett
His Hon. Judge Blacksell QC
His Hon. Judge Browne QC
His Hon. Judge Burn
His Hon. Judge Andrew Campbell
His Hon. Judge Carr
His Hon. Judge Carroll
His Hon. Judge Chapple
His Hon. Judge Clarke QC
Her Hon. Judge Coello
His Hon. Judge Cooke QC
His Hon. Judge Darling
His Hon. Judge Dawson
His Hon. Judge Davis
Her Hon. Judge Dean
His Hon. Judge Denniss
Her Hon. Judge Dhir
His Hon. Judge Dodd QC
His Hon. Judge Dodgson
His Hon. Judge Donne QC
Her Hon. Judge Downing
His Hon. Judge Dugdale
His Hon. Judge Edmunds QC
His Hon. Judge Flahive
His Hon. Judge Forrester
His Hon. Judge Fraser MVO
His Hon. Judge Freeland QC
His Hon. Judge Gledhill QC

His Hon. Judge Gold QC
His Hon. Judge Goldstaub QC
His Hon. Judge Gordon
His Hon. Judge Goymer
His Hon. Judge Alan Greenwood
His Hon. Judge Grieve QC
His Hon. Judge Grobel
Her Hon. Judge Guggenheim QC
His Hon. Judge Hand QC
His Hon. Judge Higgins
His Hon. Judge Hillen
His Hon. Judge Hone QC
His Hon. Judge Hopmeier
His Hon. Judge Huskinson
His Hon. Judge Johnson
His Hon. Judge Nicholas Jones
Her Hon. Judge Joseph QC
His Hon. Judge Karsten QC
Her Hon. Judge Karu
His Hon. Judge Kennedy
Her Hon. Judge Kent
His Hon. Judge Kinch QC
Her Hon. Judge Korner, CMG, QC
His Hon. Judge Kramer QC
His Hon. Judge Lafferty
His Hon. Judge Lamb QC
Her Hon. Judge Lees
His Hon. Judge Andrew Lees
His Hon. Judge Leonard QC
His Hon. Judge Loraine-Smith
His Hon. Judge Lowen
His Hon. Judge Lyons CBE
His Hon. Judge Marks Moore
His Hon. Judge Marron QC
His Hon. Judge Matthews
Her Hon. Judge Matthews QC
Her Hon. Judge May QC
His Hon. Judge McDowall
His Hon. Judge McGregor-Johnson

His Hon. Judge McKinnon
His Hon. Judge Fergus Mitchell
Her Hon. Judge Molyneux
His Hon. Judge Marks Moore
His Hon. Judge Anthony Morris QC
His Hon. Judge Robert Morrison
His Hon. Judge Moss QC
His Hon. Judge Murphy
His Hon. Judge Owen
Her Hon. Judge Paneth
His Hon. Judge Pardoe QC
His Hon. Judge Parker QC
His Hon. Judge Patrick
His Hon. Judge Pawlak
His Hon. Judge Pegden QC
His Hon. Judge Peters QC
His Hon. Judge Pillay
His Hon. Judge Pitts
His Hon. Judge Pontius
His Hon. Judge Price
His Hon. Judge Price QC
His Hon. Judge Radford
His Hon. Judge Richardson

His Hon. Judge Robbins
Her Hon. Judge Robinson
His Hon. Judge Peter Rook QC
His Hon. Judge John Rylance
His Hon. Judge Saggerson
His Hon. Judge Sanders
His Hon. Judge Seed QC
His Hon. Judge Shanks
His Hon. Judge Shorrock
Her Hon. Judge Sullivan
His Hon. Judge Tanzer
Her Hon. Judge Tapping
Her Hon. Judge Taylor
His Hon. Judge Testar
His Hon. Judge Thornton QC
His Hon. Judge Topolski
His Hon. Judge Worsley QC
His Hon. Judge Waller
His Hon. Judge Wide QC
His Hon. Judge Wilkinson
His Hon. Judge Winstanley
His Hon. Judge Zeidman QC

County Court

His Hon. Judge Altman
His Hon. Judge Ansell
His Hon. Judge Atkins
Her Hon. Judge Atkinson
His Hon. Judge Bailey
His Hon. Judge Birtles
Her Hon. Judge Boye
His Hon. Judge Brasse
Her Hon. Judge Brasse
His Hon. Judge Collender QC
Her Hon. Judge Corbett
Her Hon. Judge Cox
His Hon. Judge Cryan
His Hon. Judge Dight
His Hon. Judge Ellis
Her Hon. Judge Faber
His Hon. Judge Gerald
Her Hon. Judge Harris
His Hon. Judge Hornby
Her Hon. Judge Hughes
Her Hon. Judge Jakens
Her Hon. Judge Karp
Her Hon. Judge Levy
His Hon. Judge Mackie CBE QC
His Hon. Judge Mayer
His Hon. Judge Million

His Hon. Judge David Mitchell
His Hon. Judge John Mitchell
His Hon. Judge Powles QC
His Hon. Judge O'Dwyer
Her Hon. Judge Pearl
Her Hon. Judge Redgrave
Her Hon. Judge Rowe QC
Her Hon. Judge Venables
His Hon. Judge Wilding
Her Hon. Judge Sally Williams
His Hon. Judge Wright
Her Hon. Judge Caroline Wright
His Hon. Judge Wulwik

Principal Registry of the Family Division
District Judge Aitken
District Judge Bowman
District Judge Bradley
District Judge Harper
District Judge MacGregor
District Judge Reid
District Judge Robinson
District Judge Walker
District Judge Gordon-Saker
District Judge Simmonds
District Judge Gibson
District Judge Hess

DIRECTOR OF THE ROYAL COURTS OF JUSTICE
David Thompson
Director's Office, Room E331, Royal Courts of Justice, Strand, London WC2A 2LL
Tel: 0207 947 6534
Fax: 0207 947 6666
DX: 44450 STRAND

DELIVERY DIRECTOR
Sheila Proudlock
3rd Floor, Rose Court, 2 Southwark Bridge, London SE1 9HS

Tel: 020 7921 2010
DX: 154261 SOUTHWARK 12

HEAD OF CRIME
Dave Weston
3rd Floor, Rose Court, 2 Southwark Bridge, London SE1 9HS
Tel: 020 7921 2196
DX: 154261 SOUTHWARK 12

HEAD OF CIVIL, FAMILY & TRIBUNALS
Martin John
3rd Floor, Rose Court, 2 Southwark Bridge, London SE1 9HS
Tel: 020 7921 2015
DX: 154261 SOUTHWARK 12

COURT INDEX – LONDON REGION

0471	Southwark	Crown	45
2574 (6574)	Stratford (Youth)	Magistrates	102
2574 (6574)	Thames (Youth)	Magistrates	102
2572 (6572)	Tottenham (Youth)	Magistrates	102
356	Uxbridge	County	77
2578 (6578)	Uxbridge (Youth)	Magistrates	103
2574 (6574)	Waltham Forest (Youth)	Magistrates	102
359	Wandsworth	County	77
368	West London	County	78
2578 (6578)	West London LJA (Youth)	Magistrates	103
2570 (6570)	Westminster (Youth)	Magistrates	99
375	Willesden	County	78
2571 (6571)	Willesden (Youth)	Magistrates	103
2577 (6577)	Wimbledon (Youth)	Magistrates	100
0469	Wood Green	Crown	45
379	Woolwich	County	78
0472	Woolwich	Crown	45

COURT INDEX – NORTH EAST REGION

2853	South Tyneside District LJA	Magistrates	119
343	Sunderland	County	88
2855	Sunderland LJA	Magistrates	120
0460	Teesside	Crown	50
1249	Teesside LJA	Magistrates	114
357	Wakefield	County	89
2355	Wakefield & Pontefract LJA	Magistrates	118
386	York	County	83
0467	York	Crown	51
2357	York LJA	Magistrates	118

NORTHERN REGION

PRESIDING JUDGES
The Rt Hon. Lord Justice Gross, Senior Presiding Judge
The Hon. Mr Justice Holroyde
The Hon. Mr Justice Turner

VICE CHANCELLOR OF THE COUNTY PALATINE OF LANCASTER
The Hon. Mr Justice Alastair Norris

FAMILY DIVISION LIAISON JUDGE
The Hon. Mr Justice Peter Jackson

QUEEN'S BENCH LIAISON JUDGE
The Hon. Mr Justice Supperstone

CIRCUIT JUDGES

His Hon. Judge Allweis
His Hon. Judge Altham
His Hon. Judge Appleby
His Hon. Judge Armitage QC
His Hon. Judge Atherton
His Hon. Judge Aubrey QC
Her Hon. Judge Badley
His Hon. Judge Stuart Baker
Her Honour Judge Bancroft
His Hon. Judge Kevin Barnett
His Hon. Judge Batty QC
His Hon. Judge Bird
His Hon. Judge Blake
His Hon. Judge Booth
His Hon. Judge Mark Brown
Her Hon. Judge Butler
His Hon. Judge Byrne
His Hon. Judge Clarke
His Hon. Judge Clayson
His Honour Judge Conrad QC
Her Hon. Judge Coppel
His Hon. Judge Cornwall
Her Hon. Judge Daley
His Hon. Judge Peter Davies
His Hon. Judge Stephen Davies
His Honour Judge Dean QC
Her Hon. Judge De Haas QC
His Hon. Judge Dodds
His Hon. Judge Dutton
Her Hon. Judge Eaglestone
His Hon. Judge Elgan Edwards DL
His Hon. Judge Everett
His Hon. Judge Field QC
His Hon. Judge Fletcher
Her Hon. Judge Forrester
His Hon. Judge Foster QC
Her Hon. Judge Gibson
His Hon. Judge Gilbart QC
His Hon. Judge Goldstone QC
His Hon. Judge Gore QC
His Hon. Judge Greene
His Hon. Judge Halbert
His Hon. Judge Hale
His Hon. Judge Iain Hamilton
His Hon. Judge Hatton
His Hon. Judge Henshell

His Hon. Judge Hernandez
His Hon. Judge Hodge QC
His Hon. Judge Hull
His Hon. Judge Khokhar
His Hon. Judge Knopf
His Hon. Judge Knowles QC
Her Hon. Judge Kushner QC
His Hon. Judge Lakin
His Hon. Judge Lancaster
His Hon. Judge Michael Leeming
His Hon. Judge Lever
His Hon. Judge Lewis
His Hon. Judge Jeffrey Lewis
Her Hon. Judge Lloyd
His Hon. Judge Lowcock
Her Hon. Judge Lunt
Her Hon. Judge Christina Lyon
His Honour Judge Main QC
His Hon. Judge Mansell QC
His Hon. Judge Morrow QC
His Hon. Judge Mort
Her Hon. Judge Newell
Her Hon. Judge Newton
Her Hon. Judge Nield
Her Hon. Judge O'Leary
His Hon. Judge Pelling QC
Her Hon. Judge Penna
His Honour Judge Phillips CBE
His Hon. Judge Platts
Her Hon. Judge Rawkins
His Hon. Judge Raynor QC
His Hon. Judge Roberts
Her Hon. Judge Roddy
His Hon. Judge Rudland
His Hon. Judge Rumbelow QC
His Honour Judge Russell QC
Her Hon. Judge Singleton QC
His Hon. Judge Adrian Smith
His Hon. Judge Stead
His Hon. Judge Steiger TD QC
His Hon. Judge Stewart QC
His Hon. Judge Stockdale QC
His Honour Judge Sycamore
His Hon. Judge Teague QC
His Hon. Judge Thomas QC
His Honour Judge Trevor-Jones

His Hon. Judge Trigger
His Hon. Judge Waksman QC
His Hon. Judge Wallwork
His Hon. Judge Warnock
Her Hon. Judge Watson

His Hon. Judge Dennis Watson QC
His Hon. Judge Wood QC
His Hon. Judge Woodward
His Hon. Judge Woolman
His Hon. Judge Wright

DELIVERY DIRECTOR
Gill Hague
Manchester Civil Justice Centre, 1 Bridge Street West, Manchester M60 1UR
Tel: 0161 240 5800
Fax: 0161 240 5846
DX: 724780 MANCHESTER 44

HEAD OF CRIME
Paul McGladrigan
Manchester Civil Justice Centre, PO Box 4237, 1 Bridge Street West, Manchester M60 1TE
Tel: 0161 240 5913
DX: 724780 MANCHESTER 44

HEAD OF CIVIL, FAMILY & TRIBUNALS
Simon Vowles
Manchester Civil Justice Centre, PO Box 4237, 1 Bridge Street West, Manchester M60 1TE
Tel: 0161 240 5901
DX: 724780 MANCHESTER 44

HEAD OF REGIONAL SUPPORT UNIT
Sue Brooks
Manchester Civil Justice Centre, PO Box 4237, 1 Bridge Street West, Manchester M60 1TE
Tel: 0161 240 5908
DX: 724780 MANCHESTER 44

CLUSTER MANAGERS
Greater Manchester Civil, Family & Tribunals
Shirley Brown, Manchester Civil Justice Centre, 1 Bridge Street West, Manchester M60 1TE
Tel: 0161 240 5404
DX: 724780 MANCHESTER 44
Greater Manchester Crime
Clare Beech, Manchester & Salford Magistrates' Court, 3rd Floor, Crown Square, Manchester M60 1PR
Tel: 0161 830 4244
DX: 745170 MANCHESTER 75
Lancashire
Lesley Handford, Preston Combined Court, Openshaw Place, Ringway, Preston PR1 2LL
Tel: 01772 844888
DX: 702660 PRESTON 5
Cumbria
Lorraine Edgar, Kendal Court House, Burneside Road, Kendal LA9 4TJ
Tel: 01539 790516
Cheshire & Merseyside Civil, Family & Tribunals
Anita Bhardwaj, Liverpool Civil & Family Courts, 35 Vernon Street, Liverpool L2 2BX
Tel: 0151 296 2401
DX: 702600 LIVERPOOL 5
Cheshire & Merseyside Crime
Sarah Gebbie, Queen Elizabeth II Law Courts, Derby Square, Liverpool L2 1XA
Tel: 0151 471 1077
DX: 740880 LIVERPOOL 22

COURT INDEX – NORTHERN REGION

126	Birkenhead	County	61
130	Blackburn	County	62
131	Blackpool	County	62
137	Bolton	County	62
0470	Bolton	Crown	38
1731	Bolton LJA	Magistrates	126
154	Burnley	County	64
0154	Burnley	Crown	39
2014	Burnley, Pendle and Rossendale LJA	Magistrates	123
156	Bury	County	64
1724	Bury and Rochdale LJA	Magistrates	126
165	Carlisle	County	65
0412	Carlisle	Crown	40
170	Chester	County	66
0415	Chester	Crown	40
1998	Chorley LJA	Magistrates	123
181	Crewe	County	68
1725	East Lancashire LJA	Magistrates	123
1398	Furness and District LJA	Magistrates	123
1992	Fylde Coast LJA	Magistrates	123
	Greater Manchester Public Law Family Proceedings Courts and Manchester City LJA Private Law Family Proceedings Courts	Magistrates	126
235	Kendal	County	73
0767	Knutsford	Crown	43
242	Lancaster	County	74
0768	Lancaster	Crown	43
2002	Lancaster LJA	Magistrates	123
251	Liverpool	County	75
0433	Liverpool	Crown	44
1730	Liverpool and Knowsley LJA	Magistrates	121
260	Macclesfield	County	78
1178	Macclesfield LJA	Magistrates	121
262	Manchester	County	79
1733	Manchester and Salford LJA	Magistrates	126
0435	Manchester (Crown Square)	Crown	46
0436	Manchester (Minshull Street)	Crown	46
1722	North Cheshire	Magistrates	121
1727	North Cumbria LJA	Magistrates	124
288	Oldham	County	82
1734	Oldham LJA	Magistrates	126
2003	Ormskirk LJA	Magistrates	124
292	Penrith	County	82
303	Preston	County	83
0448	Preston	Crown	48
2005	Preston LJA	Magistrates	124
1722	Runcorn (Halton) LJA	Magistrates	121
315	St Helens	County	85
2268	St Helens LJA	Magistrates	121
1187	South Cheshire LJA	Magistrates	122
2007	South Ribble LJA	Magistrates	124
336	Stockport	County	87
0547	Stockport LJA	Magistrates	126
112	Tameside	County	88
1748	Tameside LJA	Magistrates	127
1742	Trafford LJA	Magistrates	127
360	Warrington	County	90
1722	Warrington LJA	Magistrates	121
1729	West Cheshire LJA	Magistrates	122

1726	West Cumbria LJA	Magistrates	124
373	West Cumbria (formerly Whitehaven)	County	91
374	Wigan	County	91
1749	Wigan and Leigh LJA	Magistrates	127
2271	Wirral LJA	Magistrates	122

SOUTH EAST REGION

PRESIDING JUDGES
The Rt Hon. Lord Justice Gross, Senior Presiding Judge
The Hon. Mr Justice Nicol
The Hon. Mr Justice Sweeney
The Hon. Mr Justice Singh
The Hon. Mr Justice Spencer

FAMILY DIVISION LIAISON JUDGE
The Hon. Mrs Justice Parker
The Hon. Mrs Justice Theis

CHANCERY SUPERVISING JUDGE
The Right Hon. Sir Terence Michael Elkan Barnet Etherton

CIRCUIT JUDGES

Her Hon. Judge Ackner
His Hon. Judge Addison
His Hon. Judge Anthony
His Hon. Judge Ball QC
His Hon. Judge Bate
His Hon. Judge Black
His Hon. Judge Bridge
His Hon. Judge Bright QC
His Hon. Judge Carey
His Hon. Judge Carroll
Her Hon. Judge Catterson
His Hon. Judge Coleman
His Hon. Judge Critchlow
His Hon. Judge Curl
Her Hon. Judge Cutts QC
His Hon. Judge Davies
His Hon. Judge Devaux
His Hon. Judge Enright
His Hon. Judge Farrell QC
His Hon. Judge Richard Foster
His Hon. Judge Goldstaub QC
His Hon. Judge Goodin
His Hon. Judge Graham
His Hon. Judge Grainger
His Hon. Judge Gratwicke
His Hon. Judge Griffith
His Hon. Judge David Griffith-Jones QC
His Hon. Judge Gullick
His Hon. Judge Gareth Hawkesworth
His Hon. Judge Jonathan Haworth
His Hon. Judge Hayward
His Hon. Judge J. Holt
His Hon. Judge S. Holt
His Hon. Judge Simon James
His Hon. Judge John
His Hon. Judge Joy
His Hon. Judge Kay QC
His Hon. Judge Kemp
His Hon. Judge Lawson QC
His Hon. Judge Lodge
His Hon. Judge Macdonald QC
His Hon. Judge Madge
Her Hon. Judge Matthews QC
Her Hon. Judge Mensah
His Hon. Judge Moloney QC

Her Hon. Judge A. Morris
His Hon. Judge Peter Moss
Her Hon. Judge Mowat
His Hon. Judge Niblett
His Hon. Judge Overbury
His Hon. Judge Owen-Jones
His Hon. Judge O'Mahony
His Hon. Judge Parkes
His Hon. Judge Plumstead
His Hon. Judge Reddihough
His Hon. Judge Rennie
His Hon. Judge Risius
His Hon. Judge Ross
His Hon. Judge John Rylance
His Hon. Judge Scott-Gall
Her Hon. Judge Zoe Smith QC
His Hon. Judge Statman
His Hon. Judge Stewart
His Hon. Judge Tain
His Hon. Judge Turner QC
His Hon. Judge Van Der Bijl
Her Hon. Judge Walden-Smith
His Hon. Judge Stephen Warner
Her Hon. Judge A. Williams
His Hon. Judge Nicholas Wood
His Hon. Judge Wood QC

COUNTY COURT
His Hon. Judge Arthur
His Hon. Judge Caddick
Her Hon. Judge Cameron
Her Hon. Judge Coates
His Hon. Judge Coltart
His Hon. Judge Corrie
His Hon. Judge Everall QC
His Hon. Judge Greene
Her Hon. Judge Hammerton
His Hon. Charles Harris QC
Her Hon. Judge Joanne Harris
His Hon. Judge Michael Hughes
His Hon. Judge Lochrane
His Hon. Judge McIntyre
His Hon. Judge Murdoch QC
Her Hon. Judge Murfitt
His Hon. Judge Nathan
His Hon. Judge Newton

His Hon. Judge O'Brien
Her Hon. Judge Plumstead
His Hon. Judge Polden
His Hon. Judge Jeremy Richards
His Hon. Judge John Rylance
His Hon. Judge Scarratt

His Hon. Judge Serota QC
His Hon. Judge Simpkiss
Her Hon. Judge Staite
Her Hon. Judge Waddicor
His Hon. Judge Wright
His Hon. Judge Yelton

DELIVERY DIRECTOR
Chris Jennings
Area 9.08, 9th Floor, 102 Petty France, London SW1H 9AJ
Tel: 020 3206 0688

COURT INDEX – SOUTH EAST REGION

Court Code	Town Name	Court Type	Page No
111	Ashford	County	60
113	Aylesbury	County	60
0401	Aylesbury	Crown	38
114	Banbury	County	60
153	Basildon	County	61
0461	Basildon	Crown	38
124	Bedford	County	61
0124	Bedford and Mid Bedfordshire LJA	Magistrates	128
1920	Berkshire LJA	Magistrates	135
150	Brighton	County	64
1921	Buckinghamshire LJA	Magistrates	135
157	Bury St Edmunds	County	64
0754	Bury St Edmunds	Crown	39
162	Cambridge	County	65
0410	Cambridge	Crown	39
163	Canterbury	County	65
0163	Canterbury	Crown	40
1960	Central Kent LJA	Magistrates	131
167	Chelmsford	County	66
0414	Chelmsford	Crown	40
172	Chichester	County	66
0172	Chichester	Crown	41
176	Colchester	County	67
184	Dartford	County	68
1957	East Kent LJA	Magistrates	131
191	Eastbourne	County	69
196	Epsom	County	69
211	Guildford	County	70
0474	Guildford	Crown	42
213	Harlow	County	71
216	Hastings	County	71
1879	Hatfield	Magistrates	128
218	Haywards Heath	County	71
221	Hertford	County	72
223	High Wycombe	County	72
225	Hitchin	County	72
227	Horsham	County	72
229	Huntingdon	County	72
1168	Huntingdonshire LJA	Magistrates	129
233	Ipswich	County	73
0426	Ipswich	Crown	42
238	King's Lynn	County	73
0765	King's Lynn	Crown	43
247	Lewes	County	74

0247	Lewes	Crown	43
256	Lowestoft	County	78
258	Luton	County	78
0769	Luton	Crown	46
1055	Luton and South Bedfordshire LJA	Magistrates	128
261	Maidstone	County	79
0434	Maidstone	Crown	46
267	Medway	County	79
388	Milton Keynes	County	80
277	Newbury	County	81
1972	Norfolk LJA	Magistrates	132
1889	North and East Hertfordshire LJA	Magistrates	128
1950	North Cambridgeshire LJA	Magistrates	129
1970	North Essex LJA	Magistrates	129
2863	North East Suffolk LJA	Magistrates	132
1966	North Kent LJA (Dartford and Medway)	Magistrates	131
2849	North Surrey LJA	Magistrates	133
285	Norwich	County	82
0443	Norwich	Crown	47
291	Oxford	County	82
0291	Oxford	Crown	48
2777	Oxfordshire LJA	Magistrates	135
294	Peterborough	County	83
0294	Peterborough	Crown	48
305	Reading	County	84
0449	Reading	Crown	48
307	Reigate	County	84
313	St Albans	County	85
0450	St Albans	Crown	49
327	Slough	County	86
1951	South Cambridgeshire LJA	Magistrates	129
1971	South Essex LJA	Magistrates	130
2866	South East Suffolk LJA	Magistrates	132
2856	South East Surrey LJA	Magistrates	133
2848	South West Surrey LJA	Magistrates	133
329	Southend	County	86
0772	Southend	Crown	49
334	Staines	County	87
2950	Sussex (Central) LJA	Magistrates	133
2948	Sussex (Eastern) LJA	Magistrates	133
2947	Sussex (Northern) LJA	Magistrates	133
2949	Sussex (Western) LJA	Magistrates	134
348	Thanet	County	89
362	Watford	County	90
1910	West and Central Hertfordshire LJA	Magistrates	128
2867	West Suffolk LJA	Magistrates	132
838	Worthing	County	92

0454	Southampton	Crown	49
1304	Southampton LJA	Magistrates	141
345	Swindon	County	88
0345	Swindon	Crown	50
347	Taunton	County	88
0459	Taunton	Crown	50
352	Torquay and Newton Abbot	County	89
354	Truro	County	89
0477	Truro	Crown	50
1510	West Dorset LJA	Magistrates	139
370	Weston-super-Mare	County	91
371	Weymouth	County	91
3021 (7021)	Wiltshire (Youth)	Magistrates	141
376	Winchester	County	91
0376	Winchester	Crown	51
385	Yeovil	County	92

HMCTS WALES

PRESIDING JUDGES
The Rt Hon. Lord Justice Gross, Senior Presiding Judge
The Hon. Mr Justice Wyn Williams
The Hon. Mrs Justice Nicola Davies

FAMILY DIVISION LIAISON JUDGE
The Hon. Mr Justice Philip Moor

CHANCERY SUPERVISING JUDGE
The Hon. Mr Justice Morgan

ADMINISTRATIVE COURT SUPERVISING JUDGE
The Hon. Mr Justice Hickinbottom

CIRCUIT JUDGES

His Hon. Judge Bidder QC
His Hon. Judge Patrick Curran QC
His Hon. Judge Huw Davies QC
His Honour Judge Denyer QC
His Hon. Judge Furness
His Hon. Judge Gaskell
His Hon. Judge Heywood
His Hon. Judge Stephen Hopkins QC
His Hon. Judge Dafydd Hughes
His Hon. Judge Hughes QC
His Hon. Judge Hughes
His Hon. Judge Jarman QC
His Hon. Judge Terence John
His Hon. Judge Gareth Jones
His Hon. Judge Keyser QC

Her Hon. Judge Helen Mifflin
His Hon. Judge David Wynn Morgan
Her Hon. Judge Parry
His Hon. Judge Parry
His Hon. Judge Perry
Her Hon. Judge Rees
His Hon. Judge Phillip Richards
His Hon. Judge Rowlands
His Honour Judge Seys-Llewellyn QC
His Hon. Judge Keith Thomas
His Hon. Judge Paul Thomas QC
His Hon. Judge Richard Twomlow
His Hon. Judge Vosper QC
His Hon. Judge Daniel Williams

DELIVERY DIRECTOR FOR HMCTS WALES
Luigi Strinati
Wales Support Unit, Churchill House, Churchill Way, Cardiff CF10 4HH
DX: 743943 Cardiff 38
Email: luigi.strinati@hmcts.gsi.gov.uk

HEAD OF CRIME FOR HMCTS WALES
Nick Albrow
Wales Support Unit, Churchill House, Churchill Way, Cardiff CF10 4HH
Email: nick.albrow@hmcts.gsi.gov.uk

COURT INDEX – HMCTS WALES

3253 (7253)	Ceredigion & Pembrokeshire LJA (Youth)	Magistrates	142
3062	Conwy LJA	Magistrates	144
178	Conwy and Colwyn	County	67
3061	Denbighshire LJA	Magistrates	144
0758	Dolgellau	Crown	41
3059	Flintshire LJA	Magistrates	144
3270 (7270)	Glamorgan Valleys LJA (Youth)	Magistrates	145
3211	Gwent LJA	Magistrates	145
3244	Gwynedd LJA	Magistrates	144
217	Haverfordwest	County	71
253	Llanelli	County	75
254	Llangefni	County	75
269	Merthyr Tydfil	County	80
0269	Merthyr Tydfil	Crown	46
271	Mold	County	80
0769	Mold	Crown	47
3355	Montgomeryshire LJA	Magistrates	143
274	Neath Port Talbot	County	80
3359	Neath Port Talbot LJA	Magistrates	143
3266	Newcastle and Ogmore LJA	Magistrates	145
280	Newport (Gwent)	County	81
0441	Newport (South Wales)	Crown	47
299	Pontypridd	County	83
308	Rhyl	County	84
344	Swansea	County	88
0457	Swansea	Crown	50
3360	Swansea LJA	Magistrates	143
366	Welshpool and Newtown	County	90
0774	Welshpool	Crown	51
384	Wrexham	County	92
3058	Wrexham Maelor LJA	Magistrates	144
3238	Ynys Mon/Anglesey LJA	Magistrates	144

HMCTS Estate by Region and Cluster

London Region
Central and South (Crime)
North and West (Crime)
Family

Midlands Region
Derbyshire and Nottinghamshire
Leicestershire, Rutland, Lincolnshire and Northamptonshire
Staffordshire and West Mercia
West Midlands

North East Region
Cleveland and Durham
Humber and South Yorkshire
North and West Yorkshire
Northumbria

North West Region
Cheshire and Merseyside
Cumbria and Lancashire
Greater Manchester

South East Region
Bedfordshire and Hertfordshire
Cambridgeshire and Essex
Kent
Norfolk and Suffolk
Surrey and Sussex
Thames Valley

South West Region
Devon, Cornwall and Dorset
Avon, Somerset and Gloucestershire
Hampshire, Isle of Wight and Wiltshire

HMCTS Wales
North Wales
Mid and West Wales
South East Wales

CROWN COURTS

Note: First tier centres deal with High Court civil cases and Crown Court criminal cases and are served by High Court and circuit judges. Second and third tier centres deal only with criminal cases. Second tier centres are served by High Court and circuit judges and third tier centres only by circuit judges.

ENGLAND AND WALES

0401 AYLESBURY (SE)
County Hall, Market Square, Aylesbury, Buckinghamshire HP20 1XD
Tel: 01296 434401
Fax: 01296 435665
Email: enquiries@aylesbury.crowncourt.gsi.gov.uk
DX: 157430 AYLESBURY 11
Court Details
County Hall, Aylesbury
Tier 3

0750 BARNSTAPLE (SW)
Exeter Comined Court, Southernhay Gardens, Exeter EX1 1UH
Tel: 01392 415300
Email: exeter.enquiries@exeter.crowncourt.gsi.gov.uk
DX: 98440 EXETER 2 or 98560 Barnstaple 2
Court Details
The Law Courts, Civic Centre, Barnstaple EX31 1DX
Tier 3

0461 BASILDON (SE)
Basildon Combined Court, The Gore, Basildon, Essex SS14 2BU
Tel: 01268 458000
Fax: 0870 324 0090
Email: enquiries@basildon.crowncourt.gsi.gov.uk
DX: 97633 BASILDON 5
Court Details
The Gore, Basildon
Tier 3

0404 BIRMINGHAM (M)
Queen Elizabeth II Law Courts, 11 Newton Street, Birmingham B4 7NA
Tel: 0121 681 3300 or 3339
Fax: 0870 324 0273
Email: birmingham.enquiries@birmingham.crowncourt.gsi.gov.uk
DX: 702033 BIRMINGHAM 8
Court Details
Queen Elizabeth II Law Courts, 1 Newton Street, Birmingham
Tier 1

0405 BODMIN
CLOSED *see* TRURO

0470 BOLTON (NW)
The Law Courts, Blackhorse Street, Bolton BL1 1SU
Tel: 01204 392881
Fax: 01204 363204
Email: enquiries@bolton.crowncourt.gsi.gov.uk
DX: 702610 BOLTON 3
Court Details
The Law Courts, Blackhorse Street, Bolton
Tier 3

0406 BOURNEMOUTH (SW)
Bournemouth Crown and County Court, Courts of Justice, Deansleigh Road, Bournemouth BH7 7DS
Tel: 01202 502800

Fax: 01202 502859
DX: 98420 BOURNEMOUTH 4
Court Details
Courts of Justice, Deansleigh Road, Bournemouth
Tier 3

0402 BRADFORD (NE)

Bradford Combined Court Centre, The Law Courts, Exchange Square, Drake Street, Bradford BD1 1JA
Tel: 01274 840274
Fax: 01274 843510
Email: enquiries@bradford.countycourt.gsi.gov.uk
DX: 702083 BRADFORD 2
Court Details
Bradford Law Courts, Exchange Square, Drake Street, Bradford
Tier 2

0753 BRIGHTON

CLOSED *see* LEWES

0408 BRISTOL (SW)

The Law Courts, Small Street, Bristol BS1 1DA
Tel: 0117 976 3030
Fax: 0870 739 4136
Email: enquiries@bristol.crowncourt.gsi.gov.uk
DX: 78128 BRISTOL
Court Details
The Law Courts, Small Street, Bristol
Tier 1

0154 BURNLEY (NW)

Burnley Combined Court Centre, The Law Courts, Hammerton Street, Burnley, Lancashire BB11 1XD
Tel: 01282 855300
Fax: 01282 414911
Email: enquiries@burnley.countycourt.gsi.gov.uk
DX: 724940 BURNLEY 4
Court Details
The Law Courts, Hammerton Street, Burnley
Tier 3

0754 BURY ST EDMUNDS (SE)

Shire Hall, Bury St Edmunds, Suffolk, IP33 1HF
Tel: 01473 228585
Fax: 01473 228560
Email: enquiries@ipswich.crowncourt.gsi.gov.uk
Court Details
Shire Hall, Bury St Edmunds, Suffolk
Tier 3

0755 CAERNARFON (WAL)

Caernarfon Criminal Justice Centre, Llanberis Road, Caernarfon LL55 2DF
Tel: 01352 707340
Fax: 0870 324 0321
Email: listing@mold.crowncourt.gsi.gov.uk
DX: 744382 CAERNARFON 6
Court Details
Caernarfon Criminal Justice Centre, Llanberis Road, Caernarfon LL55 2DF
Tier 1

0410 CAMBRIDGE (SE)

The Court House, 83 East Road, Cambridge CB1 1BT
Tel: 01223 488321
Fax: 01223 488333
DX: 97365 CAMBRIDGE 2
Email: enquiries@cambridge.crowncourt.gsi.gov.uk

Court Details
83 East Road, Cambridge
Tier 1

0163 CANTERBURY (SE)
Canterbury Combined Court Centre, The Law Courts, Chaucer Road, Canterbury CT1 1ZA
Tel: 01227 819200
Fax: 01227 819329
Email: enquiries@canterbury.countycourt.gsi.gov.uk
DX: 99710 CANTERBURY 3

Court Details
The Law Courts, Chaucer Road, Canterbury
Tier 3

0411 CARDIFF (WAL)
The Law Courts, Cathays Park, Cardiff CF10 3PG
Tel: 029 2067 8730
Email: listing@cardiff.crowncourt.gsi.gov.uk
DX: 99450 CARDIFF 5

Court Details
The Law Courts, Cathays Park, Cardiff
Tier 1

0412 CARLISLE (NW)
Carlisle Combined Court Centre, Courts of Justice, Earl Street, Carlisle CA1 1DJ
Tel: 01228 882140
Fax: 0870 324 0259
Email: enquiries@carlisle.countycourt.gsi.gov.uk
DX: 65331 CARLISLE 2

Court Details
Courts of Justice, Earl Street, Carlisle
Tier 1

0756 CARMARTHEN (WAL)
The Law Courts, St Helen's Road, Swansea SA1 4PF
Tel: 01792 637000
Fax: 01792 637049
Email: contacts@swansea.crowncourt.gsi.gov.uk
DX: 99540 SWANSEA 4
Note: *Hearings only*

Court Details
The Guildhall, Camarthen
Tier 2

0413 CENTRAL CRIMINAL COURT
see LONDON

0414 CHELMSFORD (SE)
PO Box 9, New Street, Chelmsford CM1 1EL
Tel: 01245 603000
Fax: 01245 603011
Email: enquiries@chelmsford.crowncourt.gsi.gov.uk
DX: 97375 CHELMSFORD 3

Court Details
New Street, Chelmsford
Tier 1

0415 CHESTER (NW)
The Castle, Chester CH1 2AN
Tel: 01244 317606
Email: chester.enquiries@chester.crowncourt.gsi.gov.uk
DX: 702527 CHESTER 5

Court Details
The Castle, Chester
Tier 1

0172 CHICHESTER (SE)
Chichester Combined Court Centre, Southgate, Chichester, West Sussex PO19 1SX
Tel: 01243 520742
Email: enquiries@chichester.countycourt.gsi.gov.uk
DX: 97460 Chichester 2
Court Details
The Courthouse, Southgate, Chichester, West Sussex
Tier 3

0417 COVENTRY (M)
Coventry Combined Court Centre, 140 Much Park Street, Coventry CV1 2SN
Tel: 0300 123 557
Fax: 0247 652 0443
Email: civilenquiries@coventry.countycourt.gsi.gov.uk.gsi.gov.uk
DX: 701580 COVENTRY 5
Court Details
140 Much Park Street, Coventry
Tier 3

0185 DERBY (M)
Derby Combined Court Centre, Morledge, Derby DE1 2XE
Tel: 01332 622600
Fax: 0870 324 0296
Email: enquiries@derby.countycourt.gsi.gov.uk
DX: 724060 DERBY 21
Court Details
Derby Combined Court Centre, Morledge, Derby
Tier 3

0758 DOLGELLAU (WAL)
The Law Courts, County Civic Centre, Mold CH7 1AE
Tel: 01352 707340
Fax: 01352 753874
Email: enquires@mold.crowncourt.gsi.gov.uk
DX: 702521 MOLD 2
Court Details
The County Hall, Dolgellau, Gwynedd LL40 1AU
Tier 3

0420 DONCASTER (NE)
Sheffield Crown Court, The Law Courts, West Bar, Sheffield, South Yorkshire S3 8PH
Tel: 0114 281 2400
Fax: 0114 281 2425
Email: enquiries@sheffield.crowncourt.gsi.gov.uk
DX: 703001 DONCASTER 5
Court Detail
Crown Court, College Road, Doncaster
Tier 3

0407 DORCHESTER (SW)
Dorchester Crown Court, Colliton Park, Dorchester DT1 1XJ
Tel: 01305 265867
Fax: 01305 251867
Court Details
County Hall, Dorchester
Tier 2

0422 DURHAM (NE)
The Law Courts, Old Elvet, Durham DH1 3HW
Tel: 0191 386 6714
Fax: 0191 383 0605
DX: 65112 DURHAM 4
Court Details
The Law Courts, Old Elvet, Durham
Tier 3

0198 EXETER (SW)
Exeter Crown & County Court, Southernhay Gardens, Exeter EX1 1UH
Tel: 01392 415300
Fax: 0870 324 0070
Email: enquiries@exeter.countycourt.gsi.gov.uk
DX: 98440 EXETER 2
Court Details
Southernhay Gardens, Exeter
Tier 1

0424 GLOUCESTER (SW)
Gloucestershire Crown Courthouse, Longsmith Street, Gloucester GL1 2TS
Tel: 01452 420400
Fax: 0870 324 0310
Email: gloucestercrowncourt@hmcts.gsi.gov.uk
Court Details
Longsmith Street, Gloucester
Tier 2

0208 GREAT GRIMSBY (NE)
Great Grimsby Combined Court Centre, Town Hall Square, Grimsby DN31 1HX
Tel: 01472 265250
Fax: 01472 265251
Email: enquiries@grimsby.countycourt.gsi.gov.uk
DX: 702007 GRIMSBY 3
Court Details
The Combined Court Centre, Town Hall Square, Grimsby
Tier 3

0474 GUILDFORD (SE)
Bedford Road, Guildford, Surrey GU1 4ST
Tel: 01483 468500
Fax: 01483 579545
Email: enquiries@guildford.crowncourt.gsi.gov.uk
DX: 97862 GUILDFORD 5
Court Details
Bedford Road, Guildford
Tier 3

0762 HEREFORD (M)
The Shirehall, St Peter's Square, Hereford HR1 2HY
Tel: 01432 276118
Fax: 01432 274350
DX: 721120 WORCESTER 11
Court Details
The Shirehall, Hereford
Tier 3

HOVE
see LEWES

0440 INNER LONDON SESSIONS HOUSE
see LONDON

0426 IPSWICH (SE)
The Court House, 1 Russell Road, Ipswich, Suffolk IP1 2AG
Tel: 01473 228585
Fax: 01473 228560
Email: enquiries@ipswich.crowncourt.gsi.gov.uk
DX: 729480 IPSWICH 19
Court Details
The Court House, 1 Russell Road, Ipswich
Tier 2

0475 ISLEWORTH
see LONDON

0765 KING'S LYNN (SE)
The Court House, College Lane, King's Lynn, Norfolk PE30 1PQ
Tel: 01603 728200
Fax: 01603 760848
Court Details
The Court House, College Lane, King's Lynn, Norfolk
Tier 3

0239 KINGSTON-UPON-HULL (NE)
Kingston-upon-Hull Combined Court Centre, Lowgate, Hull HU1 2EZ
Tel: 01482 586161
Fax: 01482 621148
Email: enquiries@kingstonuponhull.crowncourt.gsi.gov.uk
DX: 703010 HULL 5
Court Details
Kingston-upon-Hull Combined Court Centre, Lowgate, Hull
Tier 2

0427 KINGSTON-UPON-THAMES
see LONDON

0767 KNUTSFORD (NW)
The Castle, Chester CH1 2AN
Tel: 01244 317606
Email: chester.enquiries@chester.crowncourt.gsi.gov.uk
DX: 702527 CHESTER 5
Court Details
The Sessions House, Knutsford
Tier 3

0768 LANCASTER (NW)
The Law Courts, Openshaw Place, Ring Way, Preston PR1 2LL
Tel: 01772 844700
Fax: 01772 844759
Email: enquiries@preston.crowncourt.gsi.gov.uk
DX: 702660 PRESTON 5
Court Details
The Castle, Lancaster
Tier 3

0243 LEEDS (NE)
The Court House, 1 Oxford Row, Leeds LS1 3BG
Tel: 0113 306 2800
Fax: 0870 739 5873
Email: enquiries@leeds.countycourt.gsi.gov.uk
DX: 703016 LEEDS 6
Court Details
Leeds Combined Court Centre, The Court House, 1 Oxford Row, Leeds
Tier 1

0430 LEICESTER (M)
90 Wellington Street, Leicester LE1 6HG
Tel: 0116 222 5700
Fax: 0870 739 5873
Email: leicester.enquiries@leicester.crowncourt.gsi.gov.uk
DX: 10880 LEICESTER 3
Court Details
90 Wellington Street, Leicester
Tier 2

0247 LEWES (SE)
Lewes Combined Court Centre, The Law Courts, High Street, Lewes, East Sussex BN7 1YB
Tel: 01273 480400
Fax: 01273 485269
Email: enquiries@lewes.countycourt.gsi.gov.uk
DX: 97395 LEWES 4

Email: enquiries@nottingham.crowncourt.gsi.gov.uk
DX: 702383 NOTTINGHAM 7

Court Details
The Law Courts, 60 Canal Street, Nottingham
Tier 1

0291 OXFORD (SE)
Oxford Combined Court Centre, St Aldates, Oxford OX1 1TL
Tel: 01865 264200
Fax: 01865 264253
Email: enquiries@oxford.crowncourt.gsi.gov.uk
DX: 96450 OXFORD 4

Court Details
The Court House, St Aldate's, Oxford
Tier 1

0294 PETERBOROUGH (SE)
Peterborough Combined Court Centre, Crown Buildings, Rivergate, Peterborough PE1 1EJ
Tel: 01733 349161
Fax: 01733 891563
Email: enquiries@peterborough.crowncourt.gsi.gov.uk
DX: 702302 PETERBOROUGH 8

Court Details
Crown Buildings, Rivergate, Peterborough
Tier 3

0296 PLYMOUTH (SW)
Plymouth Combined Court Centre, The Law Courts, Armada Way, Plymouth PL1 2ER
Tel: 01752 677400
Fax: 0870 324 0096
Email: enquiries@plymouth.crowncourt.gsi.gov.uk
DX: 98470 PLYMOUTH 7

Court Details
The Law Courts, Armada Way, Plymouth
Tier 2

0302 PORTSMOUTH (SW)
Portsmouth Combined Court Centre, The Courts of Justice, Winston Churchill Avenue, Portsmouth PO1 2EB
Tel: 023 9289 3000
Fax: 0870 739 4345 or 0870 739 4357
Email: enquiries@portsmouth.countycourt.gsi.gov.uk
DX: 98490 PORTSMOUTH 5

Court Details
The Courts of Justice, Winston Churchill Avenue, Portsmouth
Tier 3

0448 PRESTON (NW)
Preston Combined Court Centre, The Law Courts, Openshaw Place, Ring Way, Preston PR1 2LL
Tel: 01772 844700
Email: enquiries@preston.crowncourt.gsi.gov.uk
DX: 310201 Preston 31 or 702660 Preston 5

Court Details
The Sessions House, Lancaster Road, Preston
Tier 1

0449 READING (SE)
The Old Shire Hall, The Forbury, Reading RG1 3EH
Tel: 0118 967 4400
Fax: 0118 967 4444
DX: 97440 READING 5

Court Details
The Old Shire Hall, The Forbury, Reading
Tier 2

0450 ST ALBANS (SE)
The Court Building, Bricket Road, St Albans, Hertfordshire AL1 3JW
Tel: 01727 753220
Fax: 0870 324 0229
Email: results@stalbans.crowncourt.gsi.gov.uk
DX: 99700 ST ALBANS 3
Court Details
The Court Building, Bricket Road, St Albans
Tier 2

0480 SALISBURY (SW)
Salisbury Combined Court Centre, The Law Courts, Wilton Road, Salisbury, SP2 7EP
Tel: 01722 345200
Fax: 0870 324 0069
Email: enquiries@salisbury.crowncourt.gsi.gov.uk
Court Details
The Law Courts, Wilton Road, Sailsbury
Tier 3

0320 SHEFFIELD (NE)
Sheffield Combined Court Centre, The Law Courts, 50 West Bar, Sheffield S3 8PH
Tel: 0114 281 2400
Fax: 0114 281 2425
Email: enquiries@sheffield.countycourt.gsi.gov.uk
DX: 703028 SHEFFIELD 6
Court Details
The Law Courts, 50 West Bar, Sheffield
Tier 1

0452 SHREWSBURY (M)
The Shirehall, Abbey Foregate, Shrewsbury SY2 6LU
Tel: 01743 260820
Fax: 01743 244236
Email: enquiries@shrewsbury.crowncourt.gsi.gov.uk
DX: 702022 SHREWSBURY 2
Court Details
The Shirehall, Abbey Foregate, Shrewsbury
Tier 2

0453 SNARESBROOK
see LONDON

0454 SOUTHAMPTON (SW)
Southampton Combined Court Centre, The Courts of Justice, London Road, Southampton SO15 2XQ
Tel: 023 8021 3200
Fax: 0870 761 7655
Email: southamptoncrnenquiries@hmcts.gsi.gov.uk
DX: 111000 SOUTHAMPTON 11
Court Details
The Courts of Justice, London Road, Southampton
Tier 3

0772 SOUTHEND (SE)
The Court House, Victoria Avenue, Southend-on-Sea, Essex SS2 6EG
Tel: 01268 458000
Fax: 01268 458100
Court Details
The Court House, Victoria Avenue, Southend-on-Sea, SS2 6EG
Tier 3

0471 SOUTHWARK
see LONDON

THE NORTHERN IRELAND COURTS AND TRIBUNALS SERVICE

CEO: Jacqui Durkin, Laganside House, 23–27 Oxford Street, Belfast BT1 3LA.
Tel: 030 0200 7812
Fax: 028 9072 8946

ANTRIM
Antrim Court Office, The Courthouse, 30 Castle Way, Antrim BT41 4AQ
Tel: 030 0200 7812

Court House
The Courthouse, Castle Way, Antrim

ARMAGH
Armagh Court Office, The Courthouse, The Mall, Armagh, Co. Armagh BT61 9DJ
Tel: 030 0200 7812

Court House
The Courthouse, The Mall, Armagh

BALLYMENA
Ballymena Court Office, The Courthouse, Albert Place, Ballymena, Co. Antrim BT43 6DY
Tel: 030 0200 7812

Court House
The Courthouse, Albert Place, Ballymena

BELFAST
Belfast Combined Courts Office, Laganside Courts, 45 Oxford Street, Belfast BT1 3LL
Tel: 030 0200 7812

Court House
Laganside Courts, Oxford Street, Belfast

COLERAINE
Coleraine Court Office, The Courthouse, 46A Mountsandel Road, Coleraine BT52 1NY
Tel: 030 0200 7812

Court House
The Courthouse, Mountsandel Road, Coleraine

CRAIGAVON
Craigavon Court Office, The Courthouse, Central Way, Craigavon BT64 1AP
Tel: 030 0200 7812

Court House
The Courthouse, Central Way, Craigavon

DOWNPATRICK
Downpatrick Court Office, The Courthouse, 21 English Street, Downpatrick BT30 6AD
Tel: 030 0200 7812

Court House
The Courthouse, English Street, Downpatrick

DUNGANNON
The Courthouse, 46 Killyman Road, Dungannon BT71 6DE
Tel: 030 0200 7812

Court House
The Courthouse, Killyman Road, Dungannon

ENNISKILLEN
Enniskillen Court Office, The Courthouse, East Bridge Street, Enniskillen BT74 7BP
Tel: 030 0200 7812

Court House
The Courthouse, East Bridge Street, Enniskillen

LISBURN
Lisburn Court Office, The Courthouse, Railway Street, Lisburn BT28 1XR
Tel: 030 0200 7812

Court House
The Courthouse, Railway Street, Lisburn

LONDONDERRY
Londonderry Court Office, The Courthouse, Bishop Street, Londonderry BT48 6PQ
Tel: 030 0200 7812

Court House
The Courthouse, Bishop Street, Londonderry

NEWRY
Newry Court Office, The Courthouse, 23 New Street, Newry BT35 6JD
Tel: 030 0200 7812

Court House
The Courthouse, New Street, Newry

NEWTOWNARDS
Newtownards Court Office, The Courthouse, Regent Street, Newtownards BT23 4LP
Tel: 030 0200 7812

Court House
The Courthouse, Regent Street, Newtownards

OMAGH
Omagh Court Office, The Courthouse, High Street, Omagh, Co. Tyrone BT78 1DU
Tel: 030 0200 7812

Court House
The Courthouse, High Street, Omagh

Crown Court Codes

0401	Aylesbury	0452	Shrewsbury
0402	Bedford (CLOSED)	0453	Snaresbrook
0402	Bradford	0454	Southampton
0403	Beverley (CLOSED)	0455	Stafford
0239	Kingston-upon-Hull	0388	Stoke-on-Trent
0404	Birmingham	0457	Swansea
0405	Bodmin (CLOSED)	0345	Swindon
0406	Bournemouth	0459	Taunton
0407	Bradford (CLOSED)	0460	Teesside
0407	Dorchester	0461	Wakefield (CLOSED)
0408	Bristol	0461	Basildon (wef 2/1/96)
0154	Burnley	0462	Warrington (CLOSED)
0410	Cambridge	0361	Warwick
0411	Cardiff	0464	Middlesex Guildhall (CLOSED)
0412	Carlisle	0376	Winchester
0413	Central Criminal Court (Old Bailey)	0380	Worcester
0414	Chelmsford	0467	York
0415	Chester	0468	Acton (CLOSED)
0172	Chichester	0468	Harrow
0417	Coventry	0469	Wood Green
0418	Croydon	0470	Bolton
0185	Derby	0471	Southwark
0420	Doncaster	0472	Woolwich
0421	Dudley (CLOSED)	0294	Peterborough
0378	Wolverhampton	0474	Guildford
0422	Durham	0475	Isleworth
0198	Exeter	0769	Luton
0424	Gloucester	0477	Truro
0208	Great Grimsby	0478	Newport (I.O.W.)
0426	Ipswich	0163	Canterbury
0427	Kingston-upon-Thames	0480	Salisbury
0428	Blackfriars	0750	Barnstaple
0243	Leeds	0751	Barrow-in-Furness
0430	Leicester	0752	Birkenhead (CLOSED)
0247	Lewes	0753	Brighton (CLOSED)
0432	Lincoln	0754	Bury St Edmunds
0433	Liverpool	0755	Caernarfon
0434	Maidstone	0756	Carmarthen
0435	Manchester (Crown Square)	0757	Devizes (CLOSED)
0436	Manchester (Minshull Street)	0758	Dolgellau
0269	Merthyr Tydfil	0759	Dorchester
0769	Mold	0760	Gravesend (CLOSED)
0278	Newcastle-upon-Tyne	0761	Haverfordwest (CLOSED)
0440	Newington Causeway (Inner LondonSessions House)	0762	Hereford
0441	Newport	0763	Huddersfield (CLOSED)
0282	Northampton	0764	Kendal (CLOSED)
0443	Norwich	0765	Kings Lynn
0444	Nottingham	0766	Kingston-upon-Hull
0291	Oxford	0767	Knutsford
0296	Plymouth	0768	Lancaster
0302	Portsmouth	0769	Luton

—

0448	Preston		0769	Mold
0449	Reading		0772	Southend
0450	St Albans		0773	Walsall (CLOSED)
0320	Sheffield		0774	Welshpool

110   ASHBY-DE-LA-ZOUCH
closed wef 1/10/84 – successor court – Burton-on-Trent

111   ASHFORD
closed wef 7/11

112   ASHTON-UNDER-LYNE AND STALYBRIDGE
renamed TAMESIDE

702   AXMINSTER AND CHARD
closed wef 5/12/94 – successor court – Yeovil

113   AYLESBURY (SE)
Walton Street, Aylesbury, Buckinghamshire HP21 7QZ
Tel: 01296 554327
Fax: 01296 554320
Email: enquiries@aylesbury.countycourt.gsi.gov.uk
DX: 97820 AYLESBURY 10
Court Details
Walton Street, Aylesbury
Bankruptcy; Children; Divorce; Domestic violence; Forced marriage; Housing possession; Money claims

114   BANBURY (SE)
The Courthouse, Warwick Road, Banbury, Oxfordshire OX16 2AW
Tel: 01295 452090
Fax: 01295 452051
Email: enquiries@banbury.countycourt.gsi.gov.uk
DX: 701967 BANBURY 2
Court Details
The Courthouse, Warwick Road, Banbury
Bankruptcy; Housing possession; Money claims

115   BANGOR
closed wef 4/7/94 – successor court – Caernarfon

116   BARGOED
closed wef 29/12/95 – successor court – Blackwood

117   BARNET
see LONDON

118   BARNSLEY (NE)
Barnsley County Court, Court House, Westgate, Barnsley S70 2DW
Tel: 01226 320000
Fax: 01226 320044
Email: enquiries@barnsley.countycourt.gsi.gov.uk
DX: 702080 BARNSLEY 3
Court Details
Barnsley County Court, Barnsley
Bankruptcy; Children; Divorce; Domestic violence; Housing possession; Money claims

119   BARNSTAPLE (SW)
The Law Courts, North Walk, Civic Centre, Barnstaple, Devon EX31 1DX
Tel: 01271 340410
Fax: 0870 324 0129
Email: hearings@barnstaple.countycourt.gsi.gov.uk
DX: 98560 BARNSTAPLE 2
Court Details
8th Floor (Civic Centre), North Walk, Barnstaple
Bankruptcy; Children; Divorce; Domestic violence; Housing possession; Money claims

120   BARROW-IN-FURNESS (NW)
Law Courts, Abbey Road, Barrow-in-Furness, Cumbria LA14 5QX
Tel: 01229 840370; 840380 (Bailiffs)
Fax: 0870 739 4409
Email: enquiries.barrowcountycourt@hmcts.gsi.gov.uk
DX: 65210 BARROW-IN-FURNESS 2

Court Details
Law Courts, Abbey Road, Barrow-in-Furness
Adoption; Bankruptcy; Children; Divorce; Domestic violence; Housing possession; Money claims

121   BARRY
closed wef 29/12/95 – successor court – Cardiff

153   BASILDON (SE)
Basildon Combined Court, The Gore, Basildon, Essex SS14 2BU
Tel: 0344 892 4000
Fax: 01268 458100
Email: enquiries@basildon.countycourt.gsi.gov.uk
DX: 97633 BASILDON 5
Court Details
The Gore, Basildon
Housing possession; Money claims

122   BASINGSTOKE (SW)
The Court House, London Road, Basingstoke RG21 4AB
Tel: 01256 318200
Fax: 01256 318217
Email: enquiries@basingstoke.countycourt.gsi.gov.uk
DX: 98570 BASINGSTOKE 3
Court Details
The Court House, London Road, Basingstoke
Children; Divorce; Domestic violence; Housing possession; Money claims

123   BATH (SW)
PO Box 4302, North Parade Road, Bath BA1 0LF
Tel: 01225 476730
Email: av-bathcounty@hmcts.gsi.gov.uk
DX: 98580 BATH 2
Court Details
The Law Courts, North Parade Road, Bath
Bankruptcy; Children; Divorce; Domestic violence; Housing possession; Money claims

124   BEDFORD (SE)
PO Box 1405, 3 St Paul's Square, Bedford MK40 9DN
Tel: 0844 892 0550
Email: enquiries@bedford.countycourt.gsi.gov.uk
DX: 97590 BEDFORD 3
Court Details
Shire Hall, 3 St Paul's Square, Bedford MK40 1SQ
Adoption; Bankruptcy; Children; Divorce; Domestic violence; Forced marriage; Housing possession; Money claims

703   BERWICK-UPON-TWEED
closed wef 15/12/97 – successor court – Morpeth and Berwick

704   BEVERLEY
closed wef 1/1/93 – successor court – Kingston-upon-Hull

126   BIRKENHEAD (NW)
76 Hamilton Street, Birkenhead, Merseyside CH41 5EN
Tel: 0151 666 5800
Fax: 0151 666 5873
Email: enquiries@birkenhead.countycourt.gsi.gov.uk
DX: 725000 BIRKENHEAD 10
Court Details
76 Hamilton Street, Birkenhead
Bankruptcy; Children; Divorce; Domestic violence; Housing possession; Money claims

127   BIRMINGHAM CIVIL JUSTICE CENTRE AND FAMILY COURTS (M)
Priory Courts, 33 Bull Street, Birmingham B4 6DS
Tel: 0300 123 1751
Email: enquiries@birmingham.countycourt.gsi.gov.uk

DX: 701987 BIRMINGHAM 7

Court Details
33 Bull Street, Birmingham
Adoption; Bankruptcy; Children; Civil partnership; Divorce; Domestic violence; Forced marriage; Housing possession

128   BISHOP AUCKLAND
closed wef 7/11 – successor courts – Darlington and Durham

129   BISHOP'S STORTFORD
closed wef 1/12/97 – successor courts – Cambridge, Harlow and Colchester

130   BLACKBURN (NW)
64 Victoria Street, Blackburn, Lancashire BB1 6DJ
Tel: 01254 299840
Fax: 0870 324 0328
Email: enquiries@blackburn.countycourt.gsi.gov.uk
DX: 702650 BLACKBURN 4

Court Details
64 Victoria Street, Blackburn
Adoption; Bankruptcy; Children; Divorce; Domestic violence; Employment; Forced marriage

131   BLACKPOOL (NW)
Blackpool County Court, The Law Courts, Chapel Street, Blackpool, Lancashire FY1 5RJ
Tel: 01253 754020
Fax: 01253 295255
Email: enquiries@blackpool.countycourt.gsi.gov.uk
DX: 724900 BLACKPOOL 10

Court Details
The Law Courts, Chapel Street, Blackpool
Bankruptcy; Children; Divorce; Domestic violence; Housing possession; Money claims

132   BLACKWOOD (WAL)
Blackwood Civil and Family Court, 8 Hall Street, Blackwood NP12 1NY
Tel: 01495 238200
Fax: 0870 324 0167
Email: blackwood.enquiries@hmcts.gsi.gov.uk
DX: 99470 BLACKWOOD 2

Court Details
Civil and Family Court, 8 Hall Street, Blackwood
Bankruptcy; Children; Divorce; Domestic violence; Housing possession

133   BLETCHLEY AND LEIGHTON BUZZARD
renamed MILTON KEYNES

134   BLOOMSBURY
see LONDON

705   BLYTH
closed wef 15/12/97 – successor court – Morpeth and Berwick

136   BODMIN (SW)
The Law Courts, Launceston Road, Bodmin, Cornwall PL31 2AL
Tel: 01208 261580
Fax: 01208 772555
Email: enquiriesbodmincc@hmcts.gsi.gov.uk
DX: 136846 BODMIN 2

Court Details
The Law Courts, Launceston Road, Bodmin
Children; Divorce; Domestic violence; Housing possession; Money claims

137   BOLTON (NW)
Bolton Combined Court Centre, The Law Courts, Blackhorse Street, Bolton, Lancashire BL1 1SU
Tel: 01204 392881
Fax: 01204 373706
Email: enquiries@bolton.countycourt.gsi.gov.uk
DX: 702610 BOLTON 3

Court Details
The Law Courts, Blackhorse Street, Bolton
Adoption; Bankruptcy; Children; Divorce; Domestic violence; Housing possession; Money claims

---

138   BOSTON (M)
Boston County Court, 55 Norfolk Street, Boston, Lincolnshire PE21 6PE
Tel: 01205 366080 (Office); 359665 (Bailiff)
Email: bostonenquiries@hmcts.gsi.gov.uk
DX: 701922 BOSTON 2
Court Details
Boston County Court, 55 Norfolk Street, Boston
Bankruptcy; Children; Divorce; Domestic violence; Housing possession; Money claims

---

139   BOURNEMOUTH (SW)
Bournemouth and Poole Crown and County Courts, Courts of Justice, Deansleigh Road, Bournemouth BH7 7DS
Tel: 01202 502800
Fax: 01202 502801
Email: enquiries@bournemouth.countycourt.gsi.gov.uk
DX: 98420 BOURNEMOUTH 4
Court Details
Courts of Justice, Deansleigh Road, Bournemouth
Adoption; Bankruptcy; Children; Divorce; Domestic violence; Housing possession; Money claims

---

140   BOW
see LONDON

---

141   BRADFORD (NE)
Bradford Combined Court Centre, The Law Courts, Exchange Square, Drake Street, Bradford, West Yorkshire BD1 1JA
Tel: 01274 840274
Fax: 01274 840275
Email: enquiries@bradford.countycourt.gsi.gov.uk
DX: 702083 BRADFORD 2
Court Details
The Law Courts, Exchange Square, Drake Street, Bradford
Bankruptcy; Children; Divorce; Domestic violence; Forced marriage; Housing possession; Money claims

---

142   BRAINTREE
closed wef 1/12/97 – successor courts Chelmsford, Harlow and Colchester

---

143   BRECKNOCK (WAL)
closed

---

144   BRENTFORD
see LONDON

---

145   BRENTWOOD
transferred to BASILDON wef 29/12/95

---

146   BRIDGEND (WAL)
Bridgend Law Courts, Sunnyside, Bridgend CF31 4AJ
Tel: 01656 673833
Fax: 0870 739 5940
Email: enquiriesbridgendlawcourts@hmcts.gsi.gov.uk
DX: 99750 BRIDGEND 2
Court Details
Bridgend Law Courts, Sunnyside, Bridgend
Bankruptcy; Children; Divorce; Domestic violence; Housing possession

---

147   BRIDGNORTH
closed wef 1/10/84 – successor court – Wellington

---

148   BRIDGWATER
closed wef 20/12/99 – successor court – Taunton

---

149   BRIDLINGTON
closed wef 24/12/97 – successor court – Scarborough

150   BRIGHTON (SE)
William Street, Brighton BN2 0RF
Tel: 01273 674421
Fax: 0870 324 0319
Email: enquiries@brighton.countycourt.gsi.gov.uk
DX: 98070 BRIGHTON 3
Court Details
William Street, Brighton
Bankruptcy; House possession; Money claims

151   BRISTOL (SW)
Bristol Civil Justice Centre, 2 Redcliff Street, Bristol BS1 6GR
Tel: 0117 366 4800
Fax: 0870 324 0048
Email: enquiries@bristol.countycourt.gsi.gov.uk
DX: 95903 BRISTOL 3
Court Details
Bristol Civil Justice Centre
Adoption; Bankruptcy; Children; Civil partnership; Divorce; Domestic violence; Forced marriage; Housing possession; Money claims

152   BROMLEY
see LONDON

154   BURNLEY (NW)
Burnley Combined Court Centre, The Law Courts, Hammerton Street, Burnley, Lancashire BB11 1XD
Tel: 01282 855300
Fax: 01282 414911
Email: enquiries@burnley.countycourt.gsi.gov.uk
DX: 724940 BURNLEY 4
Court Details
The Law Courts, Hammmerton Street, Burnley
Bankruptcy; Money claims

155   BURTON-UPON-TRENT (M)
closed wef 2013

156   BURY (NW)
The Courthouse, Tenters Street, Bury, Lancashire BL9 0HX
Tel: 0161 447 8699
Fax: 0161 763 4995
Email: enquiries@bury.countycourt.gsi.gov.uk
DX: 702615 BURY 2
Court Details
The Courthouse, Tenters Street, Bury
Bankruptcy; Divorce; Domestic violence; Housing possession; Money claims

157   BURY ST EDMUNDS (SE)
Triton House (Entrance B), St Andrew's Street North, Bury St Edmunds, Suffolk IP33 1TR
Tel: 0344 892 4000
Fax: 01284 702687
Email: enquiries@burystedmunds.countycourt.gsi.gov.uk
DX: 97640 BURY ST EDMUNDS 3
Court Details
Triton House (Entrance F), St Andrew's Street North, Bury St Edmunds
Adoption; Bankruptcy; Children; Divorce; Domestic violence; Forced marriage; Housing possession; Money claims

158   BUXTON (M)
Morledge, Derby DE1 2XE
Tel: 01332 622600
Fax: 01332 622543
Email: scmenquiries@hmcts.gsi.gov.uk

DX: 724060 DERBY 21

Note: This building is used only for occasional hearings. Please direct all correspondence to Derby County Court.

Court Details

Court House, Peak Buildings, Terrace Road, Buxton SK17 6DY

Housing possession; Money claims

159 CAERNARFON (WAL)

Court House, Llanberis Road, Caernarfon, Gwynedd LL55 2DF

Tel: 01286 684600

Fax: 01286 678965

Email: enquiries@caernarfon.countycourt.gsi.gov.uk

DX: 702483 CAERNARFON 2

Court Details

Court House, Llanberis Road, Caernarfon

Adoption; Bankruptcy; Children; Divorce; Domestic violence; Housing possession; Money claims

160 CAERPHILLY

closed wef 1/12/00 – successor courts – Cardiff, Blackwood

161 CAMBORNE AND REDRUTH

closed wef 24/12/98 – successor court – Penzance

162 CAMBRIDGE (SE)

197 East Road, Cambridge CB1 1BA

Tel: 0344 892 4000

Fax: 0870 761 7687

Email: cambridgecountyenquiries@hmcts.gsi.gov.uk

DX: 97650 CAMBRIDGE 3

Court Details

197 East Road, Cambridge

Adoption; Bankruptcy; Children; Divorce; Domestic violence; Forced marriage; Housing possession; Money claims

163 CANTERBURY (SE)

Canterbury Combined Court Centre, Law Courts, Chaucer Road, Canterbury, Kent CT1 1ZA

Tel: 01227 819200

Fax: 01227 819283

Email: enquiries@canterbury.countycourt.gsi.gov.uk

DX: 99710 CANTERBURY 3

Court Details

Law Courts, Chaucer Road, Canterbury

Adoption; Bankruptcy; Children; Divorce; Domestic violence; Forced marriage; Housing possession; Money claims

164 CARDIFF CIVIL JUSTICE CENTRE (WAL)

Cardiff Civil Justice Centre, 2 Park Street, Cardiff CF10 1ET

Tel: 029 2037 6400

Fax: 029 2037 6475

Email: enquiries@cardiff.countycourt.gsi.gov.uk

DX: 99500 CARDIFF 6

Court Details

2 Park Street, Cardiff

Adoption; Bankruptcy; Children; Civil partnership; Divorce; Domestic violence; Forced marriage; Housing possession

707 CARDIGAN

closed wef 29/12/95 – successor court – Carmarthen

165 CARLISLE (NW)

Carlisle Combined Court Centre, Courts of Justice, Earl Street, Carlisle CA1 1DJ

Tel: 01228 882140

Fax: 0870 324 0259

Email: enquiries@carlisle.countycourt.gsi.gov.uk

DX: 65331 CARLISLE 2

Court Details
Courts of Justice, Earl Street, Carlisle
Adoption; Bankruptcy; Children; Divorce; Domestic violence; Housing possession; Money claims

166   CARMARTHEN (WAL)

Carmarthen County Court and Family Court Hearing Centre, Hill House, Picton Terrace, Carmarthen SA31 3BT
Tel: 01267 228010
Fax: 0870 7617684
Email: enquiries@carmarthen.countycourt.gsi.gov.uk
DX: 99570 CARMARTHEN 2

Court Details
Guildhall, Carmarthen
Bankruptcy; Children; Divorce; Domestic violence; Housing possession; Money claims

CENTRAL LONDON
see LONDON

CHARD
see AXMINSTER AND CHARD

CHATHAM
see MEDWAY

167   CHELMSFORD (SE)

Priory Place, New London Road, Chelmsford, Essex CM2 0PP
Tel: 0344 892 4000
Fax: 01245 295395
Email: enquiries@chelmsford.countycourt.gsi.gov.uk
DX: 97660 CHELMSFORD 4

Court Details
Priory Place, New London Road, Chelmsford
Adoption; Bankruptcy; Children; Divorce; Domestic violence; Forced marriage; Housing possession; Money claims

168   CHELTENHAM
closed wef 30/6/11

169   CHEPSTOW
closed wef 1/4/02 – successor court – Newport (Gwent)

170   CHESTER (NW)

Trident House, Little St John Street, Chester CH1 1SN
Tel: 01244 404200
Fax: 0870 324 0311
Email: enquiries@chester.countycourt.gsi.gov.uk
DX: 702460 CHESTER 4

Court Details
Trident House, Little St John Street, Chester
Adoption; Bankruptcy; Children; Civil partnership; Divorce; Domestic violence; Housing possession; Money claims

171   CHESTERFIELD (M)

St Mary's Gate, Chesterfield, Derbyshire S41 7TD
Tel: 01246 501200; 501201 (Bailiffs)
Fax: 01246 501205
Email: chesterfieldcountycourt@hmcts.gsi.gov.uk
DX: 703160 CHESTERFIELD 3

Court Details
St Mary's Gate, Chesterfield
Bankruptcy; Children; Divorce; Domestic violence; Housing possession; Money claims

172   CHICHESTER (SE)

Chichester Combined Court Centre, Southgate, Chichester, West Sussex PO19 1SX
Tel: 01243 520700
Fax: 0870 324 0244

Email: enquiries@chichester.countycourt.gsi.gov.uk
DX: 97460 CHICHESTER 2
Court Details
The Courthouse, Southgate, Chichester
Adoption; Children; Divorce; Domestic violence; Forced marriage; Housing possession; Money claims

173   CHIPPENHAM
(closed wef 1/5/96 – successor courts – Swindon and Trowbridge)

353   CHIPPENHAM AND TROWBRIDGE (SW)
Chippenham Law Courts, Pewsham Way, Chippenham, Wiltshire SN15 3BF
Tel: 01249 463473
Fax: 01249 466246
Email: chipp&trowcty@hmcts.gsi.gov.uk
DX: 744850 CHIPPENHAM 5
Email: enquiries@trowbridge.countycourt.gsi.gov.uk
Court Details
Chippenham Law Courts, Pewsham Way, Chippenham
Domestic violence; Housing possession; Money claims
(***Note:*** **new divorce applications for Wiltshire are handled by Salisbury County Court wef 1/8/13**)

174   CHORLEY
closed wef 9/9/11

CIRENCESTER
see SWINDON

CLERKENWELL
see LONDON

176   COLCHESTER (SE)
Falkland House, 25 Southway, Colchester, Essex CO3 3EG
Tel: 0344 892 4000
Fax: 01206 717250
Email: enquiries@colchester.countycourt.gsi.gov.uk
DX: 97670 COLCHESTER 3
Court Details
Falkland House, 25 Southway, Colchester
Bankruptcy; Children; Divorce; Domestic violence; Housing possession; Money claims

COLWYN BAY
see CONWY AND COLWYN

177   CONSETT
closed wef 7/11 – successor courts– Durham and Gateshead

178   CONWY AND COLWYN
closed wef 30/6/10 – administration relocated to Rhyl
County Court – hearings held at Llandudno Magistrates' Court

179   CORBY
closed wef 1/3/99 – successor courts – Kettering and Peterborough

180   COVENTRY (M)
Coventry Combined Court Centre, 140 Much Park Street, Coventry CV1 2SN
Tel: 0300 123 5577
Fax: 024 7652 0443
Email: civilenquiries@coventry.countycourt.gsi.gov.uk.gsi.gov.uk
DX: 701580 COVENTRY 5
Court Details
140 Much Park Street, Coventry
Adoption; Bankruptcy; Children; Divorce; Domestic violence; Housing possession; Money claims

181 CREWE (NW)
The Law Courts, Civic Centre, Crewe, Cheshire CW1 2DP
Tel: 01270 539300
Fax: 0870 761 7649
Email: ch-crewectycivil@hmcts.gsi.gov.uk
DX: 702504 CREWE 2
Court Details
The Law Courts, Civic Centre, Crewe
Bankruptcy; Children; Divorce; Domestic violence; Housing possession; Money claims

182 CROYDON
see LONDON

183 DARLINGTON (NE)
Family Court Hearing Centre, 4 Coniscliffe Road, Darlington, County Durham DL3 7RL
Tel: 01325 463224
Fax: 01325 362829
Email: darlingtoncountycourt@hmcts.gsi.gov.uk
DX: 65109 DARLINGTON 2
Court Details
4 Coniscliffe Road, Darlington
Bankruptcy; Children; Divorce; Domestic violence; Housing possession; Money claims

184 DARTFORD (SE)
Court House, Home Gardens, Dartford, Kent DA1 1DX
Tel: 01322 627600
Fax: 01322 270902
Email: enquiries@dartford.countycourt.gsi.gov.uk
DX: 98090 DARTFORD 2
Court Details
Court House, Home Gardens, Dartford
Adoption; Children; Divorce; Domestic violence; Forced marriage; Housing possession; Money claims

185 DERBY (M)
Derby Combined Court Centre, Morledge, Derby DE1 2XE
Tel: 01332 622600
Fax: 01332 622543
Email: enquiries@derby.countycourt.gsi.gov.uk
DX: 724060 DERBY 21
Court Details
Combined Court Centre, Morledge, Derby
Adoption; Bankruptcy; Children; Divorce; Domestic violence; Forced marriage; Housing possession; Money claims

DEVIZES
see TROWBRIDGE

186 DEWSBURY
closed wef 4/12

187 DONCASTER (NE)
74 Waterdale, Doncaster, South Yorkshire DN1 3BT
Tel: 01302 381730
Fax: 01302 768090
Email: enquiries@doncaster.countycourt.gsi.gov.uk
DX: 702089 DONCASTER 4
Court Details
74 Waterdale, Doncaster
Bankruptcy; Children; Divorce; Domestic violence; Housing possession

DORCHESTER
see WEYMOUTH

188 DOVER
closed wef 30/3/96 – successor court – Canterbury

189   DUDLEY (M)
Dudley County Court and Family Court Hearing Centre, 7 Hagley Road, Stourbridge, West Midlands
DY8 1QL
Tel: 01384 397800
Fax: 01384 397802
Email: enquiries@dudley.countycourt.gsi.gov.uk
DX: 701889 STOURBRIDGE 2
Court Details
7 Hagley Road, Stourbridge, West Midlands DY8 1QL
Bankruptcy; Children; Divorce; Domestic violence; Housing possession; Money claims

190   DURHAM (NE)
Civil and Family Justice Centre, Green Lane, Old Elvet, Durham DH1 3RG
Tel: 0191 375 1840
Fax: 0870 739 5954
Email: hearingsdurhamcty@hmcts.gsi.gov.uk
DX: 65115 DURHAM 5
Court Details
Civil and Family Justice Centre, Green Lane, Old Elvet
**Adoption; Bankruptcy; Children; Divorce; Domestic violence; Housing possession; Money
claims**

191   EASTBOURNE (SE)
The Law Courts, Old Orchard Road, Eastbourne, East Sussex BN21 4UN
Tel: 01323 727518
Fax: 01323 649372
DX: 98110 EASTBOURNE 2
Court Details
The Law Courts, Eastbourne
**Adoption; Bankruptcy; Children; Divorce; Domestic violence; Forced marriage; Housing
possession; Money claims**

192   EAST GRINSTEAD
closed wef 4/1/94 – successor courts – Haywards Heath and Tunbridge Wells

194   EDMONTON
see LONDON

195   ELLESMERE PORT
closed wef 5/12/94 – successor court – Chester

196   EPSOM
closed wef 7/11

197   EVESHAM
closed wef 30/9/11 – successor court – Worcester

198   EXETER (SW)
Exeter Crown and County Court, Southernhay Gardens, Exeter, Devon EX1 1UH
Tel: 01392 415300
Fax: 01392 415350
Email: enquiries@exeter.countycourt.gsi.gov.uk
DX: 98440 EXETER 2
Court Details
Southernhay Gardens, Exeter
**Adoption; Bankruptcy; Children; Civil partnership; Divorce; Domestic violence; Housing
possession; Money claims**

FARNHAM
see ALDERSHOT AND FARNHAM

199   FOLKESTONE
closed wef 30/3/96 – successor court – Ashford

FROME
see TROWBRIDGE

201 GAINSBOROUGH
closed wef 1/1/93 – successor court – Lincoln

202 GATESHEAD (NE)
Gateshead Law Courts, Warwick Street, Gateshead, Tyne & Wear NE8 1DT
Tel: 0191 477 5821
Fax: 0870 324 0210
Email: gatesheadcivil@hmcourts-service.gsi.gov.uk
DX: 742120 GATESHEAD 6
Court Details
Gateshead Law Courts, Warwick Street
Children; Divorce; Domestic violence; Housing possession; Money claims

203 GLOUCESTER AND CHELTENHAM (SW)
Family and Civil Courts, County Court Offices, Kimbrose Way, Gloucester GL1 2DE
Tel: 01452 834900
Fax: 0870 324 0114
Email: enquiries@gloucester.countycourt.gsi.gov.uk
DX: 98660 GLOUCESTER 5
Court Details
Kimbrose Way, Gloucester
Bankruptcy; Children; Divorce; Domestic violence; Housing possession; Money claims

204 GOOLE
closed wef 4/11/96 – successor court – Doncaster

205 GRANTHAM
closed wef 9/11

206 GRAVESEND
closed wef 31/12/10

207 GRAYS THURROCK
closed wef 31/1/2000 – successor court – Basildon

208 GREAT GRIMSBY (NE)
Great Grimsby Combined Court Centre, Town Hall Square, Grimsby, Lincolnshire DN31 1HX
Tel: 01472 265200
Fax: 01472 265201
Email: enquiries@grimsby.countycourt.gsi.gov.uk
DX: 702007 GRIMSBY 3
Court Details
The Combined Court Centre, Town Hall Square, Grimsby
Adoption; Bankruptcy; Children; Divorce; Domestic violence; Forced marriage; Housing possession; Money claims

209 GREAT MALVERN
closed wef 1/1/93 – successor court – Worcester

210 GREAT YARMOUTH
closed wef 31/1/2000 – successor court – Lowestoft, Norwich

GRIMSBY
see GREAT GRIMSBY

211 GUILDFORD (SE)
The Law Courts, Mary Road, Guildford, Surrey GU1 4PS
Tel: 01483 405300
Fax: 01483 300031
Email: surreycivil@hmcts.gsi.gov.uk
DX: 97860 GUILDFORD 5
Court Details
The Law Courts, Mary Road, Guildford
Adoption; Bankruptcy; Children; Divorce; Domestic violence; Forced marriage; Housing possession; Money claims

212   HALIFAX (NE)
Prescott Street, Halifax, West Yorkshire HX1 2JJ
Tel: 01422 344700 (General Office); 369936 (Bailiffs)
Fax: 01422 360132
Email: claims@halifax.countycourt.gsi.gov.uk
DX: 702095 HALIFAX 2
Court Details
Prescott Street, Halifax
Bankruptcy; Children; Divorce; Domestic violence; Housing possession; Money claims

HANLEY
see STOKE-ON-TRENT

213   HARLOW
closed wef 31/3/11

214   HARROGATE (NE)
2 Victoria Avenue, Harrogate, North Yorkshire HG1 1EL
Tel: 01423 503921
Fax: 01423 528679
Email: enquiries@harrogate.countycourt.gsi.gov.uk
DX: 702098 HARROGATE 3
Court Details
2 Victoria Avenue, Harrogate
Bankruptcy; Children; Divorce; Domestic violence; Housing possession; Money claims

215   HARTLEPOOL (NE)
Law Courts, Victoria Road, Hartlepool TS24 8BS
Tel: 01429 268198
Fax: 01429 862550
Email: scmenquiries@hmcts.gsi.gov.uk
DX: 65121 HARTLEPOOL 2
Court Details
Law Courts, Victoria Road, Hartlepool
Children; Divorce; Domestic violence; Housing possession; Money claims

216   HASTINGS (SE)
The Law Courts, Bohemia Road, Hastings, East Sussex TN34 1QX
Tel: 01424 710280/287/291
Fax: 01424 421585
DX: 98150 HASTINGS 2
Court Details
Law Courts, Bohemia Road, Hastings
Adoption; Bankruptcy; Children; Divorce; Domestic violence; Forced marriage; Housing possession; Money claims

217   HAVERFORDWEST (WAL)
Penffynnon, Hawthorn Rise, Haverfordwest, Pembrokeshire SA61 2AX
Tel: 01437 772060; 772076 (Bailiffs)
Fax: 0870 7617734
Email: enquiries@haverfordwest.countycourt.gsi.gov.uk
DX: 99610 HAVERFORDWEST 2
Court Details
Penffynnon, Hawthorn Rise, Haverfordwest
Bankruptcy; Children; Divorce; Domestic violence; Housing possession; Money claims

218   HAYWARDS HEATH
closed wef 7/11

219   HEMEL HEMPSTEAD
closed wef 24/12/98 – successor courts – Aylesbury, Luton and Watford

220   HEREFORD (M)
First Floor, Barclays Bank Chambers, 1/3 Broad Street, Hereford HR4 9BA
Tel: 01432 357233/264118
Fax: 01432 352593
Email: scmenquiries@hmcts.gsi.gov.uk

DX: 701904 HEREFORD 2

Court Details
1/3 Broad Street, Hereford
Bankruptcy; Children; Divorce; Domestic violence; Housing possession; Money claims

221   HERTFORD (SE)
PO Box 373, Hertford SG13 9HT
Tel: 0844 892 0550
Fax: 0870 324 0115
Email: enquiries@hertford.countycourt.gsi.gov.uk
DX: 97710 HERTFORD 2

Court Details
Shire Hall, Fore Street, Hertford SG14 1BY
Adoption; Bankruptcy; Children; Divorce; Domestic violence; Forced marriage; Housing possession; Money claims

713   HEXHAM
closed wef 4/1/94 – successor court – Newcastle-upon-Tyne

223   HIGH WYCOMBE (SE)
High Wycombe County Court and Family Court Hearing Centre, The Law Courts, Windsor Road, Slough, Berkshire SL1 2HE
Tel: 01753 690 300
Fax: 01753 690 327
Email: enquiries@slough.countycourt.gsi.gov.uk
DX: 98030 SLOUGH 3

Court Details
The Law Courts, Easton Street, High Wycombe HP11 1LR
Adoption; Bankruptcy; Children; Divorce; Domestic violence; Forced marriage; Housing possession; Money claims

224   HINCKLEY
closed wef 1/10/84 – successor court – Nuneaton

225   HITCHIN
closed wef 1/7/11

226   HOLYWELL
closed wef 7/9/98 – successor courts – Rhyl and Chester

227   HORSHAM (SE)
The Law Courts, Hurst Road, Horsham, Sussex RH12 2EU
Tel: 01403 252474
Fax: 01403 258844
Email: ss.cchorsham@hmcts.gsi.gov.uk
DX: 98170 HORSHAM 2

Court Details
The Law Courts, Hurst Road, Horsham
Adoption; Children; Divorce; Domestic violence; Forced marriage; Housing possession; Money claims

228   HUDDERSFIELD (NE)
County Court, Queensgate House, Queensgate, Huddersfield HD1 2RR
Tel: 01484 421043; 535085
Fax: 01484 426366
Email: enquiries@huddersfield.countycourt.gsi.gov.uk
DX: 703013 HUDDERSFIELD 2

Court Details
County Court, Queensgate House, Queensgate, Huddersfield
Bankruptcy; Children; Divorce; Domestic violence; Housing possession; Money claims

HULL
see KINGSTON-UPON-HULL

229   HUNTINGDON
closed wef 31/3/11

230   HYDE
closed wef 31/1/87 – successor court – Tameside

231   ILFORD
see LONDON

232   ILKESTON
closed wef 16/2/96 – successor courts – Derby and Nottingham

233   IPSWICH (SE)
8 Arcade Street, Ipswich, Suffolk IP1 1EJ
Tel: 0344 892 4000
Fax: 01473 251797
Email: enquiries@ipswich.countycourt.gsi.gov.uk
DX: 97730 IPSWICH 3
Court Details
8 Arcade Street, Ipswich
Adoption; Bankruptcy; Children; Divorce; Domestic violence; Forced marriage; Housing possession; Money claims

234   KEIGHLEY
closed wef 4/12

235   KENDAL (NW)
Carlisle Combined Court Centre, Courts of Justice, Earl Street, Carlisle CA1 1DJ
Tel: 01228 882140
Fax: 0870 324 0259
Email: enquiries@carlisle.countycourt.gsi.gov.uk
DX: 65331 CARLISLE 2
Note: Court open Wednesdays and Fridays only.
Court Details
The Court House, County Court, Burneside Road, Kendal LA9 4NF
Bankruptcy; Divorce; Housing possession

236   KETTERING (M)
Dryland Street, Kettering, Northamtonshire NN16 0BE
Tel: 01536 512471
Email: enquiries@kettering.countycourt.gsi.gov.uk
DX: 701886 KETTERING 2
Court Details
Dryland Street, Kettering
Housing possession; Money claims

237   KIDDERMINSTER
closed wef 30/3/9/11 – successor court – Worcester

238   KING'S LYNN (SE)
12 King Street, King's Lynn, Norfolk PE30 1ES
Tel: 0844 892 4000
Fax: 01553 769824
DX: 97740 KING'S LYNN 2
Email: kingslynn.cty.mail@hmcts.gsi.gov.uk
Court Details
Chequer House, 12 King Street, King's Lynn
Adoption; Bankruptcy; Children; Divorce; Domestic violence; Forced marriage; Housing possession; Money claims

239   KINGSTON-UPON-HULL (NE)
Kingston-upon-Hull Combined Court Centre, Lowgate, Hull HU1 2EZ
Tel: 01482 586161
Fax: 01482 588527
Email: enquiries@kingstonuponhull.countycourt.gsi.gov.uk
DX: 703010 HULL 5
Court Details
Kingston-upon-Hull Combined Court Centre, Lowgate, Hull

Adoption; Bankruptcy; Children; Divorce; Domestic violence; Housing possession; Money claims

240   KINGSTON-UPON-THAMES
see LONDON

241   LAMBETH
see LONDON

714   LAMPETER
closed wef 5/12/94 – successor courts – Aberystwyth and Camarthen

242   LANCASTER (NW)
2nd Floor, Mitre House, Church Street, Lancaster LA1 1UZ
Tel: 01524 68112
Fax: 0870 739 4451
Email: enquiries@lancaster.countycourt.gsi.gov.uk
DX: 145880 LANCASTER 2
Court Details
County Court, 2nd Floor, Mitre House, Church Street, Lancaster
Adoption; Bankruptcy; Children; Divorce; Domestic violence; Housing possession; Money claims

715   LAUNCESTON
closed wef 5/12/95 – successor court – Bodmin

243   LEEDS (NE)
Leeds Combined Court Centre, The Courthouse, 1 Oxford Row, Leeds LS1 3BG
Tel: 0113 306 2800
Email: enquiries@leeds.countycourt.gsi.gov.uk
DX: 703016 LEEDS 6
Court Details
Leeds Combined Court Centre, The Court House, 1 Oxford Row, Leeds
Coverdale House, 13–15 East Parade, Leeds LS1 4BJ
Adoption; Bankruptcy; Children; Civil partnership; Divorce; Domestic violence; Forced marriage; Housing possession; Money claims

244   LEICESTER (M)
90 Wellington Street, Leicester LE1 6HG
Tel: 0116 222 5700
Email: enquiries@leicester.countycourt.gsi.gov.uk
DX: 17401 LEICESTER 3
Court Details
The Court House, 90 Wellington Street, Leicester
Adoption; Bankruptcy; Children; Divorce; Domestic violence; Forced marriage; Housing possession; Money claims

245   LEIGH
closed wef 2010 – successor court – Wigan. For Glazebury and Culcheth – Warrington

LEIGHTON BUZZARD
see BLETCHLEY AND LEIGHTON BUZZARD

246   LEOMINSTER
closed wef 1/10/84 – successor court – Hereford

247   LEWES (SE)
Lewes Combined Court Centre, The Law Courts, High Street, Lewes, East Sussex BN7 1YB
Tel: 01273 674421
Fax: 01273 602138
DX: 97395 LEWES 4
Email: enquiries@lewes.countycourt.gsi.gov.uk
Court Details
Law Courts, High Street, Lewes
Housing possession; Money claims

248   LICHFIELD
closed wef 3/7/00 – successor courts – Burton upon Trent, Stafford, Tamworth, Walsall

249   LINCOLN (M)
Lincoln County Court, 360 High Street, Lincoln LN5 7PS
Tel: 01522 551500
DX: 703231 LINCOLN 6
Email: enquiries@lincoln.countycourt.gsi.gov.uk
Court Details
360 High Street, Lincoln
Adoption; Bankruptcy; Children; Divorce; Domestic violence; Housing possession; Money claims

LISKEARD
see BODMIN

251   LIVERPOOL CIVIL AND FAMILY CENTRE (NW)
Liverpool Civil and Family Courts, 35 Vernon Street, Liverpool L2 2BX
Tel: 0151 296 2200
Fax: 0151 296 2201
Email: enquiries@liverpool.countycourt.gsi.gov.uk
DX: 702600 LIVERPOOL 5
Court Details
35 Vernon Street, Liverpool
Adoption; Bankruptcy; Children; Divorce; Domestic violence; Housing possession

143   LLANDRINDOD WELLS
closed wef 29/12/95 – successor court – Brecknock

253   LLANELLI (WAL)
2nd Floor, Court Buildings, Town Hall Square, Llanelli, Carmarthenshire SA15 3AL
Tel: 01554 757171
Fax: 01554 758079
Email: enquiries@llanelli.countycourt.gsi.gov.uk
DX: 99510 LLANELLI 2
Court Details
2nd Floor, Court Buildings, Town Hall Square, Llanelli
Children; Divorce; Domestic violence; Housing possession; Money claims

254   LLANGEFNI (WAL)
Caernarfon County Court and Family Court Hearing Centre, Llanberis Road, Caernarfon, Gwynedd LL55 2DF
Tel: 01286 684 600
Fax: 01286 678 965
Email: enquiries@caernarfon.countycourt.gsi.gov.uk
DX: 702480 LLANGEFNI 2
Court Details
County Court Buildings, Llangefni
Adoption; Bankruptcy; Children; Divorce; Domestic violence; Housing possession; Money claims

LONDON

117   BARNET (LON)
St Mary's Court, Regents Park Road, Finchley Central, London N3 1BQ
Tel: 020 8343 4272
Fax: 0870 324 0201
Email: enquiries@barnet.countycourt.gsi.gov.uk
DX: 122570 FINCHLEY (CHURCH END)
Court Details
St Mary's Court, Regents Park Road, Finchley Central
Adoption; Children; Divorce; Domestic violence; Housing possession; Money claims

134   BLOOMSBURY
combined with Westminster County Court to form Central London County Court – wef 14/8/92

140   BOW (LON)
96 Romford Road, Stratford, London E15 4EG
Tel: 020 8536 5200
Fax: 0870 324 0188

Email: civil@bow.countycourt.gsi.gov.uk
DX: 97490 STRATFORD (LONDON) 2

Court Details
96 Romford Road, Stratford
Children; Divorce; Domestic violence; Housing possession; Money claims

144   BRENTFORD (LON)
Alexandra Road, High Street, Brentford, Middlesex TW8 0JJ
Tel: 020 8231 8940
Fax: 0870 739 5909
Email: enquiries@brentford.countycourt.gsi.gov.uk
DX: 97840 BRENTFORD 2

Court Details
Alexandra Road, High Street, Brentford
Children; Divorce; Domestic violence; Housing possession; Money claims

152   BROMLEY (LON)
Court House, College Road, Bromley, Kent BR1 3PX
Tel: 020 8290 9620
Fax: 0870 761 7689
Email: enquiries@bromley.countycourt.gsi.gov.uk
DX: 98080 BROMLEY 2

Court Details
Court House, College Road, Bromley
Adoption; Children; Divorce; Domestic violence; Housing possession; Money claims

372   CENTRAL LONDON (LON)
County Court at Central London, Royal Courts of Justice, Thomas More Building, Royal Courts of Justice, Strand, London WC2A 2LL
Tel: 0207 947 7800
Fax: 0870 739 4144
Email: enquiries@centrallondon.countycourt.gsi.gov.uk
DX: 44453 STRAND

Court Details
Thomas More Building, Royal Courts of Justice, Strand, London WC2A 2LL
Housing possession; Money claims

321   CLERKENWELL AND SHOREDITCH (LON)
The Gee Street Courthouse, 29–41 Gee Street, London EC1V 3RE
Tel: 020 7250 7200
Fax: 0870 761 7688
Email: enquiries@clerkenwellandshoreditch.countycourt.gsi.gov.uk
DX: 121000 SHOREDITCH 2

Court Details
29–41 Gee Street
Children; Divorce; Domestic violence; Housing possession; Money claims

182   CROYDON (LON)
Croydon Civil and Family Court Centre, The Law Courts, Altyre Road, Croydon CR9 5AB
Tel: 0300 123 5577
Fax: 020 8760 0432
Email: enquiries@croydon.countycourt.gsi.gov.uk
DX: 97470 CROYDON 6

Court Details
The Law Courts, Altyre Road, Croydon
Adoption; Bankruptcy; Children; Divorce; Domestic violence; Housing possession; Money claims

194   EDMONTON (LON)
Court House, 59 Fore Street, Edmonton, London N18 2TN
Tel: 020 8884 6500
Fax: 0870 324 0314
Email: enquiries@edmonton.countycourt.gsi.gov.uk
DX: 136686 EDMONTON 3

Court Details
Court House, 59 Fore Street, Upper Edmonton
Children; Divorce; Domestic violence; Housing possession; Money claims

231   ILFORD
closed wef 31/3/12

240   KINGSTON-UPON-THAMES (LON)
County Court, St James's Road, Kingston-upon-Thames, Surrey KT1 2AD
Tel: 020 8972 8700
Fax: 0870 324 0315
Email: enquiries@kingston.countycourt.gsi.gov.uk
DX: 97890 KINGSTON-UPON-THAMES 3

Court Details
County Court, St James's Road, Kingston-upon-Thames
Bankruptcy; Children; Divorce; Domestic violence; Housing possession; Money claims

241   LAMBETH (LON)
Court House, Cleaver Street, Kennington Road, London SE11 4DZ
Tel: 020 7091 4410
Fax: 0870 324 0205
Email: enquiries@lambeth.countycourt.gsi.gov.uk
DX: 145020 KENNINGTON 2

Court Details
Court House, Cleaver Street, Kennington Road SE11 4DZ
Children; Domestic violence; Housing possession; Money claims

266   THE MAYOR'S AND CITY OF LONDON (LON)
Guildhall Buildings, Basinghall Street, London EC2V 5AR
Tel: 020 7796 5400
Fax: 020 7796 5424
Email: enquiries@mayorsandcityoflondon.countycourt.gsi.gov.uk
DX: 97520 MOORGATE (EC2)

Court Details
Guildhall Buildings, Basinghall Street, London EC2V 5AR
Housing possession

387   ROMFORD (LON)
2A Oaklands Avenue, Romford, Essex RM1 4DP
Tel: 01708 775353
Fax: 0870 324 0225
Email: enquiries@romford.countycourt.gsi.gov.uk
DX: 97530 ROMFORD 2

Court Details
2A Oaklands Avenue, Romford
Adoption; Bankruptcy; Children; Divorce; Domestic violence; Forced marriage; Housing possession

356   UXBRIDGE (LON)
501 Uxbridge Road, Hayes, Middlesex UB4 8HL
Tel: 020 8756 3520
Fax: 0870 324 0300
DX: 44658 HAYES (Middlesex)
Email: enquiries@uxbridge.countycourt.gsi.gov.uk

Court Details
501 Uxbridge Road, Hayes
Children; Divorce; Domestic violence; Housing possession; Money claims

359   WANDSWORTH (LON)
76/78 Upper Richmond Road, Putney SW15 2SU
Tel: 020 8333 4351
Fax: 020 8877 9854
Email: enquiries@wandsworth.countycourt.gsi.gov.uk
DX: 97540 PUTNEY 2

Court Details
76/78 Upper Richmond Road, Putney
Children; Divorce; Domestic violence; Housing possession; Money claims

368   WEST LONDON (LON)
Courthouse, 181 Talgarth Road, Hammersmith, London W6 8DN
Tel: 020 8600 6868
Fax: 020 8600 6860
Email: enquiries@westlondon.countycourt.gsi.gov.uk
DX: 97550 HAMMERSMITH 8

Court Details
Courthouse, 181 Talgarth Road, Hammersmith W6 8DN
Housing possession; Money claims

369   WESTMINSTER
Combined with Bloomsbury County Court to form Central London County Court – wef 14/8/92

375   WILLESDEN (LON)
9 Acton Lane, Harlesden, London NW10 8SB
Tel: 020 8963 8200
Fax: 0870 320 0034
DX: 97560 HARLESDEN 2
Email: enquiries@willesden.countycourt.gsi.gov.uk

Court Details
9 Acton Lane, Harlesden
Children; Divorce; Domestic violence; Forced marriage; Housing possession; Money claims

379   WOOLWICH (LON)
The Court House, 165 Powis Street, Woolwich, London SE18 6JW
Tel: 020 8301 8700
Fax: 0870 324 0285
Email: enquiries@woolwich.countycourt.gsi.gov.uk
DX: 123450 WOOLWICH 8

Court Details
The Court House, Powis Street
Children; Domestic violence; Housing possession; Money claims

255   LOUGHBOROUGH
closed wef 31/12/98 – successor courts – Derby, Leicester and Nottingham

256   LOWESTOFT
closed wef 31/3/11

257   LUDLOW
closed wef 9/11

258   LUTON (SE)
2nd Floor, Cresta House, Alma Street, Luton, Bedfordshire LU1 2PU
Tel: 0844 892 0550
Email: enquiries@luton.countycourt.gsi.gov.uk
DX: 97760 LUTON 4

Court Details
2nd Floor, Cresta House, Alma Street, Luton
Adoption; Bankruptcy; Children; Divorce; Domestic violence; Forced marriage; Housing possession; Money claims

260   MACCLESFIELD (NW)
2nd Floor, Silk House, Park Green, Macclesfield SK11 7NA
Tel: 01625 412800
Fax: 01625 501262
Email: enquiries@macclesfield.countycourt.gsi.gov.uk
DX: 702498 MACCLESFIELD 3

Court Details
2nd Floor, Silk House, Park Green, Macclesfield
Adoption; Bankruptcy; Children; Divorce; Domestic violence; Housing possession; Money claims

261 MAIDSTONE (SE)
The Law Courts, Barker Road, Maidstone, Kent ME16 8EQ
Tel: 01622 202000
Fax: 01622 202002
Email: enquiries@maidstone.countycourt.gsi.gov.uk
DX: 130065 MAIDSTONE 7
Court Details
The Law Courts, Barker Road, Maidstone
Adoption; Bankruptcy; Children; Divorce; Domestic violence; Forced marriage; Housing possession; Money claims

719 MALDON
closed wef 30/6/92 – successor court – Chelmsford

720 MALTON
closed wef 4/1/94 – successor court – York

262 MANCHESTER (NW)
Civil Justice Centre, 1 Bridge Street West, Manchester M60 9DJ
Tel: 0161 240 5000
Fax: 0161 240 5050
Email: family@manchester.countycourt.gsi.gov.uk; bailiffs@manchester.countycourt.gsi.gov.uk; hearings@manchester.countycourt.gsi.gov.uk; e-filing@manchester.countycourt.gsi.gov.uk
DX: 724783 MANCHESTER 44
Court Details
1 Bridge Street West, Manchester
Adoption; Bankruptcy; Children; Civil partnership; Divorce; Domestic violence; Forced marriage; Housing possession; Money claims

263 MANSFIELD (M)
The Court House, Rosemary Street, Mansfield, Nottinghamshire NG19 6EE
Tel: 01623 451500
Fax: 01623 451502
Email: mansfieldcty.enquiries@hmcts.gsi.gov.uk
DX: 179560 MANSFIELD 9
Court Details
The Court House, Rosemary Street, Mansfield
Children; Divorce; Domestic violence; Housing possession; Money claims

MARGATE
see THANET

264 MARKET DRAYTON
closed wef 27/10/95 – successor courts – Shrewsbury and Stoke-on-Trent

265 MATLOCK
closed wef 16/2/96 – successor courts – Burton, Chesterfield and Derby

266 MAYOR'S AND CITY OF LONDON
see LONDON

267 MEDWAY COUNTY AND FAMILY COURT (SE)
Anchorage House, 47–67 High Street, Chatham, Kent ME4 4DW
Tel: 01634 887900
Email: enquiries@medway.countycourt.gsi.gov.uk
DX: 98180 CHATHAM 4
Court Details
Anchorage House, High Street, Chatham
Adoption; Bankruptcy; Children; Divorce; Domestic violence; Forced marriage; Housing possession; Money claims

268 MELTON MOWBRAY (M)
closed – successor courts – Kettering, Nottingham, Peterborough, Leicester

269 MERTHYR TYDFIL (WAL)
Merthyr Tydfil Combined Court Centre, Glebeland Place, Merthyr Tydfil, Mid Glamorgan CF47 8BH
Tel: 01685 727600
Fax: 0870 7395981

Email: enquiries@merthyrtydfil.countycourt.gsi.gov.uk
DX: 99582 MERTHYR TYDFIL 2

Court Details
The Law Courts, Glebeland Place, Merthyr Tydfil
Bankruptcy; Children; Divorce; Domestic violence; Housing possession; Money claims

270   MIDDLESBROUGH (NE)
Teesside Combined Court Centre, Russell Street, Middlesbrough, Cleveland TS1 2AE
Tel: 01642 340000/067
Fax: 01642 340002
Email: enquiries@middlesbrough.countycourt.gsi.gov.uk
DX: 65152 MIDDLESBROUGH 2

Court Details
Russell Street, Middlesbrough
Adoption; Bankruptcy; Housing possession; Money claims

388   MILTON KEYNES (SE)
351 Silbury Boulevard, Witan Gate East, Milton Keynes MK9 2DT
Tel: 01908 302800
Email: enquiries@miltonkeynes.countycourt.gsi.gov.uk
DX: 136266 MILTON KEYNES 6

Court Details
351 Silbury Boulevard, Milton Keynes
Adoption; Bankruptcy; Children; Divorce; Domestic violence; Forced marriage; Housing possession; Money claims

271   MOLD (WAL)
Wrexham Law Courts, Bodhyfryd, Wrexham LL12 7BP
Tel: 01978 317400
Fax: 01978 358213
Email: enquires@wrexham.countycourt.gsi.gov.uk
DX: 702521 MOLD 2 or 721921 WREXHAM 4

Court Details
Law Courts, County Civic Centre, Mold
Housing possession; Money claims

272   MONMOUTH
closed wef 1/4/02 – successor court – Newport (Gwent)

273   MORPETH AND BERWICK (NE)
Fountain House, Newmarket, Morpeth, Northumberland NE61 1LA
Tel: 01670 512221
Fax: 01670 504188
Email: no-morpethcc@hmcts.gsi.gov.uk
DX: 65124 MORPETH 2

Court Details
Fountain House, Newmarket, Morpeth
Children; Divorce; Domestic violence; Housing possession; Money claims

274   NEATH PORT TALBOT (WAL)
Forster Road, Neath, West Glamorgan SA11 3BN
Tel: 01639 642267; 635088 (Bailiffs)
Fax: 0870 761 7675
Email: enquiries@neath.countycourt.gsi.gov.uk
DX: 99550 NEATH 2

Court Details
Forster Road, Neath
Bankruptcy; Children; Divorce; Domestic violence; Housing possession; Money claims

275   NELSON
closed wef 31/1/10 – successor court – Burnley

276   NEWARK
closed wef 9/11

277 NEWBURY
Hearing centre only wef 1/7/11 – all enquiries to Reading County Court

278 NEWCASTLE-UPON-TYNE (NE)
Newcastle-upon-Tyne Combined Court Centre, The Law Courts, Quayside, Newcastle-upon-Tyne NE1 3LA
Tel: 0191 201 2000
Fax: 0870 324 0243
Email: civil@newcastle.countycourt.gsi.gov.uk
DX: 65127 NEWCASTLE UPON TYNE 2
Court Details
The Law Courts, Quayside, Newcastle-upon-Tyne
Adoption; Bankruptcy; Children; Civil partnership; Divorce; Domestic violence; Forced marriage; Housing possession; Money claims

279 NEWPORT ISLE OF WIGHT (SW)
Crown and County Courts, The Law Courts, Quay Street, Newport, Isle of Wight PO30 5YT
Tel: 01983 535100
Fax: 01983 821039
Email: enquiries@newportiow.countycourt.gsi.gov.uk
DX: 98460 NEWPORT IW 2
Court Details
The Law Courts, Quay Street, Newport, Isle of Wight
Bankruptcy; Children; Divorce; Domestic violence; Housing possession; Money claims;Social security

280 NEWPORT (GWENT) CIVIL & FAMILY COURT (WAL)
Clarence House, 5th Floor, Clarence Place, Newport, South Wales NP19 7AA
Tel: 01633 245040
Fax: 0870 324 0308
Email: enquiries@newportgwent.countycourt.gsi.gov.uk
DX: 99480 NEWPORT (South Wales) 4
Court Details
The Concourse, Clarence House, Clarence Place, Newport
Adoption; Bankruptcy; Children; Divorce; Domestic violence; Housing possession

281 NEWTON ABBOT
closed wef 30/3/96 – amalgamated with Torquay

NEWTOWN
see WELSHPOOL AND NEWTOWN

283 NORTH SHIELDS (NE)
Kings Court, Earl Grey Way, Royal Quays, North Shields, Tyne & Wear NE29 6AR
Tel: 0191 298 2339
Fax: 0870 761 7692
DX: 65137 NORTH SHIELDS 2
Court Details
2nd Floor, Kings Court, Earl Grey Way, North Shields
Children; Divorce; Domestic violence; Housing possession; Money claims

722 NORTHALLERTON
closed wef 1/4/92 – successor court – Darlington

282 NORTHAMPTON (M)
Northampton Combined Court Centre, 85/87 Lady's Lane, Northampton NN1 3HQ
Tel: 01604 470400
Fax: 01604 232398
Email: enquiries@northampton.countycourt.gsi.gov.uk
DX: 725380 NORTHAMPTON 21
Court Details
Combined Court Centre, 85/87 Lady's Lane, Northampton
Adoption; Bankruptcy; Children; Divorce; Domestic violence; Housing possession; Money claims

284 NORTHWICH
closed wef 29/7/11

285 NORWICH (SE)
Norwich Combined Court Centre, The Law Courts, Bishopgate, Norwich NR3 1UR
Tel: 0344 892 4000
Fax: 01603 760863
Email: enquiries@norwich.countycourt.gsi.gov.uk
DX: 97385 NORWICH 5
Court Details
The Law Courts, Bishopgate, Norwich
Adoption; Bankruptcy; Children; Divorce; Domestic violence; Forced marriage; Housing possession; Money claims

286 NOTTINGHAM (M)
Nottingham County Court, The Law Courts, 60 Canal Street, Nottingham NG1 7EJ
Tel: 0115 910 3500
Email: enquiries@nottingham.countycourt.gsi.gov.uk
DX: 702380 NOTTINGHAM 7
Court Details
The Law Courts, 60 Canal Street, Nottingham
Adoption; Bankruptcy; Children; Divorce; Domestic violence; Housing possession; Money claims

287 NUNEATON (M)
Warwickshire Justice Centre, Vicarage Street, Nuneaton CV11 4WX
Tel: 0300 123 5577
Fax: 02476 352835
Email: enquiries@nuneaton.countycourt.gsi.gov.uk
DX: 701940 NUNEATON 2
Court Details
Warwickshire Justice Centre, Vicarage Street, Nuneaton
Housing possession; Money claims

288 OLDHAM (NW)
The County Court House, New Radcliffe Street, Oldham OL1 1NL
Tel: 0161 290 4200
Fax: 0161 290 4222
Email: enquiries@oldham.countycourt.gsi.gov.uk
DX: 702595 OLDHAM 2
Court Details
The County Court House, New Radcliffe Street, Oldham
Bankruptcy; Children; Divorce; Domestic violence; Housing possession; Money claims

289 OSWESTRY
closed wef 30/9/11

290 OTLEY
closed wef 2/1/96 – successor courts – Bradford, Harrogate, Leeds and Skipton

291 OXFORD (SE)
Oxford Combined Court Centre, St Aldate's, Oxford OX1 1TL
Tel: 01865 264200
Fax: 01865 790773
Email: enquiries@oxford.countycourt.gsi.gov.uk
DX: 96450 OXFORD 4
Court Details
The Court House, St Aldate's, Oxford
Adoption; Bankruptcy; Children; Divorce; Domestic violence; Forced marriage; Housing possession; Money claims

292 PENRITH
closed wef 26/7/11

293 PENZANCE
closed wef 30/6/11

294 PETERBOROUGH (SE)

Peterborough Combined Court Centre, Crown Buildings, Rivergate, Peterborough PE1 1EJ
Tel: 0344 892 4000
Fax: 01733 557348
Email: enquiries@peterborough.countycourt.gsi.gov.uk
DX: 702302 PETERBOROUGH 8
Court Details
Crown Buildings, Rivergate, Peterborough
Adoption; Bankruptcy; Children; Divorce; Domestic violence; Forced marriage; Housing possession; Money claims

296 PLYMOUTH (SW)

Plymouth Combined Court Centre, The Law Courts, Armada Way, Plymouth, Devon PL1 2ER
Tel: 01752 677400
Fax: 0870 324 0096
Email: enquiries@plymouth.countycourt.gsi.gov.uk
DX: 98470 PLYMOUTH 7
Court Details
The Law Courts, Armada Way, Plymouth
Adoption; Bankruptcy; Children; Divorce; Domestic violence; Housing possession; Money claims
Note: open by appointment only

297 PONTEFRACT

closed wef 4/12

298 PONTYPOOL

closed wef 31/7/11

299 PONTYPRIDD (WAL)

The Courthouse, Courthouse Street, Pontypridd, Mid Glamorgan CF37 1JR
Tel: 01443 490800
Fax: 01443 480305
Email: enquiries@pontypridd.countycourt.gsi.gov.uk
DX: 99620 PONTYPRIDD 2
Court Details
The Courthouse, Courthouse Street, Pontypridd
Adoption; Bankruptcy; Children; Divorce; Domestic violence; Housing possession

300 POOLE

closed wef 30/6/11

302 PORTSMOUTH (SW)

Portsmouth Combined Court Centre, The Courts of Justice, Winston Churchill Avenue, Portsmouth PO1 2EB
Tel: 023 9289 3000
Fax: 023 9282 6385
Email: enquiries@portsmouth.countycourt.gsi.gov.uk
DX: 98490 PORTSMOUTH 5
Court Details
The Courts of Justice, Winston Churchill Avenue, Portsmouth
Adoption; Bankruptcy; Children; Divorce; Domestic violence; Housing possession; Money claims

PORT TALBOT

see NEATH AND PORT TALBOT

303 PRESTON (NW)

Preston Combined Court Centre, The Law Courts, Openshaw Place, Ring Way, Preston PR1 2LL
Tel: 01772 844700
Fax: 01772 844710
Email: enquiries@preston.countycourt.gsi.gov.uk
DX: 702660 PRESTON 5
Court Details
The Law Courts, Openshaw Place, Ring Way, Preston
Bankruptcy; Children; Divorce; Domestic violence; Housing possession; Money claims

304 RAWTENSTALL
closed wef 30/9/11

305 READING (SE)
160–163 Friar Street, Reading RG1 1HE
Tel: 0118 987 0500
Fax: 0870 324 0329
Email: enquiries@reading.countycourt.gsi.gov.uk
DX: 98010 READING 6
Court Details
160–163 Friar Street, Reading
Adoption; Bankruptcy; Children; Divorce; Domestic violence; Housing possession; Money claims

306 REDDITCH
closed wef 30/9/11 – successor court – Worcester

REDHILL
see REIGATE

REDRUTH
see CAMBORNE AND REDRUTH

307 REIGATE (SE)
The Law Courts, Mary Road, Guildford, Surrey GU1 4PS
Tel: 01483 405 300 or 01483 468 500
Fax: 01483 300 031
Email: reigatecountycourt.enquiries@hmcts.gsi.gov.uk
DX: 97860 Guildford 5
Court Details
Law Courts, Hatchlands Road, Redhill RH1 6BL
Adoption; Bankruptcy; Children; Divorce; Domestic violence; Forced marriage; Housing possession; Money claims

308 RHYL (WAL)
The Courthouse, Clwyd Street, Rhyl, Denbighshire LL18 3LA
Tel: 01745 352940
Fax: 01745 336726
Email: enquiries@rhyl.countycourt.gsi.gov.uk
DX: 702489 RHYL 2
Court Details
The Courthouse, Clwyd Street, Rhyl
Adoption; Bankruptcy; Children; Divorce; Domestic violence; Housing possession

309 ROCHDALE
closed wef 7/9/98 – successor courts – Oldham and Rawtenstall

387 ROMFORD
see LONDON

310 ROTHERHAM (NE)
Rotherham Law Courts, The Statutes, Rotherham S60 1YW
Tel: 01709 839339
Fax: 01709 788414
Email: enquiries@rotherham.countycourt.gsi.gov.uk
DX: 703025 ROTHERHAM 4
Court Details
Rotherham Law Courts, The Statutes, off Main Street, Rotherham
Children; Divorce; Domestic violence; Housing possession

311 RUGBY
closed wef 30/9/11

312 RUNCORN
closed wef 29/7/11

313   ST ALBANS (SE)
The Court Building, Bricket Road, St Albans, Hertfordshire AL1 3JW
Tel: 0844 892 0550
Fax: 0870 324 0127
Email: enquiries@stalbans.countycourt.gsi.gov.uk
DX: 97770 ST ALBANS 2
Court Details
The Court Building, Bricket Road, St Albans
Bankruptcy; Housing possession; Money claims

314   ST AUSTELL
closed wef 30/3/96 – successor courts – Bodmin and Truro

315   ST HELENS (NW)
St Helens County Court, St Helens Courthouse, Corporation Street, St Helens WA10 1SZ
Tel: 01744 620244
Fax: 01744 627288
Email: sthelens.cty.ge@hmcts.gsi.gov.uk
DX: 725020 ST HELENS 5
Court Details
The Law Courts, Corporation Street, St Helens
Children; Divorce; Domestic violence; Housing possession; Money claims

316   SALFORD
closed wef 5/8/11 – successor court – Manchester

317   SALISBURY (SW)
Salisbury Combined Court Centre, The Law Courts, Wilton Road, Salisbury SP2 7EP
Tel: 01722 345200
Fax: 0870 324 0071
Email: enquiries@salisbury.crowncourt.gsi.gov.uk
DX: 98500 SALISBURY 2
Court Details
The Law Courts, Wilton Road, Salisbury
Bankruptcy; Children; Divorce; Housing possession; Money claims

318   SCARBOROUGH (NE)
The Law Courts, Northway, Scarborough, North Yorkshire YO12 7AE
Tel: 01723 505000
Fax: 0870 7394411
Email: enquiries@scarborough.countycourt.gsi.gov.uk
DX: 65140 SCARBOROUGH 2
Court Details
The Law Court, Northway, Scarborough
Bankruptcy; Children; Divorce; Domestic violence; Housing possession; Money claims

319   SCUNTHORPE (NE)
Scunthorpe Court Centre, Corporation Road, Scunthorpe, Lincolnshire DN15 6QB
Tel: 01724 281100
Fax: 01724 281890
Email: scunthorpe.countycourt-enquiries@hmcts.gsi.gov.uk
DX: 742212 SCUNTHORPE 10
Court Details
Scunthorpe Court Centre, Laneham Street, Scunthorpe, Humberside DN15 6JY
Bankruptcy; Children; Divorce; Domestic violence; Housing possession; Money claims

723   SEVENOAKS
closed wef 5/4/94 – successor court – Tunbridge Wells

724   SHAFTESBURY
closed wef 5/12/94 – successor court – Yeovil

725   SHEERNESS
closed wef 5/4/94 – successor court – Sittingbourne

320   SHEFFIELD (NE)
Sheffield Combined Court Centre, The Law Courts, 50 West Bar, Sheffield S3 8PH
Tel: 0114 281 2400
Fax: 0114 281 2491
Email: enquiries@sheffield.countycourt.gsi.gov.uk
DX: 703028 SHEFFIELD 6
Court Details
The Law Courts, 50 West Bar, Sheffield
Adoption; Bankruptcy; Children; Divorce; Domestic violence; Housing possession; Money claims

321   SHOREDITCH
see LONDON

322   SHREWSBURY
closed wef 30/9/11

323   SITTINGBOURNE
closed wef 30/3/96 – successor courts – Maidstone and Medway

324   SKEGNESS
closed wef 9/11

325   SKIPTON (NE)
The Law Courts, Otley Street, Skipton, North Yorkshire BD23 1RH
Tel: 01756 692650
Fax: 01756 692655
DX: 703031 SKIPTON 2
Court Details
The Law Courts, Otley Street, Skipton
Children; Divorce; Domestic violence; Housing possession; Money claims

326   SLEAFORD
closed wef 16/2/96 – successor courts – Boston, Grantham, Lincoln and Newark

327   SLOUGH (SE)
The Law Courts, Windsor Road, Slough SL1 2HE
Tel: 01753 690300
Fax: 01753 575990
Email: enquiries@slough.countycourt.gsi.gov.uk
DX: 98030 SLOUGH 3
Court Details
The Law Courts, Windsor Road, Slough
Bankruptcy; Children; Divorce; Domestic violence; Housing possession; Money claims

328   SOUTHAMPTON (SW)
Southampton Combined Court Centre, The Courts of Justice, London Road, Southampton, Hampshire SO15 2XQ
Tel: 023 8021 3200
Fax: 0870 761 7750
Email: family@southampton.countycourt.gsi.gov.uk
DX: 111000 SOUTHAMPTON 11
Court Details
The Courts of Justice, London Road, Southampton
Adoption; Bankruptcy; Children; Divorce; Domestic violence; Employment; Housing possession; Money claims; Social security

329   SOUTHEND (SE)
County Court, Tylers House, Tylers Avenue, Southend-on-Sea, Essex SS1 2AW
Tel: 0344 892 4000
Fax: 01702 603090
Email: enquiries@southend.countycourt.gsi.gov.uk
DX: 97780 SOUTHEND ON SEA 2
Court Details
Tylers House, Tylers Avenue, Southend-on-Sea

Adoption; Bankruptcy; Children; Divorce; Domestic violence; Forced marriage; Housing possession; Money claims

330   SOUTHPORT
closed wef 29/7/11

331   SOUTH SHIELDS (NE)
South Tyneside Law Courts, Millbank, Secretan Way, South Shields, Tyne & Wear NE33 1RG
Tel: 0191 455 8800 or 0191 456 3343
Fax: 0870 324 0214
Email: southshields.cty.cm@hmcts.gsi.gov.uk
DX: 65143 SOUTH SHIELDS 3
Court Details
Law Courts, Millbank, Secretan Way
Children; Divorce; Domestic violence; Housing possession; Money claims

332   SPALDING
closed wef 16/2/96 – successor courts – Boston, Grantham and Peterborough

333   STAFFORD (M)
Stafford Combined Court Centre, Victoria Square, Stafford ST16 2QQ
Tel: 01785 610730
Fax: 01785 213250
Email: enquiries@stafford.countycourt.gsi.gov.uk
DX: 703190 STAFFORD 4
Court Details
Combined Court Centre, Victoria Square, Stafford
Bankruptcy; Divorce; Domestic violence; Housing possession; Money claims

334   STAINES (SE)
The Law Courts, Mary Road, Guildford, Surrey GU1 4PS
Tel: 01483 405 300 or 01483 468 500
Fax: 01483 300 031
Email: surreycivil@hmcts.gsi.gov.uk
DX: 98040 STAINES 2
Court Details
The Law Courts, Knowle Green, Staines TW18 1XH
Adoption; Children; Divorce; Domestic violence; Forced marriage; Housing possession

335   STAMFORD
closed wef 1/10/84 – successor court – Peterborough

336   STOCKPORT (NW)
Stockport Courthouse, Edward Street, Stockport SK1 3NF
Tel: 0161 477 2020
Fax: 0161 968 9733
Email: enquiries@stockport.countycourt.gsi.gov.uk
DX: 702620 STOCKPORT 4
Court Details
Stockport Courthouse, Stockport
Adoption; Bankruptcy; Children; Divorce; Domestic violence; Housing possession; Money claims

337   STOCKTON-ON-TEES
closed wef 2/11/94 – resited to form Teeside Combined Court Centre

338   STOKE-ON-TRENT (M)
Stoke-on-Trent Combined Court Centre, Bethesda Street, Hanley, Stoke-on-Trent ST1 3BP
Tel: 01782 854 000
Fax: 01782 854 046
Email: enquiries@stoke.countycourt.gsi.gov.uk
DX: 703360 HANLEY 3
Court Details
Bethesda Street, Hanley, Stoke-on-Trent
Adoption; Bankruptcy; Children; Divorce; Domestic violence; Housing possession; Money claims

339   STOURBRIDGE
closed wef 30/9/11

340   STRATFORD-UPON-AVON
closed wef 30/9/11

341   STROUD
closed wef 4/7/94 – successor court – Gloucester

342   SUDBURY
closed wef 5/4/94 – successor courts – Bury St Edmund's, Braintree, Colchester and Ipswich

343   SUNDERLAND (NE)
The Court House, 44 John Street, Sunderland SR1 1RB
Tel: 0191 568 0750
Fax: 0191 514 3028
Email: enquiries@sunderland.countycourt.gsi.gov.uk
DX: 65149 SUNDERLAND 2
Court Details
The Court House, John Street, Sunderland
Adoption; Bankruptcy; Children; Divorce; Domestic violence; Housing possession

344   SWANSEA (WAL)
Caravella House, Quay West, Quay Parade, Swansea SA1 1SP
Tel: 01792 485800
Fax: 01792 485810
Email: enquiries@swansea.countycourt.gsi.gov.uk
DX: 99740 SWANSEA 5
Court Details
Caravella House, Quay West, Quay Parade, Swansea
Adoption; Bankruptcy; Children; Divorce; Domestic violence; Housing possession

345   SWINDON (SW)
Swindon Combined Court Centre, The Law Courts, Islington Street, Swindon, Wiltshire SN1 2HG
Tel: 01793 690500
Fax: 01793 690555
Email: swindon.cty.enq@hmcts.gsi.gov.uk
DX: 98430 SWINDON 5
Court Details
The Law Courts, Islington Street, Swindon
Adoption; Bankruptcy; Children; Divorce; Domestic violence; Housing possession; Money claims

112   TAMESIDE (NW)
PO Box 166, Henry Square, Ashton-under-Lyne, Lancashire OL6 7TP
Tel: 0161 331 5614
Fax: 0161 331 5649
Email: tameside.cty@hmcts.gsi.gov.uk
DX: 702625 ASHTON-U-LYNE 2
Court Details
Henry Square, Ashton-under-Lyne
Bankruptcy; Divorce; Domestic violence; Housing possession

346   TAMWORTH
closed wef 30/9/11

347   TAUNTON (SW)
Taunton County Court, Shire Hall, Taunton, Somerset TA1 4EU
Tel: 01823 281110
Email: enquiries@taunton.countycourt.gsi.gov.uk
DX: 98410 TAUNTON 2
Court Details
Shire Hall, Taunton
Adoption; Bankruptcy; Children; Divorce; Domestic violence; Housing possession

364   TELFORD (M)
Telford County Court, Telford Square, Malinsgate, Town Centre, Telford, Shropshire TF3 4JP
Tel: 01952 238280
Fax: 01952 291601
Email: enquiry@telford.countycourt.gsi.gov.uk
DX: 701976 TELFORD 3
Court Details
Telford Square, Malinsgate, Telford
Adoption; Bankruptcy; Children; Divorce; Domestic violence; Housing possession; Money claims

348   THANET (SE)
The Court House, 2nd Floor, Cecil Square, Margate, Kent CT9 1RL
Tel: 01843 221722
Fax: 01843 222730
Email: enquiries@thanet.countycourt.gsi.gov.uk
DX: 98210 CLIFTONVILLE 2
Court Details
The Court House, 2nd Floor, Cecil Square, Margate
Adoption; Children; Divorce; Domestic violence; Forced marriage; Housing possession; Money claims

350   THORNE
closed wef 4/1/94 – successor court – Doncaster

351   TONBRIDGE
closed wef 1/10/84 – successor court – Tunbridge Wells

727   TODMORDEN
CLOSED wef 28/10/91 – successor court – Halifax

352   TORQUAY AND NEWTON ABBOT (SW)
The Willows, Nicholson Road, Torquay, Devon TQ2 7AZ
Tel: 01803 617880
Fax: 01803 616795
Email: civil@torquayandnewtonabbotcountycourt.gsi.gov.uk
DX: 98740 TORQUAY 4
Court Details
Nicholson Road, Torquay
Bankruptcy; Children; Divorce; Domestic violence; Housing possession; Money claims

353   TROWBRIDGE (SW)
CLOSED WEF 29/3/13 – renamed Chippenham and Trowbridge (SW)

354   TRURO (SW)
Truro County Court, Courts of Justice, Edward Street, Truro, Cornwall TR1 2PB
Tel: 01872 267460
Email: civilsection.trurocountycourt@hmcts.gsi.gov.uk
DX: 135396 TRURO 2
Court Details
Courts of Justice, Edward Street, Truro
Adoption; Bankruptcy; Children; Divorce; Domestic violence; Housing possession; Money claims; Social security

356   UXBRIDGE
see LONDON

357   WAKEFIELD (NE)
Wakefield Civil Justice Centre, Emerald House, 1 Mulberry Way, Wakefield WF1 2QN
Tel: 01924 207900
Fax: 01924 207959
Email: wakefieldurgents@hmcts.gsi.gov.uk
DX: 703022 WAKEFIELD 24
Court Details
Wakefield Civil Justice Centre, Emerald House, Wakefield
Bankruptcy; Children; Divorce; Domestic violence; Housing possession

358   WALSALL (M)
Bridge House, Bridge Street, Walsall, West Midlands WS1 1JQ
Tel: 01922 728855
Fax: 01922 728891
Email: enquiries@walsall.countycourt.gsi.gov.uk
DX: 701943 WALSALL 2
Court Details
Bridge House, Bridge Street, Walsall
Bankruptcy; Children; Divorce; Domestic violence; Housing possession; Money claims

359   WANDSWORTH
see LONDON

360   WARRINGTON (NW)
Law Courts, Legh Street, Warrington WA1 1UR
Tel: 01925 256700
Fax: 01925 413335
Email: enquiries@warrington.countycourt.gsi.gov.uk
DX: 702501 WARRINGTON 3
Court Details
Law Courts, Legh Street, Warrington
Adoption; Bankruptcy; Children; Divorce; Domestic violence; Housing possession; Money claims

361   WARWICK (M)
Warwickshire Justice Centre, Newbold Terrace, Leamington Spa, Warwickshire CV32 4EL
Tel: 0300 123 5577
Fax: 01926 682517
Email: enquiries@warwick.countycourt.gsi.gov.uk
DX: 701964 LEAMINGTON 7
Court Details
Warwickshire Justice Centre, Leamington Spa
Bankruptcy; Housing possession; Money claims

362   WATFORD (SE)
Cassiobury House, 11–19 Station Road, Watford, Hertfrodshire WD17 1EZ
Tel: 0844 892 0550
Fax: 0870 739 4015
Email: enquiries@watford.countycourt.gsi.gov.uk
DX: 122740 WATFORD 5
Court Details
Cassiobury House, 11–19 Station Road, Watford
Adoption; Children; Divorce; Domestic violence; Forced marriage; Housing possession; Money claims

363   WELLINGBOROUGH
closed wef 30/9/11

364   WELLINGTON
renamed TELFORD

WELLS
see BRISTOL

366   WELSHPOOL AND NEWTOWN (WAL)
Wrexham Law Courts, Bodhyfryd, Wrexham LL2 7BP
Tel: 01978 317400
Fax: 01978 358213
Email: enquiries@wrexham.countycourt.gsi.gov.uk
DX: 745320 WREXHAM 9 or 702524 WELSHPOOL 2
Note: All administration details as Wrexham.
Court Details
The Mansion House, 24 Severn Street, Welshpool
Bankruptcy; Children; Divorce; Domestic violence; Housing possession; Money claims

367 WEST BROMWICH
(closed wef 24/12/98 – successor courts – Birmingham, Dudley and Walsall)

373 WHITEHAVEN
see 373 WEST CUMBRIA

373 WEST CUMBRIA (NW)
West Cumbria County Court, Hall Park, Ramsey Brow, Workington CA14 4AS
Tel: 01900 609609
Fax: 0870 324 0242
Email: enquiries@westcumbria.countycourt.gsi.gov.uk
DX: 743420 WORKINGTON 5
Court Details
West Cumbria County Court, Workington
Adoption; Bankruptcy; Children; Divorce; Domestic violence; Housing possession; Money claims

368 WEST LONDON
see LONDON

369 WESTMINSTER
see LONDON

370 WESTON-SUPER-MARE (SW)
The Hedges, St George's, Weston-super-Mare BS22 7BB
Tel: 01934 528686
Fax: 0870 739 5826
Email: weston-s-marecountycourt@hmcts.gsi.gov.uk
DX: 152361 WESTON-SUPER-MARE 5
Court Details
The Hedges, St George's, Weston-super-Mare
Children; Divorce; Housing possession; Money claims

371 WEYMOUTH (SW)
Weymouth & Dorchester Combined Court Centre, Westwey Road, Weymouth, Dorset DT4 8BS
Tel: 01305 752510
Fax: 0870 739 5856
Email: enquiries@weymouth.countycourt.gsi.gov.uk
DX: 98820 WEYMOUTH 3
Court Details
Westwey House, Westwey Road, Weymouth
Bankruptcy; Children; Divorce; Domestic violence; Housing possession; Money claims

730 WHITBY
closed wef 4/1/94 – successor court – Scarborough

374 WIGAN (NW)
Wigan & Leigh Courthouse, Darlington Street, Wigan, Lancashire WN1 1DW
Tel: 01942 405405
Fax: 01942 405499
Email: enquiries@wigan.countycourt.gsi.gov.uk
DX: 724820 WIGAN 9
Court Details
Darlington Street, Wigan
Bankruptcy; Children; Divorce; Domestic violence; Housing possession; Money claims

375 WILLESDEN
see LONDON

376 WINCHESTER (SW)
Winchester Combined Court Centre, The Law Courts, Winchester, Hampshire SO23 9EL
Tel: 01962 814100
Fax: 01962 814260
Email: winchestercustomerservice@hmcts.gsi.gov.uk
DX: 98520 WINCHESTER 3

Court Details
The Law Courts, Winchester
Bankruptcy; Children; Divorce; Domestic violence; Housing possession; Money claims

377 WISBECH
closed wef 29/9/95 – successor court – King's Lynn

378 WOLVERHAMPTON (M)
Wolverhampton Combined Court Centre, Pipers Row, Wolverhampton, West Midlands WV1 3LQ
Tel: 01902 481000
Fax: 01902 481001
Email: enquiries@wolverhampton.countycourt.gsi.gov.uk
DX: 702019 WOLVERHAMPTON 4
Court Details
Combined Court Centre, Pipers Row, Wolverhampton
Adoption; Bankruptcy; Children; Divorce; Domestic violence; Housing possession; Money claims

379 WOOLWICH
see LONDON

380 WORCESTER (M)
Worcester Combined Court Centre, The Shirehall, Foregate Street, Worcester WR1 1EQ
Tel: 01905 730800
Fax: 0870 324 0277
DX: 721120 WORCESTER 11
Court Details
The Shirehall, Foregate Street, Worcester
Adoption; Bankruptcy; Children; Divorce; Domestic violence; Housing possession; Money claims

381 WORKINGTON
closed wef 2/1/01 – successor court – West Cumbria (formerly Whitehaven)

382 WORKSOP
closed wef 9/11

383 WORTHING (SE)
The Law Courts, Christchurch Road, Worthing, West Sussex BN11 1JD
Tel: 01903 221920
Fax: 01903 235559
DX: 98230 WORTHING 4
Court Details
Law Courts, Christchurch Road,Worthing
Adoption; Children; Divorce; Domestic violence; Forced marriage; Housing possession; Money claims

384 WREXHAM (WAL)
Wrexham Law Courts, Bodhyfryd, Wrexham LL12 7BP
Tel: 01978 317400; 01978 317407 (Bailiff)
Fax: 01978 358213
Email: enquiries@wrexham.countycourt.gsi.gov.uk
DX: 745320 WREXHAM 9
Court Details
Wrexham Law Courts, Bodhyfryd
Adoption; Bankruptcy; Children; Divorce; Domestic violence; Housing possession; Money claims

385 YEOVIL (SW)
22 Hendford, Yeovil, Somerset BA20 2QD
Tel: 01935 382150
Fax: 0870 324 0162
Email: info@yeovil.countycourt.gsi.gov.uk
DX: 98830 YEOVIL 2

Court Details
22 Hendford, Yeovil
Bankruptcy; Children; Divorce; Domestic violence; Housing possession; Money claims

386   YORK (NE)
Piccadilly House, 55 Piccadilly, York YO1 9WL
Tel: 01904 688550
Fax: 01904 679963
Email: enquiries@york.countycourt.gsi.gov.uk
DX: 65165 YORK 4

Court Details
Piccadilly House, 55 Piccadilly, York
Adoption; Bankruptcy; Children; Divorce; Domestic violence; Housing possession; Money claims

NORTHERN IRELAND

ARDS
Mrs K. Coey, Newtownards Court Office, The Courthouse, Regent Street, Newtownards, County Down BT23 4LP
Tel: 030 0200 7812
Court Houses: Newtownards; Downpatrick

ARMAGH AND SOUTH DOWN
Mrs G. Campbell, Newry Court Office, The Courthouse, 23 New Street, Newry BT35 6JD
Tel: 030 0200 7812
Court Houses: Armagh; Newry

BELFAST (BELFAST RECORDER'S COURT)
Mrs P. McCourt, Business Manager, Belfast Combined Courts, Laganside Courts, 45 Oxford Street, Belfast BT1 3LL
Tel: 030 0200 7812
Fax: 028 9041 2283
Court Houses: Laganside Courts; Old Town Hall; Mays Chambers

FERMANAGH AND TYRONE
Mrs S. Hughes, Omagh Court Office, The Courthouse, High Street, Omagh, County Tyrone BT78 1DU
Tel: 030 0200 7812
Court Houses: Omagh; Dungannon; Enniskillen; Strabane

LONDONDERRY (LONDONDERRY RECORDER'S COURT)
Mrs S. Moore, Londonderry Court Office, The Courthouse, Bishop Street, Londonderry BT48 6PQ
Tel: 030 0200 7812
Court Houses: Londonderry; Limavady; Magherafelt

ANTRIM
Mr M. Little, Antrim Court Office, The Courthouse, 30 Castle Way, Antrim, County Antrim BT41 4AQ
Tel: 030 0200 7812
Court Houses: Ballymena; Coleraine; Antrim

CRAIGAVON
Mr D. Harkin, Craigavon Court Office, The Courthouse, Central Way, Craigavon BT64 1AP
Tel: 030 0200 7812
Court Houses: Craigavon; Lisburn

Part III

COURTS OF SUMMARY JURISDICTION

ABBREVIATIONS

CPS	Crown Prosecution Service
DDC	Dedicated Drugs Court
Dir	Directions
Enf	Enforcement
FPC	Family Proceedings Court
JP	Justice of the Peace
Misc	Miscellaneous
NP	Non-police
RTC	Road Traffic Court
SDVC	Special Domestic Violence Court
SIC	Sensitive Issues Court
TFOs	Transfer of Fine Orders
VC	Video Court
YC	Youth Court

LONDON REGION

LOCAL JUSTICE AREAS IN THE GREATER LONDON AREA

LONDON – CENTRAL AND SOUTH (CRIME)

CENTRAL LONDON LJA (ADULT COURT 2570, YOUTH COURT 6570)

WESTMINSTER MAGISTRATES' COURT
Westminster Magistrates' Court, 181 Marylebone Road, London NW1 5BR
Tel: 020 3126 3050 (Listing); 3040 (Legal Aid); 3020 (Applications); 3030 (Post Court); 3010 (International Jurisdiction)
Fax: 020 3126 3051 (Listing); 3041 (Legal Aid); 3031 (Applications/Post Court); 3011 (International Jurisdiction)
DX: 120551 MARYLEBONE 9
Email: westminster.mc@hmcts.gsi.gov.uk

Courts and times
Westminster Magistrates' Court, 181 Marylebone Road, London NW1 5BR
Court building open: 9am to 4:30pm (1pm Saturdays)

CITY OF LONDON MAGISTRATES' COURT
All correspondence and telephone enquiries to: Westminster Magistrates' Court, 181 Marylebone Road, London NW1 5BR
Tel: 020 3126 3050 (Westminster); 3040 (Legal Aid)
Fax: 020 3126 3355
DX: 120551 MARYLEBONE 9
Email: westminster.mc@hmcts.gsi.gov.uk

Courts and times
City of London Magistrates' Court, 1 Queen Victoria Street, London EC4N 4XY
Court counter open: 9am to 4:30pm; Court building open: 9am to 4:30pm

HAMMERSMITH MAGISTRATES' COURT
All correspondence to: Westminster Magistrates' Court, 181 Marylebone Road, London NW1 5BR
Tel: 020 8700 9360 (Customer Services/Post Court/Resulting); 9350 (Listing/Pre Court)
Fax: 020 8700 9344 (Listing/Pre Court); 9355 (Post Court)
DX: 124800 HAMMERSMITH 8
Email: gl-westlondonmcenq@hmcts.gsi.gov.uk

Courts and times
Hammersmith Magistrates' Court, 181 Talgarth Road, Hammersmith, London W6 8DN
Court building open: Monday to Friday 9am to 4:30pm; Court counter open: 9am to 11am and 1:45pm to 2:30pm

SOUTH LONDON LJA (ADULT COURT 2576, YOUTH COURT 6576)

CAMBERWELL GREEN MAGISTRATES' COURT
South London Administration Centre, Camberwell Green Magistrates' Court, 15 D'Eynsford Road, Camberwell Green, London SE5 7UP
Tel: 020 7805 9851/60 (Customer Services); 9852 (Legal Aid)
Fax: 020 7805 9898
DX: 157730 CAMBERWELL GREEN 3
Email: gl-southgroupmcenq@hmcts.gsi.gov.uk

Courts and times
Camberwell Green Magistrates' Court, 15 D'Eynsford Road, Camberwell Green, London SE5 7UP
Court building open: 9:15am to 4:30pm; Court counter open: 9:30am to 4:30pm

TOWER BRIDGE MAGISTRATES' COURT
Court closed. All correspondence to: South London Administration Centre, Camberwell Green Magistrates' Court, 15 D'Eynsford Road, Camberwell Green, London SE5 7UP

CROYDON MAGISTRATES' COURT
All correspondence to: South London Administration Centre, Camberwell Green Magistrates' Court, 15 D'Eynsford Road, Camberwell Green, London SE5 7UP
Tel: 020 7805 9851 or 020 7805 9860
Fax: 020 8680 9801
DX: 157730 Camberwell Green 3
Email: gl-southgroupmcenq@hmcts.gsi.gov.uk

Courts and times
The Magistrates Court, Barclay Road, Croydon CR9 3NG
Court building open: 9am to 4:30pm
Court counter open: 9:15am to 11:30am and 1:30pm to 2:30pm

SOUTH EAST LONDON LJA (ADULT COURT 2575, YOUTH COURT 6575)

BROMLEY MAGISTRATES' COURT
South East London Administration Centre, The Court House, London Road, Bromley, Kent BR1 71RA
Tel: 020 8437 3585/3500/3618
Fax: 0870 324 0223
DX: 156800 BROMLEY 10
Email: gl-bromleymcenq@hmcts.gsi.gov.uk

Courts and times
Bromley Magistrates' Court, The Court House, London Road, Bromley, Kent BR1 71RA
Court building open: 9am to 5pm; Court counter open: 9am to 2:30pm

BEXLEY MAGISTRATES' COURT
All correspondence to: South East London Administration Centre, The Court House, London Road, Bromley, Kent BR1 71RA
Tel: 020 8437 3585/3500/3618
Fax: 0870 324 0223
DX: 156800 BROMLEY 10
Email: gl-bromleymcenq@hmcts.gsi.gov.uk

Courts and times
Bexley Magistrates' Court, Norwich Place, Bexleyheath DA6 7NB
Court building open: 9am to 4:30pm
Court counter open: 9am to 4pm (closed 1pm to 2pm)

GREENWICH MAGISTRATES' COURT
All correspondence to: South East London Administration Centre, The Court House, London Road, Bromley, Kent BR1 71RA
Tel: 020 8437 3585/3500/3618
Fax: 0870 324 0223
DX: 156800 BROMLEY 10
Email: gl-bromleymcenq@hmcts.gsi.gov.uk

Courts and times
Greenwich Magistrates' Court, 9 Blackheath Road, Greenwich SE10 8PG
Court building open: 9am to 4:30pm
Court counter open: 9am to 11am, 12pm to 12:30pm and 1:30pm to 4pm

SOUTH WEST LONDON LJA (ADULT COURT 2577, YOUTH COURT 6577)

LAVENDER HILL MAGISTRATES' COURT
South West London Administration Centre, 176A Lavender Hill, Battersea, London SW11 1JU
Tel: 020 7805 1447
Fax: 020 7805 1448
DX: 58559 CLAPHAM JUNCTION
Email: swglondonmc@hmcts.gsi.gov.uk

Courts and times
Lavender Hill Magistrates' Court, 176A Lavender Hill, Battersea, London SW11 1JU
Court building open: 9am to 4:30pm

RICHMOND MAGISTRATES' COURT
All correspondence to: South West London Administration Centre, 176A Lavender Hill, Battersea, London SW11 1JU
Tel: 0300 123 1711
Fax: 0870 739 5829
Email: richmond_ia_goldfax@hmcts.gsi.gov.uk

Courts and times
The Court House, Parkshot, Richmond
Court building open: 9am to 5pm

WIMBLEDON MAGISTRATES' COURT
All correspondence to: South West London Administration Centre, 176A Lavender Hill, Battersea, London SW11 1JU
Tel: 020 8946 8642
Fax: 020 8946 7030
DX: 58559 CLAPHAM JUNCTION
Email: wimbledon.mc@hmcts.gsi.gov.uk

Courts and times
The Law Courts, Alexandra Road, Wimbledon
Court building open: 9am to 4pm; Court counter open: 9am to 4pm

BEXLEY MAGISTRATES' COURT
see **2575/6575 South East London LJA**

BROMLEY MAGISTRATES' COURT
see **2575/6575 South East London LJA**

CITY OF LONDON MAGISTRATES' COURT
see **2570/6570 Central London LJA**

CITY OF WESTMINSTER MAGISTRATES' COURT
see **2570/6570 Central London LJA**

CROYDON MAGISTRATES' COURT
see **2576/6576 South London LJA**

GREENWICH MAGISTRATES' COURT
see **2575/6575 South East London LJA**

WOOLWICH MAGISTRATES' COURT
closed wef 1/7/11

CAMBERWELL GREEN MAGISTRATES' COURT
see **2576/6576 South London LJA**

GREENWICH, LEWISHAM & SOUTHWARK YOUTH COURTS
see **6576 South London LJA**

TOWER BRIDGE MAGISTRATES' COURT
closed wef 2013

SUTTON MAGISTRATES' COURT
closed wef 3/6/11

LONDON – NORTH AND WEST (CRIME)

EAST LONDON LJA (ADULT COURT 2574, YOUTH COURT 6574)

THAMES MAGISTRATES' COURT
58 Bow Road, London E3 4DJ
Tel: 020 8271 1530/1533
Fax: 0870 324 0220
DX: 157540 Bow 3
Email: gl-thamesmclist@hmcts.gsi.gov.uk

Courts and times
Thames Magistrates' Court, 58 Bow Road, London E3 4DJ
Court building open: Monday to Friday 9am to 5pm; Court counter open: 9am to 11am then 1:30pm to 2:30pm

STRATFORD MAGISTRATES' COURT
58 Bow Road, London E3 4DJ
Tel: 020 8271 1530/1533
Fax: 0870 324 0220
DX: 157540 Bow 3
Email: gl-thamesmclist@hmcts.gsi.gov.uk

Courts and times
Stratford Magistrates' Court, 389–397 High Street, London E15 4SB
Court building open: Monday to Friday 9am to 4:30pm; Court counter open: 9am to 11am and 1:30pm to 2:30pm

WALTHAM FOREST MAGISTRATES' COURT
58 Bow Road, London E3 4DJ
Tel: 020 8271 1530/1533
Fax: 0870 324 0220
DX: 157540 Bow 3
Email: gl-thamesmclist@hmcts.gsi.gov.uk

Courts and times
The Court House, 1 Farnan Avenue, Walthamstow, London E17 4NX
Court building open: 9am to 4:30pm (4:15pm Friday)

NORTH LONDON LJA (ADULT COURT 2572, YOUTH COURT 6572)

HIGHBURY CORNER MAGISTRATES' COURT
Postal address: North London Administration Centre, PO Box 52693, London N7 1AF
Tel: 020 7506 3100/3156/3221
Fax: 0870 739 5768
DX: 153700 HIGHBURY 4
Email: gl-hcornermcenq@hmcts.gsi.gov.uk

Courts and times
Highbury Corner Magistrates' Court, 51 Holloway Road, London N7 8JA
Court building open: 9am; Court counter open: 9am to 11am and 1:30pm to 2:30pm; Court counter open: (Application counter) 9am to 10am

TOTTENHAM MAGISTRATES' COURT
All correspondence to: North London Administration Centre, PO Box 52693, London N7 1AF
Tel: 020 7506 3100/3156/3221
Fax: 020 8885 4343
DX: 153700 HIGHBURY 4
Email: gl-hcornermcenq@hmcts.gsi.gov.uk

Courts and times
Tottenham Magistrates Court, The Court House, Lordship Lane, Tottenham, London N17 6RT
Court building open: 9am; Court counter open: 9am to 11:30am and 1:30pm to 3pm

NORTH EAST LONDON LJA (ADULT COURT 2573, YOUTH COURT 6573)

BARKINGSIDE MAGISTRATES' COURT
850 Cranbrook Road, Barkingside, Ilford, Essex IG6 1HW
Tel: 020 8437 6525
Fax: 0870 739 4187
DX: 156842 ILFORD 9
Email: gl-barkingsidemcenq@hmcts.gsi.gov.uk

Courts and times
Barkingside Magistrates' Court, 850 Cranbrook Road, Barkingside, Ilford, Essex IG6 1HW
Court building open: Monday to Friday 9am to 4:30pm (Monday – Friday)

ROMFORD MAGISTRATES' COURT
All correspondence to: North East London Administration Centre, Barkingside Magistrates' Court, 850 Cranbrook Road, Barkingside, Ilford, Essex IG6 1HW
Tel: 020 8437 6525
Fax: 020 8437 6561
DX: 156842 ILFORD 9
Email: gl-barkingsidemcenq@hmcts.gsi.gov.uk

Courts and times
Romford Magistrates' Court, Main Road, Romford, Essex RM1 3BH
Court building open: Monday to Friday 8:30am to 4:30pm; Court counter open: 8:30am to 4:30pm

NORTH WEST LONDON LJA (ADULT COURT 2571, YOUTH COURT 6571)

WILLESDEN MAGISTRATES' COURT
Willesden Magistrates' Court, 448 High Road, Willesden, London NW10 2DZ
Tel: 020 8955 0555
Fax: 0870 324 0240
DX: 110850 WILLESDEN 2
Email: gl-brentmcenq@hmcts.gsi.gov.uk

Courts and times
Willesden Magistrates' Court, 448 High Road, Willesden, London NW10 2DZ
Court building open: Monday to Friday 9am to 4:30pm; Court counter open: 9am to 11:30am; Court counter open: 1pm to 2:30pm

HENDON MAGISTRATES' COURT
The Court House, The Hyde, Hendon, London NW9 7BY
Tel: 020 8955 0555
Fax: 0870 324 0240
DX: 110850 WILLESDEN 2
Email: gl-barnetmcenq@hmcts.gsi.gov.uk

Courts and times
Hendon Magistrates' Court, The Court House, Hendon
Court building open: Monday to Friday 9am to 4:30pm; Court counter open: 9:15am to 11.30am and 1:30pm to 2:30pm

WEST LONDON LJA (ADULT COURT 2578, YOUTH COURT 6578)

EALING MAGISTRATES' COURT
Willesden Magistrates' Court, 448 High Road, Willesden, London NW10 2DZ
Tel: 020 8955 0555
Fax: 0870 324 0240
DX: 110850 WILLESDEN 2
Email: gl-brentmcenq@hmcts.gsi.gov.uk

Courts and times
Ealing Magistrates' Court, The Court House: Green Man Lane, Ealing
Court building open: Monday to Friday 9am to 4:30pm; Court counter open: Monday, Wednesday and Friday 9:30am to 10:30am. Tuesday and Thursday 9am to 10am

FELTHAM MAGISTRATES' COURT
Hanworth Road, Feltham, Middlesex TW13 5AF
Tel: 020 8955 0555
Fax: 0870 324 0240
DX: 110850 WILLESDEN 2
Email: gl-brentmcenq@hmcts.gsi.gov.uk
Courts and times
Feltham Magistrates' Court, Hanworth Road, Feltham
Court building open: Monday to Thursday 9am to 4:30pm; Court counter open: 9:30am to 10:30am
and 1:30pm to 2:30pm

UXBRIDGE MAGISTRATES' COURT
The Court House, Harefield Road, Uxbridge, Middlesex UB8 1PQ
Tel: 020 8955 0555
Fax: 0870 324 0240
DX: 110850 WILLESDEN 2
Email: gl-brentmcenq@hmcts.gsi.gov.uk
Courts and times
Uxbridge Magistrates' Court, The Court House, Harefield Road, Uxbridge UB8 1PQ
Court building open: Monday to Friday 9am to 4:30pm; Court counter open: 9am to 11:30am and
1pm to 2:30pm

BARKING MAGISTRATES' COURT
closed wef 30/9/11

HENDON MAGISTRATES' COURT
see **2571/6571 North West London LJA**

BRENT MAGISTRATES' COURT
see **2578/6578 West London LJA**

HIGHBURY CORNER MAGISTRATES' COURT
see **2572/6572 North London LJA**

EALING MAGISTRATES' COURT
see **2578/6578 West London LJA**

ACTON MAGISTRATES' COURT
closed wef 28/4/11

ENFIELD MAGISTRATES' COURT
see **2572/6572 North London LJA**

THAMES MAGISTRATES' COURT
see **2574/6574 East London LJA**

WEST LONDON MAGISTRATES' COURT
see **2570/6570 Central London LJA**

HARINGEY MAGISTRATES' COURT
see **2572/6572 North London LJA**

HARROW MAGISTRATES' COURT
closed wef 30/6/11

HAVERING MAGISTRATES' COURT
see **2573/6573 North East London LJA**

UXBRIDGE MAGISTRATES' COURT
see **2578/6578 West London LJA**

BRENTFORD MAGISTRATES' COURT
closed wef 30/12/11

FELTHAM MAGISTRATES' COURT
see **2578/6578 West London LJA**

LAMBETH AND WANDSWORTH YOUTH COURTS (BALHAM YOUTH COURT)
closed wef 30/12/11

KINGSTON-UPON-THAMES MAGISTRATES' COURT
closed wef 30/6/11

WIMBLEDON MAGISTRATES' COURT
see **London – Central and South (Crime) – 2577/6577 South West London LJA**

STRATFORD MAGISTRATES' COURT
see **2574/6574 East London LJA**

REDBRIDGE MAGISTRATES' COURT
see **2573/6573 North East London LJA**

RICHMOND-UPON-THAMES MAGISTRATES' COURT
see **London – Central and South (Crime) – 2577/6577 South West London LJA**

WALTHAM FOREST MAGISTRATES' COURT
see **2574/6574 East London LJA**

SOUTH WESTERN MAGISTRATES' COURT
see **London – Central and South (Crime) – 2577/6577 South West London LJA**

HIGHGATE MAGISTRATES' COURT
closed wef 2013

LONDON – FAMILY

PRINCIPAL REGISTRY OF THE FAMILY DIVISION (PRFD)
First Avenue House, 42–49 High Holborn, London WC1V 6NP
Tel: 0207 947 6000
DX: 610010 KINGSWAY 7
Probate Manager: Tel: 0207 947 6945

MIDLANDS REGION

DERBYSHIRE AND NOTTINGHAMSHIRE

1430 HIGH PEAK LJA
Peak Buildings, Terrace Road, Buxton, Derbyshire SK17 6DY
Tel: 01298 23951 (General Enquiries)
Fax: 08707 394 480
DX: 701980 BUXTON 2
Email: db-buxtonmccourt@hmcts.gsi.gov.uk

Courts and times
Court House, Peak Buildings, Terrace Road, Buxton
Court building open: 9am to 4pm; Court counter open: 9:45am to 4pm

2087 MANSFIELD LJA
Mansfield Magistrates' Court, Rosemary Street, Mansfield, Nottinghamshire NG19 6EE
Tel: 01623 451500
Fax: 01623 451658
DX: 179560 MANSFIELD 9
Email: mansfieldcty.enquiries@hmcts.gsi.gov.uk

Courts and times
Mansfield Magistrates' Court, Rosemary Street, Mansfield
Court building open: Monday to Friday 9am to 5pm (4:30pm Friday); Court counter open: 10am to 2pm

2567 NEWARK AND SOUTHWELL LJA
closed wef 30/9/11

1432 NORTH EAST DERBYSHIRE AND DALES LJA
Chesterfield Court House, Tapton Lane, Chesterfield, Derbyshire S41 7TW
Tel: 01246 224040
Fax: 01246 246492
DX: 742041 CHESTERFIELD 7

Courts and times
Court House, Tapton Lane, Chesterfield
Court building open: 8:30am to 4pm; Court counter open: 10am to 4pm

2086 NOTTINGHAM LJA
Nottingham Magistrates' Court, Carrington Street, Nottingham NG2 1EE
Tel: 0115 955 8111
Fax: 0870 739 4391
DX: 719030 NOTTINGHAM 32

Courts and times
Nottingham Magistrates' Court, Carrington Street, Nottingham NG2 1EE
Court building open: Monday to Thursday 9am to 5pm (4:30pm on Friday); Court counter open: 9:30am to 4pm (3:30pm Friday)

1428 SOUTHERN DERBYSHIRE LJA
The Court House, St Mary's Gate, Derby DE1 3JR
Tel: 01332 362000
Fax: 01332 333183
DX: 707570 DERBY 8

Courts and times
The Court House, St Mary's Gate, Derby
Court building open: 9am to 5pm; Court counter open: 9am to 4pm

2087 WORKSOP AND RETFORD LJA
Mansfield Magistrates' Court, The Court House, Rosemary Street, Mansfield, Nottinghamshire NG19 6EE
Tel: 01623 451 500
Fax: 01623 451 648
DX: 743240 WORKSOP 4

Courts and times
The Court House, Potter Street, Worksop
Court building open: Only when court sitting until close of business.

LEICESTERSHIRE, RUTLAND, LINCOLNSHIRE, NORTHAMPTONSHIRE

2047 ASHBY-DE-LA-ZOUCH LJA
closed wef 31/7/11

2073 BOSTON LJA
combined with **2082 SKEGNESS LJA** to form **2085 EAST LINCOLNSHIRE LJA**

2321 CORBY LJA
Regent's Pavilion, Summerhouse Road, Moulton Park, Northampton NN3 6AS
Tel: 01604 497000
Fax: 01604 497010
DX: 151720 NORTHAMPTON 27
Courts and times
The Court House, Elizabeth Street, Corby
Court building open: Monday to Friday 9am to 1pm and 1:45pm until close of business

2322 DAVENTRY LJA
closed wef 31/3/11

2085 EAST LINCOLNSHIRE LJA
The Court House, Park Avenue, Skegness PE25 1BH
Tel: 01522 528218
Fax: 0870 324 0247
DX: 743030 SKEGNESS 3
Email: li-skegness@hmcts.gsi.gov.uk
Courts and times
Court House, Park Avenue, Skegness
Court building open: 9am to 4:30pm

2076 ELLOES, BOURNE AND STAMFORD LJA
combined with **2077 GRANTHAM AND SLEAFORD LJA** to form **2105 SOUTH LINCOLNSHIRE LJA**

2075 GAINSBOROUGH LJA
closed wef 31/7/11

2077 GRANTHAM AND SLEAFORD LJA
combined with **2076 ELLOES, BOURNE AND STAMFORD LJA** to form **2105 SOUTH LINCOLNSHIRE LJA**

2323 KETTERING LJA
Regent's Pavilion, Summerhouse Road, Moulton Park, Northampton NN3 6AS
Tel: 01604 497000
Fax: 01604 497010 497020
DX: 151720 NORTHAMPTON 27
Courts and times
The Court House, London Road, Kettering
Court building open: Monday to Friday 9am to 1pm and 1:45pm until close of business

2089 LEICESTER LJA
15 Pocklingtons Walk, Leicester LE1 6BT
Tel: 0116 255 3666
Fax: 0870 739 4250
DX: 10828 LEICESTER
Email: le-leicmcenq@hmcts.gsi.gov.uk
Courts and times
15 Pocklingtons Walk, Leicester
Times on application

2079 LINCOLN DISTRICT LJA
now **2083 NORTH WEST LINCOLNSHIRE LJA**

2090 LOUGHBOROUGH LJA
The Court House, 60 Pinfold Gate, Loughborough, Leicestershire LE11 1AZ
Tel: 01509 215715
Fax: 0870 739 4126
DX: 716116 LOUGHBOROUGH 4
Email: le-loughmcprect@hmcts.gsi.gov.uk

Courts and times
The Court House, 60 Pinfold Gate, Loughborough
Court building open: 9am to 4:30pm (except every 2nd Friday each month at 1pm); Court counter open: 9:30am to Mon to Thurs 4pm Friday 3pm (except every 2nd Friday each month 12:30pm)

2050 MARKET BOSWORTH LJA
Combined with Hinckley

2051 MARKET HARBOROUGH AND LUTTERWORTH LJA
closed wef 31/7/11

2045 MELTON, BELVOIR AND RUTLAND LJA
closed wef 31/7/11

2083 NORTH WEST LINCOLNSHIRE LJA
The Court House, 358 High Street, Lincoln LN5 7QA
Tel: 01522 528218
Fax: 0870 324 0256
DX: 703232 LINCOLN 6
Email: li-lincoln@hmcts.gsi.gov.uk

Courts and times
The Court House, 358 High Street, Lincoln
Court building open: 9am to 5pm or until Courts in session finish

2325 NORTHAMPTON LJA
Regent's Pavilion, Summerhouse Road, Moulton Park, Northampton NN3 6AS
Tel: 01604 497000
Fax: 01604 497010; 497020
DX: 151720 NORTHAMPTON 27

Courts and times
The Court House, Campbell Square, Northampton
Court building open: Monday to Friday 9am until close of business

2082 SKEGNESS LJA (FORMERLY SPILSBY AND SKEGNESS DIVISION)
combined with **2073 BOSTON LJA** to form **2085 EAST LINCOLNSHIRE LJA**

2105 SOUTH LINCOLNSHIRE LJA
The Court House, Harlaxton Road, Grantham NG31 7SB
Tel: 01476 563438
Fax: 0870 324 0246
DX: 711100 GRANTHAM 4
Email: li-granthammcadmin@hmcts.gsi.gov.uk

Courts and times
Magistrates' Court, Harlaxton Road, Grantham
Court building open: 9am, hearings from 9am to 5pm Monday – Thursday, 4:30pm Friday; Enquiry Office open: 9am for Magistrates' Court enquiries

2327 TOWCESTER LJA
closed wef 31/3/11

2328 WELLINGBOROUGH LJA
Regent's Pavilion, Summerhouse Road, Moulton Park, Northampton NN3 6AS
Tel: 01604 497000
Fax: 01604 497010
DX: 151720 NORTHAMPTON 27

Courts and times
The Court House, Midland Road, Wellingborough
Court building open: Monday to Friday 9am to 1pm and 1:45pm until close of business

STAFFORDSHIRE AND WEST MERCIA

1840 BROMSGROVE AND REDDITCH LJA
Magistrates' Court, Grove Street, Redditch, Worcestershire B98 8DB
Tel: 01562 514000
Fax: 0870 324 0280
Email: hw-redditchmc_ctsup@hmcts.gsi.gov.uk

Courts and times
Magistrates' Court, Grove Street, Redditch
Court building open: Monday to Friday 9am to 5pm

2799 CENTRAL AND SOUTH WEST STAFFORDSHIRE LJA
The Court House, South Walls, Stafford ST16 3DW
Tel: 01785 275700
Fax: 0870 739 4179
DX: 14575 STAFFORD 1

Courts and times
The Court House, South Walls, Stafford
Court building open: 9am until close of court business; Court counter open: 9am to 4pm (3:45pm Friday)

1841 HEREFORDSHIRE LJA
The Magistrates' Court, Bath Street, Hereford HR1 2HE
Tel: 01562 514000
Fax: 0870 324 0318
Email: hw-herefordmc_ctsup@hmcts.gsi.gov.uk

Courts and times
The Court House, Bath Street, Hereford
Court building open: Monday to Friday 9am to 5pm

1842 KIDDERMINSTER LJA
The Magistrates' Courts, Comberton Place, Kidderminster, Worcestershire DY10 1QQ
Tel: 01562 514000
Fax: 0870 324 0279

Courts and times
Comberton Place, Kidderminster
Court building open: 9am to 5pm

2786 NORTH STAFFORDSHIRE LJA
Ryecroft, Newcastle-under-Lyme, Staffordshire ST5 2DT
Tel: 01782 741641/70
Fax: 0870 439 4453
DX: 708600 NEWCASTLE UNDER LYME 3

Courts and times
The Court House, Ryecroft, Newcastle-under-Lyme
Court building open: Monday to Friday 9am until business finishes

3282 SHREWSBURY AND NORTH SHROPSHIRE LJA
Telford Magistrates' Court, Telford Square, Malinsgate, Telford, Shropshire TF3 4HX
Tel: 01952 204 500
Fax: 0870 739 4386

Courts and times
The Court House, Preston Street, Shrewsbury SY2 5NX
Court building open: 9am to 4:30pm

2799 SOUTH EAST STAFFORDSHIRE LJA
The Court House, South Walls, Stafford ST16 3DW
Tel: 01785 275700
Fax: 0870 739 4179
DX: 14575 STAFFORD 1

Courts and times
Magistrates' Court, Horninglow Street, Burton-upon-Trent

Court building open: 9am until close of court business; Court counter open: 9am to 4pm (3:45pm Friday)

1843 SOUTH WORCESTERSHIRE LJA
Castle Street, Worcester WR1 3QZ
Tel: 01905 743200
Fax: 0870 324 0295

Courts and times
Magistrates' Courts, Castle Street, Worcester

3282 TELFORD AND SOUTH SHROPSHIRE LJA
Court Office, Telford Square, Malinsgate, Telford TF3 4HX
Tel: 01952 204500
Fax: 0870 739 4386

Courts and times
Magistrates' Court, Telford Square, Malinsgate, Telford
Court building open: Monday to Friday 9am to 5pm

WEST MIDLANDS AND WARWICKSHIRE

2922 BIRMINGHAM LJA
Victoria Law Courts, Corporation Street, Birmingham B4 6QA
Tel: 0121 212 6600
Fax: 0870 324 0274
DX: 715205 BIRMINGHAM 39
Email: wm-customerservicesbirmingham@hmcts.gsi.gov.uk

Courts and times
Victoria Law Courts, Corporation Street, Birmingham
Court building open: Monday to Friday 9am to 5pm; Court counter open: 9am to 5pm

2910 COVENTRY DISTRICT LJA
Magistrates' Court, Little Park Street, Coventry CV1 2SQ
Tel: 024 7663 0666
Fax: 0870 324 0298
DX: 701583 COVENTRY 5
Email: family@coventry.county.gsi.gov.uk

Courts and times
Magistrates' Court, Little Park Street, Coventry
Court building open: 8:30am to 5pm; Court counter open: 9am to 5pm

2911 DUDLEY LJA
combined with **2912 STOURBRIDGE AND HALESOWEN LJA** to form **2911 DUDLEY AND HALESOWEN LJA**

2911 DUDLEY AND HALESOWEN LJA
Magistrates' Courts, The Inhedge, Dudley DY1 1RY
Tel: 01384 211411
Fax: 0870 739 5776
DX: 745750 Dudley 11

Courts and times
Magistrates' Courts, The Inhedge, Dudley
Court building open: 9:15am to 4:30pm

2914 SANDWELL LJA
The Court House, Oldbury Ringway, Oldbury, West Midlands B69 4JN
Tel: 0121 511 2222
Fax: 0870 739 5777
DX: 741369 OLDBURY 5
Email: wm-warleymcadmin@hmcts.gsi.gov.uk

Courts and times
The Court House, Oldbury
Court building open: 9am to 5pm; Court counter open: 9am to 5pm

2916 SOLIHULL LJA
Victoria Law Courts, Corporation Street, Birmingham, West Midlands B4 6QA
Tel: 0121 212 6600
Fax: 0870 324 0274
DX: 715205 Birmingham 39

2912 STOURBRIDGE AND HALESOWEN LJA
combined with **2911 DUDLEY LJA** to form **2911 DUDLEY AND HALESOWEN LJA**

2909 SUTTON COLDFIELD LJA
closed wef 30/6/11

2917 WALSALL AND ALDRIDGE LJA
Magistrates' Court, Stafford Street, Walsall WS2 8HA
Tel: 01922 638222
Fax: 0870 739 4019
DX: 745540 Walsall 11
Email: wm-walsallmcadmin@hmcts.gsi.gov.uk
Courts and times
Magistrates' Court, Stafford Street, Walsall
Court building open: Monday to Friday 9am to 5pm; Court counter open: 9:30am to 4pm

2914 WARLEY LJA
combined with **2915 WEST BROMWICH LJA** to form **2914 SANDWELL LJA**

2905 WARWICKSHIRE LJA
Magistrates' Court, Warwickshire Justice Centre, PO Box 10, Newbold Terrace, Leamington Spa
CV32 4EL
Tel: 01926 429133
Fax: 0870 324 0255
DX: 701964 LEAMINGTON 7
Courts and times
Warwickshire Justice Centre – Leamington Spa, PO Box 10, Newbold Terrace, Leamington Spa
CV32 4EL
Court building open: Monday to Friday 8am to 6pm; Court counter open: 10am to 2pm

2915 WEST BROMWICH LJA
combined with **2914 WARLEY LJA** to form **2914 SANDWELL LJA**

2919 WOLVERHAMPTON LJA
Law Courts, North Street, Wolverhampton WV1 1RA
Tel: 01902 773151
Fax: 0870 739 4167
DX: 10419
Email: wm-wolvesmcadmin@hmcts.gsi.gov.uk
Courts
The Law Courts, North Street, Wolverhampton
Court building open: Monday to Friday 9am to 5pm; Court counter open: Monday to Friday 9am to 5pm

North East Region

CLEVELAND AND DURHAM

1585/5585 COUNTY DURHAM AND DARLINGTON LJA
Magistrates' Court, Newcastle Road, Chester-le-Street, County Durham DH3 3UA
Tel: 0191 387 0700
Fax: 0191 387 0746
DX: 721663 CHESTER-LE-STREET 2
Email: du-durhammcnorthenq@hmcts.gsi.gov.uk

Courts and times
Durham Civil & Family Justice Centre, Old Elvet, Durham DH1 3HW
Court building open: This is a satellite court house and is only operational during court sessions

1247 HARTLEPOOL LJA
The Law Courts, Victoria Road, Hartlepool TS24 8AG
Tel: 01429 271451 or 01429 268198
Fax: 01429 866696
DX: 68706 HARTLEPOOL 2

Courts and times
The Law Courts, Victoria Road, Hartlepool
Court building open: Monday to Friday 9am to 4pm; Court counter open: 9am to 1pm

1248 LANGBAURGH EAST LJA
closed wef 1/12

1583 NORTH DURHAM LJA
combined with **1584 SOUTH DURHAM LJA** to form **1585 and 5585 COUNTY DURHAM AND DARLINGTON LJA**

1584 SOUTH DURHAM LJA
combined with **1583 NORTH DURHAM LJA** to form **1585 and 5585 COUNTY DURHAM AND DARLINGTON LJA**

1249 TEESSIDE LJA
Teesside Law Courts, Victoria Square, Middlesbrough TS1 2AS
Tel: 01642 240301
DX: 60562 MIDDLESBROUGH
Email: postbox@hmcts.gsi.gov.uk

Courts and times
Magistrates' Court, Teesside Law Courts, Victoria Square, Middlesbrough
Court building open: Monday to Friday 8:45am to 5pm; Court counter open: 9am to 1pm

HUMBER AND SOUTH YORKSHIRE

2770 BARNSLEY LJA
Court House, PO Box 17, Barnsley, South Yorkshire S70 2DW
Tel: 01226 320013
Fax: 01226 320044
DX: 702080 BARNSLEY 3

Courts and times
Court House, Westgate, Barnsley
Court building open: Monday to Friday 9am to 5pm; Court counter open: 10am to 2pm; Telephone
Enquiries from: 9am to 5pm

1942 BEVERLEY AND THE WOLDS LJA
combined with **1941 BRIDLINGTON LJA** to form **2353 EAST YORKSHIRE LJA**

1941 BRIDLINGTON LJA
combined with **1942 BEVERLEY AND THE WOLDS LJA** to form **2353 EAST YORKSHIRE LJA**

2771 DONCASTER LJA
PO Box 49, The Law Courts, College Road, Doncaster, South Yorkshire DN1 3HT
Tel: 01302 366711
Fax: 01302 347359
DX: 742840 DONCASTER 20

Courts and times
The Law Courts, College Road, Doncaster
Court building open: Monday to Friday 9am to 5pm; Court counter open: 9am to 5pm

1928 EAST YORKSHIRE LJA
Beverley Magistrates' Court, Champney Road, Beverley, East Yorkshire HU17 9EJ
Tel: 01482 861607
Fax: 0870 739 4398
DX: 742200 Beverley 5
Email: hu-beverleymcadmin@hmcts.gsi.gov.uk

Courts and times
The Court House, Champney Road, Beverley
Court building open: Monday to Friday 8:30am to 5pm; Court counter open: 8:30am to 4pm

1928 GOOLE AND HOWDENSHIRE LJA
closed wef 12/11

1940 GRIMSBY AND CLEETHORPES LJA
Victoria Street, Grimsby, North East Lincolnshire DN31 1NH
Tel: 01472 320444
Fax: 01472 320440
DX: 707680 GRIMSBY 5
Email: hu-grimsbymcadmin@hmcts.gsi.gov.uk

Courts and times
Magistrates' Court, Victoria Street, Grimsby
Court building open: Monday to Friday 8:30am to 5pm (4:30pm Friday); Court counter open: No
payment Counter. Enquiry Counter opens at 9.30am

1943 HULL AND HOLDERNESS LJA
PO Box 2, Market Place, Kingston-upon-Hull HU1 2AD
Tel: 01482 328914
Fax: 01482 219790
DX: 742160 HULL 20
Email: hu-hullmcadmin@hmcts.gsi.gov.uk

Courts and times
The Courthouse, Market Place, Kingston-upon-Hull
Court building open: Monday to Friday 9am to 5pm; Court counter open: 9:30am to 4pm

0319 NORTH LINCOLNSHIRE LJA
Court Centre Office, Corporation Road, Scunthorpe DN15 6QB
Tel: 01724 281100

Fax: 01724 281890
DX: 742212 SCUNTHORPE 10
Email: scunmcadmin@hmcts.gsi.gov.uk

Courts and times
Scunthorpe Court Centre, Laneham Street, Scunthorpe
Court building open: Monday to Friday 8:30am to 5pm (4:30pm Friday); Court counter open: 10am to 2pm

2772 ROTHERHAM LJA
The Law Courts, The Statutes, PO Box 15, Rotherham, South Yorkshire S60 1YW
Tel: 01709 839339
Fax: 01709 370082
DX: 703025 ROTHERHAM 4
Email: sy-rotherhammcadmin@hmcts.gsi.gov.uk

Courts and times
The Statutes, Rotherham
Court building open: Monday to Friday 9am to 4pm; Magistrates' Court open: 9am to 4pm

2773 SHEFFIELD LJA
Magistrates' Court, Castle Street, Sheffield S3 8LU
Tel: 0114 276 0760
Fax: 0114 252 1860
DX: 10599 SHEFFIELD 1
Email: sy-sheffmcclerical@hmcts.gsi.gov.uk

Courts and times
Magistrates' Court, Castle Street, Sheffield
Court building open: Monday to Friday 9am until close of business; Court counter open: 9am to 4pm

NORTH AND WEST YORKSHIRE

2996 BATLEY AND DEWSBURY LJA
closed wef 4/12

2354 BRADFORD AND KEIGHLEY LJA
The Court Office, PO Box 187, The Tyrls, Bradford, West Yorkshire BD1 1JL
Tel: 01274 390111
Fax: 0870 739 4466
DX: 743850 BRADFORD 25
Email: wy-bradfordmags@hmcts.gsi.gov.uk
Courts and times
The Tyrls, Bradford
Court building open: 9am to 5pm; Court counter open: 9:30am to 4pm

2997 CALDERDALE LJA
The Court Office, PO Box 32, Harrison Road, Halifax, West Yorkshire HX1 2AN
Tel: 01422 360695
Fax: 08707 394450
Email: wy-halifaxmags@hmcts.gsi.gov.uk
Courts and times
Harrison Road, Halifax
Court building open: 9am to 5pm (4:30pm on Friday); Court counter open: 9am to 5pm (4:30pm on Friday)

2358 HARROGATE AND SKIPTON LJA
The Court House, PO Box 72, Victoria Avenue, Harrogate, North Yorkshire HG1 1EL
Tel: 01423 722000
Fax: 0870 739 4462
DX: 742910 HARROGATE 3; 703031 SKIPTON 2
Email: ny-harrogatemcenq@hmcts.gsi.gov.uk
Courts and times
Court House, Victoria Avenue, Harrogate
Court building open: 9am; Court counter open: 9:30am Monday to Friday to 4pm (3:30pm Friday)

2987 HUDDERSFIELD LJA
see 2987 KIRKLEES LJA

2979 KEIGHLEY LJA
closed wef 4/12

2987 KIRKLEES LJA
The Court Office, Civic Centre, Huddersfield, West Yorkshire HD1 2NH
Tel: 01484 423552
Fax: 0870 739 4408
DX: 743880 HUDDERSFIELD 20
Email: wy-huddersfieldmags@hmcts.gsi.gov.uk
Courts and times
Court House, Civic Centre, Huddersfield
Court building open: 9am to 5pm; Court counter open: 9am to 5pm

2992 LEEDS DISTRICT LJA
The Court House, PO Box No. 97, Westgate, Leeds LS1 3JP
Tel: 0113 245 9653
Fax: 0870 739 4267
DX: 743890 LEEDS (Westgate)
Email: wy-leedsmags@hmcts.gsi.gov.uk
Courts and times
The Court House, Westgate, Leeds
Court building open: Monday to Friday 9am to 5pm; Court enquiries open: 9am to 4pm

2543 NORTHALLERTON AND RICHMOND LJA
3 Racecourse Lane, Northallerton, North Yorkshire DL7 8QZ
Tel: 01609 788200

Fax: 0870 7394449
DX: 742420 NORTHALLERTON
Email: ny-nallertonmcenq@hmcts.gsi.gov.uk

Courts and times
3 Racecourse Lane, Northallerton
Court counter open: Monday to Friday 9am to 5pm (4:30pm on Friday); Court building open:
Monday to Friday 9am to 5pm (4:30pm Friday)

2994 PONTEFRACT LJA
CLOSED wef 3/2013 *see* **2355 WAKEFIELD AND PONTEFRACT LJA**

2536 SCARBOROUGH LJA
Law Courts, Northway, Scarborough, North Yorkshire YO12 7AE
Tel: 01723 505000
Fax: 0870 7394411
DX: 65140 Scarborough 2

Courts and times
Law Court, Northway, Scarborough
Court building open: Monday to Friday 9:15am to 4pm; Court counter open: 10am to 2pm

2537 SELBY LJA
CLOSED wef 3/2013 *see* **2357 YORK AND SELBY LJA**

2538 SKIPTON LJA
see **2358 HARROGATE AND SKIPTON LJA**

2355 WAKEFIELD AND PONTEFRACT LJA
The Court Office, Cliff Parade, Wakefield WF1 2TW
Tel: 01924 231100
Fax: 0870 7394390
DX: 743910 WAKEFIELD 20
Email: wy-wakefieldmags@hmcts.gsi.gov.uk

Courts and times
Court House, Cliff Parade, Wakefield; Enquiry Office open: 9am to 4pm; Court building open:
Monday to Friday, 8:45am to 4pm

2357 YORK AND SELBY LJA
Law Courts, Clifford Street, York YO1 9RE
Tel: 01904 818300
Fax: 0870 739 4476
DX: 744330 YORK 41
Email: ny-yorkmcenq@hmcts.gsi.gov.uk

Courts and times
Law Courts, Clifford Street, York
Court building open: Monday to Friday 9:30am to 5pm; Court counter open: 9:30am to 4pm

NORTHUMBRIA

2347 ALNWICK LJA
closed wef 31/3/11 – successor courts – South East Northumberland and Berwick-upon-Tweed

2348 BERWICK-UPON-TWEED LJA
40 Church Street, Berwick-upon-Tweed, Northumberland TD15 1DX
Tel: 01289 306885
Fax: 0870 324 0209
DX: 551540 BERWICK 3 TD
Email: no_berwick@hmcts.gsi.gov.uk
Courts
40 Church Street, Berwick-upon-Tweed
Court building open: 9:15am to 4pm; Court counter open: 9:15am to 4pm

2850 GATESHEAD DISTRICT LJA
Gateshead Magistrates' Court, Warwick Street, Gateshead, Tyne-and-Wear NE8 1DT
Tel: 0191 477 5821
Fax: 0870 324 0210
DX: 742120 GATESHEAD 6
Email: no_gatesheadcourt@hmcts.gsi.gov.uk
Courts and times
Gateshead Law Courts, Warwick Street, Gateshead
Court building open: 9am to 5pm; Court counter open: 9am to 5pm

2854 HOUGHTON-LE-SPRING LJA
closed wef 31/3/11. Enquiries to Sunderland Magistrates' Court Tel: 0191 514 1621

2351 NEWCASTLE-UPON-TYNE LJA
Magistrates' Courts, PO Box 839, Market Street, Newcastle-upon-Tyne NE99 1AU
Tel: 0191 232 7326
Fax: 0191 221 0025
DX: 61098 NEWCASTLE UPON TYNE
Email: no_newcastle@hmcts.gsi.gov.uk
Courts and times
Magistrates' Court, Market Street, Newcastle-upon-Tyne
Court building closed: 4pm; Court building open: 9am to 4pm

2852 NORTH TYNESIDE DISTRICT LJA
The Courthouse, Tynemouth Road, North Shields, Tyne-and-Wear NE30 1AG
Tel: 0191 296 0099
Fax: 0870 324 0224
Email: no-ceuadmin@hmcts.gsi.gov.uk
Courts and times
The Court House, Tynemouth Road, North Shields
Court building open: 9am; Court counter closed: 4pm

2352 SOUTH EAST NORTHUMBERLAND LJA
The Law Courts, Bedlington, Northumberland NE22 7LX
Tel: 01670 531100
Fax: 0870 3240204
DX: 62705 BEDLINGTON
Email: no_senorthmc@hmcts.gsi.gov.uk
Courts and times
The Law Courts, Bedlington
Court building open: 9am to 5pm; Court counter open: 9am to 4pm

2853 SOUTH TYNESIDE DISTRICT LJA
South Tyneside Magistrates' Court, Millbank, Secretan Way, South Shields NE33 1RG
Tel: 0191 455 8800
Fax: 0870 324 0214
DX: 65143 SOUTH SHIELDS 3
Email: no-stynesidemclist@hmcts.gsi.gov.uk

Courts and times
Magistrates' Court, Millbank, South Shields
Court building open: 9am to 5pm; Court counter open: 9am to 4pm

2855 SUNDERLAND LJA
Magistrates' Courts, Gillbridge Avenue, Sunderland SR1 3AP
Tel: 0191 514 1621
Fax: 0870 324 0213
DX: 742740 SUNDERLAND 17
Email: no-sunderlandmc@hmcts.gsi.gov.uk

Courts and times
Magistrates' Courts, Gillbridge Avenue, Sunderland
Court building open: 9am to 4pm

2346 TYNEDALE LJA
closed wef 31/3/11. Enquiries to Newcastle-upon-Tyne Magistrates' Court Tel: 0191 232 7326

North West Region

CHESHIRE AND MERSEYSIDE

1188 CHESTER, ELLESMERE PORT AND NESTON LJA
see **1729 WEST CHESHIRE LJA**

3340 COMMUNITY JUSTICE CENTRE, NORTH LIVERPOOL
closed

1177 HALTON LJA
combined with **1180 WARRINGTON LJA** to form **1722 NORTH CHESHIRE LJA**

2266 KNOWSLEY LJA
closed wef 12/11

2267 LIVERPOOL LJA
see **1730 LIVERPOOL AND KNOWSLEY LJA**

1730 LIVERPOOL AND KNOWSLEY LJA
City Magistrates' Courts, 107 Dale Street, Liverpool L2 2JQ
Tel: 0151 243 5500/88
Fax: 0870 324 0040
DX: 707900 LIVERPOOL 8
Email: me-customersupportliverpool@hmcts.gsi.gov.uk
Courts and times
Magistrates' Courts, Dale Street, Liverpool
Court building open: Monday to Friday 9am to 4pm

1178 MACCLESFIELD LJA
The Law Courts, Civic Centre, Crewe, Cheshire CW1 2DT
Tel: 01270 655920
Fax: 0870 761 7661
DX: 702504 CREWE 2
Email: ch-crewemcadmin@hmcts.gsi.gov.uk
Courts and times
The Law Courts, Hibel Road, Macclesfield
Court building open: 9am to 4:30pm

1722 NORTH CHESHIRE LJA
Winmarleigh Street, Warrington, Cheshire WA1 1PB
Tel: 01925 236 250
DX: 17793 WARRINGTON 1
Email: ch-warrmcadmin@hmcts.gsi.gov.uk
Courts and times
Warrington Magistrates' Court, Arpley Street, Warrington WA1 1LQ
Court counter open: 9:30am to 4pm; Court building open: Monday to Friday 9:30am to 4pm

2269 NORTH SEFTON DISTRICT LJA
closed wef 9/11

2268 ST HELENS LJA
The Court House, Corporation Street, St Helens, Merseyside WA10 1SZ
Tel: 01744 620244
Fax: 01744 627249
DX: 725020 St Helens 4
Courts and times
The Court House, St Helens
Court building open: Monday to Friday 9am to 5pm; Court counter open: 9am to 4pm

1728 SEFTON LJA
The Magistrates' Court, Merton Road, Bootle, Merseyside L20 3XX
Tel: 0151 933 6999
Fax: 0870 739 4401
Email: me-courtsupport@hmcts.gsi.gov.uk

Courts and times
Magistrates' Courts, Merton Road, Bootle
Court building open: 9am to 5pm

1187 SOUTH CHESHIRE LJA
Law Courts, Civic Centre, Crewe, Cheshire CW1 2DT
Tel: 01270 655920
Fax: 0870 761 7661
DX: 702504 CREWE 2
Email: ch-crewemcadmin@hmcts.gsi.gov.uk

2270 SOUTH SEFTON DISTRICT LJA
see **1728 SEFTON LJA**

1179 VALE ROYAL LJA
closed wef 9/11

1180 WARRINGTON LJA
combined with **1177 HALTON LJA** to form **1722 NORTH CHESHIRE LJA**

1729 WEST CHESHIRE LJA
Chester Magistrates' Court, Grosvenor Street, Chester CH1 2XA
Tel: 01244 405 790
Fax: 08707 394 394
Email: customerenquirieschestermc@hmcts.gsi.gov.uk

Courts and times
Chester Magistrates' Court, Grosvenor Street, Chester
Court building open: 9am to 4pm; Court counter open: 9:30am to 4pm

2271 WIRRAL LJA
The Sessions Courts, Chester Street, Birkenhead, Merseyside CH41 5HW
Tel: 0151 285 4100
Fax: 0870 761 7657
DX: 17888 BIRKENHEAD
Email: me-wirralcrime@hmcts.gsi.gov.uk

Courts and times
Birkenhead
Court building open: 9am to 4:30pm; Enquiry Office open: 9am to 4pm (closed from 1pm to 1:30pm)

CUMBRIA AND LANCASHIRE

2012 BLACKBURN, DARWEN AND RIBBLE VALLEY LJA
see **1725 EAST LANCASHIRE LJA**

2014 BURNLEY, PENDLE AND ROSSENDALE LJA
The Court House, Parker Lane, Burnley BB11 2BS
Tel: 01282 800100
Fax: 0870 324 0292
DX: 745300 BURNLEY 11
Email: ln-reedleymcenq@hmcts.gsi.gov.uk
Courts and times
Court House, Parker Lane, Burnley
Court building open: 9:15am to 4.30pm; Court counter open: 09:15am to close of Court business

1322 CARLISLE AND DISTRICT LJA
see **1727 NORTH CUMBRIA LJA**

1998 CHORLEY LJA
Court House, St Thomas's Square, Chorley, Lancashire PR7 1RZ
Tel: 01257 240500
Fax: 0870 324 0217
DX: 707530 CHORLEY 5
Email: ln-chorleymcenq@hmcts.gsi.gov.uk
Courts and times
Court House, St Thomas's Square, Chorley
Court building open: Monday to Friday 9am until close of business; Court counter open: Monday to
Friday 9am to 4pm

1725 EAST LANCASHIRE LJA
Court House, Northgate, Blackburn, Lancashire BB2 1AA
Tel: 01254 687500 (General Listings); 687510 (Listings)
Fax: 0870 739 4254
DX: 742020 BLACKBURN 10
Email: ln-blackburnmcenq@hmcts.gsi.gov.uk
Courts and times
Court House, Northgate, Blackburn
Court building open: 9:15am to 4:30pm

1324 EDEN LJA
closed wef 1/12

1398 FURNESS AND DISTRICT LJA
South Cumbria Magistrates' Court, Abbey Road, Barrow-in-Furness, Cumbria LA14 5QX
Tel: 01229 820161
Fax: 01229 870287
DX: 63909 BARROW-IN-FURNESS 2
Email: furness.magistrates@hmcts.gsi.gov.uk

1992 FYLDE COAST LJA
The Magistrates' Court, Civic Centre, Chapel Street, Blackpool, Lancashire FY1 5DQ
Tel: 01253 757000
Fax: 08703 240203
DX: 741861 BLACKPOOL 16
Email: ln-blackpoolmcenq@hmcts.gsi.gov.uk
Courts and times
Chapel Street, Blackpool
Court building open: 8:30am; Court counter open: 10am to 4pm

2010 HYNDBURN LJA
see **1725 EAST LANCASHIRE LJA**

2002 LANCASTER LJA
Blackpool Magistrates' Court, Civic Centre, Chapel Street, Blackpool, Lancashire FY1 5DQ
Tel: 01524 597000

Fax: 08703 240203
DX: 741861 BLACKPOOL 16
Email: ln-blackpoolmcenq@hmcts.gsi.gov.uk

Courts and times
Magistrates' Court, George Street, Lancaster LA1 1XZ
Court building open: 8am; Court counter open: 10am to 4pm

1727 NORTH CUMBRIA LJA
North Cumbria Magistrates' Court, Rickergate, Carlisle, Cumbria CA3 8QH
Tel: 01228 518800
Fax: 01228 518844
DX: 63018 CARLISLE
Email: cumbria.north.magistrates@hmcts.gsi.gov.uk

Courts and times
The Court House, Rickergate, Carlisle
Court building open: 9am to 5pm

2003 ORMSKIRK LJA
Court House, St Thomas's Square, Chorley, Lancashire PR7 1RZ
Tel: 01257 240500
Fax: 01257 261948
DX: 707530 CHORLEY 5
Email: ln-chorleymcenq@hmcts.gsi.gov.uk

Courts and times
The Court House, Derby Street, Ormskirk
Court building open: 9am

2005 PRESTON LJA
Magistrates' Court, PO Box 52, Lawson Street, Preston, Lancashire PR1 2RD
Tel: 01772 208000
Fax: 0870 324 0190
DX: 702663 PRESTON 5
Email: ln-prestonmcenq@hmcts.gsi.gov.uk

Courts and times
Magistrates' Court, Lawson Street, Preston
Court building open: 9am to 5pm; Court counter open: 10am to 4pm

1398 SOUTH LAKELAND LJA
South Cumbria, Magistrates' Court, Abbey Road, Barrow-in-Furness, Cumbria LA14 5QX
Tel: 01229 820161
Fax: 0870 739 4409
DX: 65210 BARROW-IN-FURNESS 2
Email: cumbria.south.magistrates@hmcts.gsi.gov.uk

Courts and times
Abbey Road, Barrow-in-Furness
Court building open: 9am to 5pm; Court counter open: 9am to 5pm

2007 SOUTH RIBBLE LJA
Court House, St Thomas's Square, Chorley, Lancashire PR7 1RZ
Tel: 01257 240500 or 01772 208 000
Fax: 0870 324 0217
DX: 707530 CHORLEY 5
Email: ln-chorleymcenq@hmcts.gsi.gov.uk

Courts and times
Court House, Chorley
Court building open: Monday to Friday 9am until close of business; Court counter open: Monday to Friday 9am to 4pm

1325 WEST ALLERDALE AND KESWICK LJA
see **1726 WEST CUMBRIA LJA**

1726 WEST CUMBRIA LJA
West Cumbria Magistrates' Courts, West Cumbria Court House, Hall Park, Ramsay Brow, Workington, Cumbria CA14 4AS
Tel: 01900 62244
Fax: 0870 324 0242

DX: 743420 WORKINGTON 5
Email: cm-workingtonmcenq@hmcts.gsi.gov.uk

Courts and times
West Cumbria Magistrates' Courts, Ramsay Brow, Workington
Court building open: Monday to Friday 9am to 5pm; Court counter open: 9am to 4pm

1375 WHITEHAVEN LJA
closed wef 6/11 (see **1726 WEST CUMBRIA LJA**)

GREATER MANCHESTER

1731 BOLTON LJA
The Courts, Civic Centre, Le Mans Crescent, Bolton BL1 1UA
Tel: 01204 558200
Fax: 01204 366978
DX: 745180 BOLTON 22

Courts and times
The Courts, Civic Centre, Bolton
Court building open: 9am to 5pm; Court counter open: 9am to 4pm

1732 BURY LJA
see **1724 BURY AND ROCHDALE LJA**

1724 BURY AND ROCHDALE LJA
Magistrates' Court, The Courthouse, Tenters Street, Bury BL9 0HX
Tel: 0161 447 8600
Fax: 0161 447 8630/50
DX: 702615 BURY 2

Courts and times
Magistrates' Court, Tenters Street, Bury
Court building open: 9am to 5pm; Court counter open: 9am to 4pm

1747 CITY OF SALFORD LJA
closed wef 12/11

GREATER MANCHESTER PUBLIC LAW FAMILY PROCEEDINGS COURTS AND MANCHESTER CITY LJA PRIVATE LAW FAMILY PROCEEDINGS COURTS
Civil Justice Centre, 1 Bridge Street West, Manchester M3 3FX
Tel: 0161 240 5000
Fax: 0161 240 5455

Courts and times
Civil Justice Centre, 1 Bridge Street West, Manchester M3 3FX
Court building open: Monday to Friday 8:30am to 5pm

1733 MANCHESTER AND SALFORD LJA
City Magistrates' Court, Crown Square, Manchester M60 1PR
Tel: 0161 830 4200
DX: 745170 MANCHESTER 75
Email: gm-manmcadmin@hmcts.gsi.gov.uk

Courts and times
Magistrates' Court, Crown Square, Manchester
Court building open: Monday to Friday 9am to 5pm; Court counter open: 9am to 5pm

1733 MANCHESTER CITY LJA
see **1733 MANCHESTER AND SALFORD LJA**

1734 OLDHAM LJA
Magistrates' Court, St Domingo Place, West Street, Oldham OL1 1QE
Tel: 0161 620 2331
Fax: 0161 652 0172
DX: 745190 OLDHAM 8

Courts and times
Magistrates' Court, St Domingo Place, Oldham
Court building open: 9am to 5pm

1750 ROCHDALE, MIDDLETON AND HEYWOOD LJA
closed wef 12/11 (see **1724 BURY AND ROCHDALE LJA**)

547 STOCKPORT LJA
The Courthouse, Stockport Magistrates' Court, PO Box 155, Edward Street, Stockport SK1 3NF
Tel: 0161 477 2020
Fax: 0161 968 9733

DX: 702620 STOCKPORT 4
Email: family@stockport.countycourt.gsi.gov.uk

Courts and times
The Courthouse, Edward Street, Stockport
Court building open: Monday to Friday 9am to 5pm; Court counter open: 9am to 4pm

1748 TAMESIDE LJA
Magistrates' Court, Henry Square, Ashton-under-Lyne OL6 7TP
Tel: 0161 330 2023/331 5645
Fax: 0161 339 9632
DX: 702625 ASHTON UNDER LYNE 2
Email: gm-tamesidemcadmin@hmcts.gsi.gov.uk

Courts and times
Magistrates' Court, Henry Square, Ashton-under-Lyne
Court building open: 9am to 5pm; Court counter open: 9am to 4pm

1742 TRAFFORD LJA
Magistrates' Court, PO Box 13, Ashton Lane, Sale, Cheshire M33 7NR
Tel: 0161 976 3333
Fax: 0161 975 4628
DX: 708290 SALE 6

Courts and times
Magistrates' Court, Ashton Lane, Sale
Court building open: 9am to 5pm; Court counter open: 9am to 4pm

1749 WIGAN AND LEIGH LJA
Magistrates' Court, Darlington Street, Wigan WN1 1DW
Tel: 01942 405405
Fax: 01942 405444
DX: 724820 WIGAN 9

Courts and times
Darlington Street, Wigan
Court building open: 8:30am to 5pm; Court counter open: 9am to 4pm

SOUTH EAST REGION

BEDFORDSHIRE AND HERTFORDSHIRE

124 BEDFORD AND MID BEDFORDSHIRE LJA
Luton & South Bedfordshire Magistrates' Court and Family Hearing Centre, Stuart Street, Luton,
Bedfordshire LU1 5BL
Tel: 01234 319100
Fax: 01234 319114
DX: 729420 BEDFORD 10 or 151660 LUTON 16
Email: bd-bedfordmcenq@hmcts.gsi.gov.uk

Courts and times
Shire Hall, 3 St Paul's Square, Bedford
Court building open: Monday to Friday 9am to 5pm (4:30pm Friday)

1892 CENTRAL HERTFORDSHIRE LJA
combined with **1893 WEST HERTFORDSHIRE LJA** to form **1910 WEST** and **CENTRAL
HERTFORDSHIRE LJA**

1888 EAST HERTFORDSHIRE LJA
combined with **1889 NORTH HERTFORDSHIRE LJA** to form **1889 NORTH** and **EAST
HERTFORDSHIRE LJA**

1879 HATFIELD MAGISTRATES' COURT
Clarendon Road, Watford, Hertfordshire WD17 1ST
Tel: 01923 281300
Fax: 01923 281318
DX: 51509 WATFORD 2

Courts and times
Hatfield Magistrates' Court, Comet Way, Hatfield
Court building open: 8:30am to close of business

1055 LUTON AND SOUTH BEDFORDSHIRE LJA
Luton and South Bedfordshire Magistrates' Courts, Stuart Street, Luton LU1 5BL
Tel: 01582 524200
Fax: 01582 524252
DX: 151660 LUTON 16
Email: bd-lutonmcenq@hmcts.gsi.gov.uk

Courts and times
Luton Magistrates' Court, Stuart Street, Luton
Court building open: Monday to Friday 9am to 5pm (4:30pm Friday); Court counter open: 9:30am to
2pm

1889 NORTH HERTFORDSHIRE LJA
combined with **1888 EAST HERTFORDSHIRE LJA** to form **1889 NORTH AND EAST
HERTFORDSHIRE LJA**

1889 NORTH AND EAST HERTFORDSHIRE LJA
Bayley House, Sish Lane, Stevenage SG1 3SS
Tel: 01923 281300
Fax: 01923 281318
DX: 153620 OLD STEVENAGE 2

Courts and times
Bayley House, Sish Lane, Stevenage
Court building open: 9am to 4pm

1893 WEST HERTFORDSHIRE LJA
combined with **1892 CENTRAL HERTFORDSHIRE LJA** to form **1910 WEST AND CENTRAL
HERTFORDSHIRE LJA**

1910 WEST AND CENTRAL HERTFORDSHIRE LJA
The Court House, Clarendon Road, Watford WD17 1ST
Tel: 01923 281300; 01234 319081 (Central Enforcement Unit)
Fax: 01923 281318
DX: 51509 WATFORD 2

CAMBRIDGESHIRE AND ESSEX

1165 CAMBRIDGE LJA
combined with **1166 EAST CAMBRIDGESHIRE LJA** to form **SOUTH CAMBRIDGESHIRE LJA** – wef 1/1/12

1166 EAST CAMBRIDGESHIRE LJA
combined with **1165 CAMBRIDGE LJA** to form **SOUTH CAMBRIDGESHIRE LJA** – wef 1/1/12

1167 FENLAND LJA
combined with **1162 PETERBOROUGH** to form **NORTH CAMBRIDGESHIRE LJA** – wef 1/1/12

1168 HUNTINGDONSHIRE LJA
Magistrates' Court, Bridge Street, Peterborough PE1 1ED
Tel: 0845 310 0575
Fax: 01733 313749
DX: 742250 PETERBOROUGH 23
Email: cb-enquiries@hmcts.gsi.gov.uk

Courts and times
Magistrates' Court, Bridge Street, Peterborough
Court building open: 9am to 4:30pm; Telephone Enquiries from: 9am to 5pm

1612 MID-NORTH ESSEX LJA
combined with **1613 NORTH-EAST ESSEX LJA** and **1619 NORTH WEST ESSEX LJA** to form **1970 NORTH ESSEX LJA**

1610 MID-SOUTH ESSEX LJA
combined with **1629 SOUTH-EAST ESSEX LJA** and **1626 SOUTH-WEST ESSEX LJA** to form **1971 SOUTH ESSEX LJA**

NORTH CAMBRIDGESHIRE LJA
Magistrates' Court, Bridge Street, Peterborough PE1 1ED
Tel: 0845 310 0575
Fax: 01733 313749
DX: 742250 PETERBOROUGH 23
Email: cb-enquiries@hmcts.gsi.gov.uk

Courts and times
Magistrates' Court, Peterborough
Court building open: 9am to 4:30pm; Telephone Enquiries from: 9am to 5pm

1613 NORTH-EAST ESSEX LJA
combined with **1612 MID-NORTH ESSEX LJA** and **1619 NORTH-WEST ESSEX LJA** to form **1970 NORTH ESSEX LJA**

1970 NORTH ESSEX LJA
Essex Magistrates' Courts Business Centre, PO Box 10754, Chelmsford CM1 9PZ
Tel: 01245 313300
Fax: 0870 324 0091
DX: 151020 Chelmsford 17
Email: es-osprey.general@hmcts.gsi.gov.uk

Courts and times
10 New Street, Chelmsford CM1 1NT
Court building open: 9am to close of court business

1619 NORTH-WEST ESSEX LJA
combined with **1612 MID-NORTH ESSEX LJA** and **1613 NORTH EAST ESSEX LJA** to form **1970 NORTH ESSEX LJA**

1162 PETERBOROUGH LJA
combined with **1167 FENLAND** to form **NORTH CAMBRIDGESHIRE LJA** – wef 1/1/12

SOUTH CAMBRIDGESHIRE LJA
Magistrates' Court, Bridge Street, Peterborough PE1 1ED
Tel: 0845 310 0575
Fax: 01733 313749
DX: 742250 PETERBOROUGH 23

Email: cb-enquiries@hmcts.gsi.gov.uk

Courts and times
Magistrates' Court, Peterborough
Court building open: 9am to 4:30pm; Telephone Enquiries from: 9am to 5pm

1971 SOUTH ESSEX LJA
Essex Magistrates' Courts Business Centre, PO Box 10754, Chelmsford CM1 9PZ
Tel: 01245 313300
Fax: 0870 324 0091
DX: 151020 Chelmsford 17
Email: es-osprey.general@hmcts.gsi.gov.uk

Courts and times
10 New Street, Chelmsford CM1 1NT
Court building open: 9am to close of court business

1629 SOUTH-EAST ESSEX LJA
combined with **1610 MID-SOUTH ESSEX LJA** and **1626 SOUTH WEST ESSEX LJA** to form **1971 SOUTH ESSEX LJA**

1626 SOUTH-WEST ESSEX LJA
combined with **1610 MID-SOUTH ESSEX LJA** and **1629 SOUTH-EAST ESSEX LJA** to form **1971 SOUTH ESSEX LJA**

KENT

1959 CENTRAL KENT LJA
Maidstone Magistrates' Court, The Courthouse, Palace Avenue, Maidstone ME15 6LL
Tel: 01634 830232
Fax: 0870 324 0037
DX: 152303 MAIDSTONE 19 (Maidstone Magistrates' Court)
Enquiries: ke-ck_nk_admin@hmcts.gsi.gov.uk

Courts and times
Maidstone Magistrates' Court, Maidstone
Court building open: 9am to 5pm; Court counter open: 9am to 5pm

1955 EAST KENT LJA
Court Admin Office, The Magistrates' Court, Pencester Road, Dover CT16 1BS
Tel: 01304 218600
Fax: 0870 739 5848
Email: ke-dovermclist@hmcts.gsi.gov.uk

Courts and times
The Magistrates' Court, Pencester Road, Dover
Court building open: Monday to Friday 9:30am to 4pm; Court counter open: 9:30am to 4pm

1966 NORTH KENT LJA (DARTFORD AND MEDWAY)
Court Admin Office, PO Box CH 4, The Court House, The Brook, Chatham ME4 4JZ
Tel: 01634 830232
Fax: 01634 847400

Courts and times
The Court House, Chatham
Court building open: 9.00am to 5.00pm; Court counter open: 9.00am to 4.00pm

NORFOLK AND SUFFOLK

1442 CENTRAL NORFOLK LJA
combined with **1443 GREAT YARMOUTH LJA, 1444 NORTH NORFOLK LJA, 1445 NORWICH LJA, 1446 SOUTH NORFOLK LJA, 1447 WEST NORFOLK LJA** to form **1972 NORFOLK LJA**

1443 GREAT YARMOUTH LJA
combined with **1442 CENTRAL NORFOLK LJA, 1444 NORTH NORFOLK LJA, 1445 NORWICH LJA, 1446 SOUTH NORFOLK LJA, 1447 WEST NORFOLK LJA** to form **1972 NORFOLK LJA**

2863 NORTH EAST SUFFOLK LJA
Lowestoft Magistrates' Court and Family Court Hearing Centre, Elm Street, Ipswich, Suffolk IP1 2AP
Tel: 01473 217 261 or 01502 501 060
Fax: 01502 513875
DX: 97750 LOWESTOFT 2
Email: suffolkadmin@hmcts.gsi.gov.uk

Courts and times
The Magistrates' Court, Old Nelson Street, Lowestoft
Court building open: Monday to Thursday, 9am until close of business

1444 NORTH NORFOLK LJA
combined with **1442 CENTRAL NORFOLK LJA, 1443 GREAT YARMOUTH LJA, 1445 NORWICH LJA, 1446 SOUTH NORFOLK LJA, 1447 WEST NORFOLK LJA** to form **1972 NORFOLK LJA**

1445 NORFOLK LJA
combined with **1442 CENTRAL NORFOLK LJA, 1443 GREAT YARMOUTH LJA, 1445 NORWICH LJA, 1446 SOUTH NORFOLK LJA, 1447 WEST NORFOLK LJA** to form **1972 NORFOLK LJA**

1972 NORFOLK LJA
The Magistrates' Court, Bishopgate, Norwich NR3 1UP
Tel: 01603 679500
Fax: 01603 663263
DX: 97389 NORWICH 5
Email: norwich.court@hmcts.gsi.gov.uk

Courts and times
The Magistrates' Court, Bishopgate, Norwich
Court building open: 9am to 5pm

2866 SOUTH EAST SUFFOLK LJA
The Magistrates' Court, Elm Street, Ipswich IP1 2AP
Tel: 01473 217261
Fax: 01473 231249
DX: 3232 IPSWICH
Email: suffolkadmin@hmcts.gsi.gov.uk

Courts and times
The Magistrates' Court, Elm Street, Ipswich
Court building open: Monday to Friday 9am to 4pm

1446 SOUTH NORFOLK LJA
combined with **1442 CENTRAL NORFOLK LJA, 1443 GREAT YARMOUTH LJA, 1444 NORTH NORFOLK LJA, 1445 NORWICH LJA, 1447 WEST NORFOLK LJA** to form **1972 NORFOLK LJA**

1447 WEST NORFOLK LJA
combined with **1442 CENTRAL NORFOLK LJA, 1443 GREAT YARMOUTH LJA, 1444 NORTH NORFOLK LJA, 1445 NORWICH LJA, 1446 SOUTH NORFOLK LJA** to form **1972 NORFOLK LJA**

2867 WEST SUFFOLK LJA
The Magistrates' Court, Elm Street, Ipswich IP1 2AP
Tel: 01473 217261
Fax: 01473 231249
DX: 3232 IPSWICH
Email: suffolkadmin@hmcts.gsi.gov.uk

Courts and times
The Courthouse, Shire Hall, Bury St Edmunds
Court building open: 9am to 4pm

SURREY AND SUSSEX

2841 NORTH SURREY LJA
Surrey Magistrates' Courts Business Centre and Family Court Hearing Centre, PO Box 36, The Law Courts, Mary Road, Guildford, Surrey GU1 4AS
Tel: 01483 405 300
Fax: 01483 461 791
DX: 97865 GUILDFORD 5 or 98045 STAINES 2
Email: su-guildfordmcadmin@hmcts.gsi.gov.uk
Courts and times
The Law Courts, Knowle Green, Staines
Court building open: Monday to Friday 9am to 4pm; Telephone Enquiries from: 9am to 5pm

2857 NORTH WEST SURREY LJA
closed wef 31/12/11

2856 SOUTH EAST SURREY LJA
Surrey Magistrates' Courts and Family Court Hearing Centre Business Centre, PO Box 36, The Law Courts, Mary Road, Guildford, Surrey GU1 4AS
Tel: 01483 405 300
Fax: 01483 461 791
DX: 97865 GUILDFORD 5
Courts and times
The Law Courts, Hatchlands Road, Redhill
Court building open: Monday to Friday 9am to 5pm

2856 SOUTH WEST SURREY LJA
Guildford Magistrates' Court and Family Court Hearing Centre, Mary Road, Guildford, Surrey GU1 4PS
Tel: 01483 405300
Fax: 01483 461791
DX: 97865 GUILDFORD 5
Email: su-guildfordmcadmin@hmcts.gsi.gov.uk
Courts and times
Magistrates' Court, Mary Road, Guildford
Court building open: Monday to Friday 9am to 4pm; Telephone Enquiries from: 9am to 5pm

2950 SUSSEX (CENTRAL) LJA
Brighton Magistrates' Court, The Law Courts, Edward Street, Brighton BN2 0LG
Tel: 01273 670888
Fax: 0870 761 7669
DX: 153460 BRIGHTON 17
Email: ss-sussexadmin@hmcts.gsi.gov.uk
Courts and times
Law Courts, Edward Street, Brighton
Court building open: Monday to Friday 8:30am to 4:30pm

2948 SUSSEX (EASTERN) LJA
Hastings Magistrates' Court, The Law Courts, Horntye Park, Bohemia Road, Hastings TN34 1ND
Tel: 01424 710 280 or 01424 710 287 or 01424 710 291
Fax: 01424 421585
DX: 98150 HASTINGS 2
Courts and times
The Law Courts, Horntye Park, Bohemia Road, Hastings
Court building open: Monday to Friday 9am to 4:30pm; Court counter open: For urgent appointments only; Telephone Enquiries from: 9am to 5pm

2947 SUSSEX (NORTHERN) LJA
Brighton Magistrates' Court, The Law Courts, Edward Street, Brighton BN2 0LG
Tel: 01273 670888
Fax: 0870 761 7669
DX: 153460 BRIGHTON 17
Email: ss-sussexadmin@hmcts.gsi.gov.uk

Courts and times
The Law Courts, Edward Street, Brighton
Court building open: Monday to Friday 8:30am to 4:30pm

2949 SUSSEX (WESTERN) LJA
Brighton Magistrates' Court, The Law Courts, Edwards Street, Brighton, East Sussex BN2 0LG
Tel: 01273 670888
Fax: 0870 761 7669
DX: 153460 BRIGHTON 17
Email: ss-sussexadmin@hmcts.gsi.gov.uk

Courts and times
The Law Courts, Christchurch Road, Worthing
Magistrates' Court, 6 Market Avenue, Chichester
Worthing: Court building open: Monday to Friday 8:45am to 4:30pm
Chichester: Court building open: When court is sitting

SOUTH EAST REGION

THAMES VALLEY

1076 BERKSHIRE LJA
Reading Magistrates' Court, Civic Centre, Reading RG1 7TQ
Tel: 0118 980 1800
Fax: 0118 980 1830
DX: 151160 READING 25
Email: tv-berkshiremcenq@hmcts.gsi.gov.uk
Courts and times
Magistrates' Court, Civic Centre, Reading
Court building open: 9am to 5pm Monday to Thursday, 4:30pm Friday

1124 BUCKINGHAMSHIRE LJA
Magistrates' Court, 301 Silbury Boulevard, Witan Gate East, Milton Keynes MK9 2AJ
Tel: 01908 451145
Fax: 01296 554320
DX: 149920 AYLESBURY 10
Courts and times
The Law Courts, Walton Street, Aylesbury HP21 7QZ.
Court building open: 8:45am – 4:45pm

1129 CENTRAL BUCKINGHAMSHIRE LJA
combined with **1129 CENTRAL BUCKINGHAMSHIRE LJA** and **1130 WYCOMBE AND BEACONSFIELD LJA** to form **1124 BUCKINGHAMSHIRE LJA**

1072 EAST BERKSHIRE LJA
combined with **1075 WEST BERKSHIRE LJA** and **1076 READING LJA** to form **1076 BERKSHIRE LJA**

1124 MILTON KEYNES LJA
combined with **1129 CENTRAL BUCKINGHAMSHIRE LJA** and **1130 WYCOMBE AND BEACONSFIELD LJA** to form **1124 BUCKINGHAMSHIRE LJA**

2775 NORTHERN OXFORDSHIRE LJA
combined with **2777 OXFORD LJA** and **2774 SOUTHERN OXFORDSHIRE LJA** to form **2777 OXFORDSHIRE LJA**

2777 OXFORD LJA
combined with **2775 NORTHERN OXFORDSHIRE LJA** and **2774 SOUTHERN OXFORDSHIRE LJA** to form **2777 OXFORDSHIRE LJA**

2777 OXFORDSHIRE LJA
The Court House, Speedwell Street, Oxford, Oxfordshire OX1 1RZ
Tel: 01865 448020
Fax: 01865 448024
DX: 96452 OXFORD 4
Email: tv-oxfordmcenq@hmcts.gsi.gov.uk
Courts and times
Oxford Magistrates' Court, Speedwell Street, Oxford OX1 1XP.
Court counter and building open: 9am to 4:30pm (4pm Friday)

1076 READING LJA
combined with **1072 EAST BERKSHIRE LJA** and **1075 WEST BERKSHIRE LJA** to form **1076 BERKSHIRE LJA**

2774 SOUTHERN OXFORDSHIRE LJA
combined with **2777 OXFORD LJA** and **2775 NORTHERN OXFORDSHIRE LJA** to form **2777 OXFORDSHIRE LJA**

1075 WEST BERKSHIRE LJA
combined with **1072 EAST BERKSHIRE LJA** and **1076 READING LJA** to form **1076 BERKSHIRE LJA**

1130 WYCOMBE AND BEACONSFIELD LJA
combined with **1124 MILTON KEYNES LJA** and **1129 CENTRAL BUCKINGHAMSHIRE LJA** to form
1124 BUCKINGHAMSHIRE LJA

SOUTH WEST REGION

AVON, SOMERSET AND GLOUCESTERSHIRE

1022 BATH AND WANSDYKE LJA
see **1022 SOMERSET LJA**

1013 BRISTOL LJA
Magistrates' Court, Marlborough Street, Bristol BS1 3NU
Tel: 0117 930 2400
Fax: 0870 739 4080
DX: 78126 BRISTOL
Email: av-bristol.mc@hmcts.gsi.gov.uk

Courts and times
Marlborough Street, Bristol
Court building open: 9am to 4:30pm; Telephone Enquiries from: 8:30am to 5pm

1692 GLOUCESTERSHIRE LJA
HMCTS Gloucestershire, PO Box 9051, Gloucester, Gloucestershire GL1 2XG
Tel: 01452 334400
Fax: 0870 324 0171
DX: 7598 GLOUCESTER 3
Email: gs-glosmcadmin@hmcts.gsi.gov.uk

Courts and times
The Courthouse, Barbican Way, Gloucester
Court building open: 9am until close of business when court sitting

1021 NORTH AVON LJA
Magistrates' Court, Kennedy Way, Yate, South Gloucestershire BS37 4PY
Tel: 01454 310505/3338219
DX: 743500 YATE 2
Email: av-yate.mc@hmcts.gsi.gov.uk

Courts and times
Magistrates' Court, Kennedy Way, Yate
Court counter open: 9:45am to 2pm

1023 NORTH SOMERSET LJA
see **1022 SOMERSET LJA**

2706 SEDGEMOOR LJA
closed wef 4/12

1022 SOMERSET LJA
Magistrates' Court, The Law Courts, North Parade Road, Bath BA1 0LF
Tel: 01225 463281
Fax: 0870 324 0189
DX: 98580 BATH 2
Email: av-bath.mc@hmcts.gsi.gov.uk

Courts and times
Magistrates' Court, North Parade Road, Bath
Court building open: Monday to Friday 9am to 4:30pm; Telephone Enquiries from: 8:30am to 5pm;
Court counter open: 10am to 2pm

2716 SOUTH SOMERSET AND MENDIP LJA
see **1022 SOMERSET LJA**

2709 TAUNTON DEANE AND WEST SOMERSET LJA
see **1022 SOMERSET LJA**

DEVON, CORNWALL AND DORSET

1292 CENTRAL DEVON LJA
combined with **1291 NORTH DEVON LJA** to form **1292 NORTH AND EAST DEVON LJA**

1301 CORNWALL LJA
The Law Courts, Launceston Road, Bodmin, Cornwall PL31 2AL
Tel: 01208 262700
Fax: 01208 77198
DX: 740535 BODMIN 4 PL
Email: dcmcc.eastcornwall@hmcts.gsi.gov.uk
The Magistrates' Court, Tremorvah Wood Lane, Mitchell Hill, Truro TR1 1HZ
Tel: 01872 321900
Fax: 01872 276227
DX: 140880 TRURO 5
Email: westcornwall@hmcts.gsi.gov.uk
Notes:
Family Court Administration Department is located at The Truro County Court, Courts of Justice, Edward Street, Truro TR1 2PB. Tel: 01872 267460. DX: 135396 TRURO 2.

Courts and times
The Law Courts, Launceston Road, Bodmin
The Magistrates' Court, Tremorvah Wood Lane, Mitchell Hill, Truro
Bodmin: Court building open: 9am to 4pm; Court counter open: 9am to 4pm
Truro: Court building open: Monday to Friday 9am to 4:30pm; Court counter open: 9am to 4pm

DORSET COMBINED FAMILY PANEL AND UNIFIED FAMILY OFFICE
The Combined Court, Deansleigh Road, Bournemouth BH7 7DS
Tel: 01202 502800
Fax: 01202 502801
DX: 98420 BOURNEMOUTH 4
Email: enquiries@bournemouth.countycourt.gsi.gov.uk

Courts and times
The Family Court Suite at The Law Courts, Stafford Road, Bournemouth
The Law Courts, Westwey Road, Weymouth
Dates and venues as required

5522/5523 DORSET COMBINED YOUTH PANEL
The Law Courts, Westwey Road, Weymouth, Dorset DT4 8BS
Tel: 01305 752510
DX: 98820 WEYMOUTH 3

Courts
The Law Courts, Park Road, Poole
The Law Courts, Westwey Road, Weymouth
Dates and venues as required

1289 EAST CORNWALL LJA
combined with **1288 WEST CORNWALL LJA** to form **1301 CORNWALL LJA**

1522 EAST DORSET LJA
The Law Courts, Stafford Road, Bournemouth, Dorset BH1 1LA
Tel: 01202 745309
Fax: 01202 711999
DX: 157500 BOURNEMOUTH 24

Courts and times
The Law Courts, Stafford Road, Bournemouth
Court building open: 8:30am to 5pm; Court counter open: 9am to 5pm (Mon-Thu) & 4:30pm (Fri)

1291 NORTH DEVON LJA
combined with **1292 CENTRAL DEVON LJA** to form **1292 NORTH AND EAST DEVON LJA**

1292 NORTH AND EAST DEVON LJA
East Devon Magistrates' Courts, Southernhay Gardens, Exeter EX1 1UH
Tel: 01392 415 300
Fax: 0870 324 0076

DX: 98440 EXETER 2
Email: de-exetermcadm@hmcts.gsi.gov.uk
The Law Courts, Civic Centre, Barnstaple, Devon EX31 1DX
Tel: 01271 340410
Fax: 0870 324 0128
DX: 98560 BARNSTAPLE 2
Email: nedmc@hmcts.gsi.gov.uk

Courts and times
Court House, Heavitree Road, Exeter
The Law Courts, Civic Centre, Barnstaple
Exeter: Court building closed: 4pm; Court building open: 9am to 4pm
Barnstaple: Court building open: Monday to Friday 9am until close of business; Court counter open: 9:30am to 2pm

1290 PLYMOUTH DISTRICT LJA

Magistrates' Court, St Andrew Street, Plymouth PL1 2DP
Tel: 01752 206200
Fax: 0870 3240 186
DX: 98670 Plymouth 7
Email: de-plymouthmclist@hmcts.gsi.gov.uk

Courts and times
Magistrates' Court, St Andrew Street, Plymouth
Court building open: 9am to 5pm; Court counter open: 9am to 4pm

1302 SOUTH DEVON LJA

HMCTS South Devon, Nicholson Road, Torquay, Devon TQ2 7AZ
Tel: 01803 617880
Fax: 01803 616795
DX: 98740 TORQUAY 4
Email: southdevonmc@hmcts.gsi.gov.uk

Courts and times
The Court House, Union Street, Torquay
Court building open: 9.00am

1288 WEST CORNWALL LJA

combined with **1289 EAST CORNWALL LJA** to form **1301 CORNWALL LJA**

1510 WEST DORSET LJA

The Law Courts, Westwey Road, Weymouth, Dorset DT4 8BS
Tel: 01305 783891
Fax: 01305 761418
DX: 98820 WEYMOUTH 3

Courts and times
The Law Courts, Westwey Road, Weymouth
Court building open: 8:30am to 5pm (Mon to Thu) & 4:30pm (Fri); Court counter open: 8:30am to 5pm (Mon to Thu) & 4:30pm (Fri)

HAMPSHIRE, ISLE OF WIGHT AND WILTSHIRE

1945 ISLE OF WIGHT LJA
The Magistrates' Court, The Law Courts, Quay Street, Newport, Isle of Wight PO30 5YT
Tel: 01983 535100
Fax: 0870 761 7625
DX: 98460 NEWPORT IW 2
Email: iow.magistrates@hmcts.gsi.gov.uk

Courts and times
Magistrates' Court, The Law Courts, Quay Street, Newport, Isle of Wight
Court building open: Monday to Friday 9am to 5pm; Court counter open: 10am to 4pm

1779 NEW FOREST LJA
closed wef 1/04/11

1305 NORTH HAMPSHIRE LJA
     5305 (YC)
Basingstoke Magistrates' Court, The Court House, London Road, Basingstoke RG21 4AB
Tel: 01256 318 200
DX: 98570 Basingstoke 3
Email: ha.basmags@hmcts.gsi.gov.uk
Aldershot Magistrates' Court, The Court House, Civic Centre, Aldershot GU11 1NY
Tel: 01252 366000
Fax: 0870 739 4087
DX: 98570 BASINGSTOKE 3
Email: ha.aldmags@hmcts.gsi.gov.uk

Courts and times
The Court House, London Road, Basingstoke
The Court House, Civic Centre, Aldershot
Basingstoke: Court building open: Monday to Friday 9am to 5pm; Court counter open: 9am to 4:30pm
Aldershot: Court building open: Monday to Friday, 9am to 5pm; Court counter open: 9am to 4:30pm

1780 NORTH EAST HAMPSHIRE LJA
combined with **1781 NORTH WEST HAMPSHIRE LJA** to form **1305/5305 NORTH HAMPSHIRE LJA**

1781 NORTH WEST HAMPSHIRE LJA
combined with **1780 NORTH EAST HAMPSHIRE LJA** to form **1305/5305 NORTH HAMPSHIRE LJA**

3026 NORTH WEST WILTSHIRE LJA
See **3012 WILTSHIRE LJA**

1782 SOUTH EAST HAMPSHIRE LJA
The Law Courts, Winston Churchill Avenue, Portsmouth, Hampshire PO1 2DQ
Tel: 023 9281 9421 or 023 9285 7904 or 023 9285 7992
Fax: 023 9229 3085
DX: 98494 PORTSMOUTH 5
Email: ha-portsmcenquiry@hmcts.gsi.gov.uk

Courts and times
The Law Courts, Winston Churchill Avenue, Portsmouth
Court building open: 9.00am to 5.00pm (4.30pm Friday); Court counter open: 9.00am to 4.30pm (4.00pm Friday)

3027 SOUTH EAST WILTSHIRE LJA
See **3012 WILTSHIRE LJA**

1783 SOUTH HAMPSHIRE LJA
The Law Courts, Winston Churchill Avenue, Portsmouth, Hampshire PO1 2DQ
Tel: 023 9281 9421 or 023 9285 7904 or 023 9285 7992
Fax: 023 9229 3085
DX: 98494 PORTSMOUTH 5
Email: ha-portsmcenquiry@hmcts.gsi.gov.uk

Courts and times
The Court House, Trinity Street, Fareham
Court building open: Closed every Monday. Open Tues-Fri: 9am to 5pm (4:30pm Friday); Court counter open: 9am to 4:30pm (4pm Friday); Telephone Enquiries from: 9am to 5pm

---

1775 SOUTHAMPTON LJA
See **1304 WEST HAMPSHIRE LJA**

3015 SWINDON LJA
See **3012 WILTSHIRE LJA**

1304 WEST HAMPSHIRE LJA
Southampton Magistrates' Court, 100 The Avenue, Southampton SO17 1EY
Tel: 023 8038 4200
DX: 135986 SOUTHAMPTON 32
Email: ha-swestenq@hmcts.gsi.gov.uk

Courts and times
Southampton Magistrates' Court, 100 The Avenue, Southampton
Court building open: Monday to Friday 9am to 5pm; Court counter open: 9am to 4:30pm (4pm on Friday); Fixed penalty office: 9:30am to 12pm and 1:30pm to 3:30pm

---

3015 WILTSHIRE LJA
7021 (YC)
Swindon Magistrates' Court, Princes Street, Swindon, Wiltshire SN1 2JB
Tel: 01793 699800 or 01793 699 814
Fax: 01793 699863
DX: 118725 SWINDON 7
Email: wi-swindonmcadmin@hmcts.gsi.gov.uk

Courts and times
Swindon Magistrates' Court, Princes Street, Swindon
Court building open: 9am to 4:30pm (3:45pm Friday); Court counter open: 9am to 4:30pm (3:45pm Friday) – Admin only

---

HMCTS WALES

MID AND WEST WALES

3250 BRECKNOCK AND RADNORSHIRE LJA
7250 (YC)
Magistrates' Court, The Law Courts, Glebeland Place, Merthyr Tydfil CF47 8BH
Tel: 01685 727600
Fax: 0870 3240338
DX: 99582 MERTHYR TYDFIL 2
Email: sw-merthyrmcenq@hmcts.gsi.gov.uk

Courts and times
The Law Courts, Glebeland Place
Court building open: Monday to Friday 9am to 5pm; Court counter open: 10am to 2pm

3138 CARMARTHEN LJA
combined with **3140 DINEFWR AND 3122 LLANELLI LJAS** to form **3252 CARMARTHENSHIRE LJA**

3252 CARMARTHENSHIRE LJA
Llanelli Magistrates' Court, Town Hall Square, Llanelli SA15 3AW
Tel: 01554 757201
Fax: 0870 739 4284
DX: 99512 LLANELLI 2
Email: llanellimagscrt@hmcts.gsi.gov.uk

Courts and times
Town Hall Square, Llanelli
Court building open: 9am to 5pm; Court counter open: 10am to 2pm

3135 CEREDIGION LJA
combined with **3356 PEMBROKESHIRE LJA** to form **3253 CEREDIGION AND PEMBROKESHIRE LJA**

3253 CEREDIGION AND PEMBROKESHIRE LJA
7253 (YC)
Aberystwyth Justice Centre, Y Lanfa, Trefechan, Aberystwyth, Ceredigion SY23 1AS
Tel: 01970 621250
Fax: 0870 739 4223
DX: 99560 ABERYSTWYTH 2
Email: aberystwythjusticecentre@hmcts.gsi.gov.uk
Haverfordwest Law Courts, Penffynnon, Hawthorn Rise, Haverfordwest SA61 2AX
Tel: 01437 772090
Fax: 0870 739 4344
DX: 99610 HAVERFORDWEST 2
Email: dy-pembsmcinfo@hmcts.gsi.gov.uk

Courts and times
Aberystwyth Justice Centre, Y Lanfa, Trefechan, Aberystwyth
Magistrates' Court, Penffynnon, Haverfordwest
Aberystwyth: Court building open: Monday to Friday, 9am to 5pm; Court enquiries open: 10am to 2pm
Haverfordwest: Court counter open: 10am to 2pm

3350 DE BRYCHEINIOG LJA
combined with **3357 RADNORSHIRE AND NORTH BRECKNOCK LJA** to form **3250 BRECKNOCK AND RADNORSHIRE LJA**

3140 DINEFWR LJA
combined with **3138 CARMARTHEN AND 3122 LLANELLI LJAS** to form **3252 CARMARTHENSHIRE LJA**

3122 LLANELLI LJA
combined with **3138 CARMARTHEN AND 3140 DINEFWR LJAS** to form **3252 CARMARTHENSHIRE LJA**

3355 MONTGOMERYSHIRE LJA
Mansion House, 24 Severn Street, Welshpool, Powys SY21 7UX
Tel: 01938 555968
Fax: 0870 324 0339
Email: dy-powysmcinfo@hmcts.gsi.gov.uk

Courts and times
Mansion House, Welshpool
Court building open: Monday to Friday 9am to 4pm; Court counter open: Thursday 10am to 2pm

3359 NEATH PORT TALBOT LJA
Magistrates' Clerk's Office, Fairfield Way, Neath SA11 1RF
Tel: 01639 765900
Fax: 01639 641456

3356 PEMBROKESHIRE LJA
combined with **3135 CEREDIGION LJA** to form **3253 CEREDIGION AND PEMBROKESHIRE LJA**

3351 RADNORSHIRE AND NORTH BRECKNOCK LJA
combined with **3350 DE BRYCHEINIOG** to for **3250 BRECKNOCK AND RADNORSHIRE LJA**

3360 SWANSEA LJA
Magistrates' Court, Grove Place, Swansea SA1 5DB
Tel: 01792 478300
Fax: 0870 739 4327
Email: sw-swanseamagscrt@hmcts.gsi.gov.uk

Courts and times
Magistrates' Court, Grove Place, Swansea
Court building open: 9am to 5pm; Court counter open: 10am to 2pm

NORTH WALES

3062 CONWY LJA
The Courthouse, Conwy Road, Llandudno LL30 1GA
Tel: 01492 871333
Fax: 0870 327 0327
DX: 11365 LLANDUDNO
Email: nw-llandudnomcenq@hmcts.gsi.gov.uk

Courts and times
The Courthouse, Conwy Road, Llandudno
Court building open: 9am to Monday to Thursday 5pm, Friday 4:30pm; Court counter open: 9am to 4:30pm

3061 DENBIGHSHIRE LJA
The Courthouse, Conwy Road, Llandudno LL30 1GA
Tel: 01492 871333
Fax: 0870 327 0327
DX: 11365 LLANDUDNO
Email: nw-llandudnomcenq@hmcts.gsi.gov.uk

Courts and times
The Courthouse, Victoria Road, Prestatyn
Court building open: Monday to Friday 9am to 4:30pm

3059 FLINTSHIRE LJA
The Law Courts, Mold, Flintshire CH7 1AE
Tel: 01352 707330
Fax: 0870 739 4239
DX: 702521 Mold 2
Email: nw-wrexhammcenq@hmcts.gsi.gov.uk.cjsm.net

Courts and times
The Law Courts, Mold
Court building open: Monday to Friday 9am to 5pm; Court counter open: 9am to 5pm

3244 GWYNEDD LJA
Criminal Justice Centre, Llanberis Road, Caernarfon, Gwynedd LL55 2DF
Tel: 01286 669700
Fax: 0870 739 4384
DX: 744382 CAERNARFON 6
Email: nw-caernarfonmcenq@hmcts.gsi.gov.uk

Courts and times
Criminal Justice Centre, Caernarfon
Court building open: 9am to 5pm Monday to Thursday; Friday: 4:30pm; Court counter open: 9am to 5pm Monday to Thursday; Friday: 4:30pm

3058 WREXHAM MAELOR LJA
Wrexham Magistrates' Court and Family Court, Bodhyfryd, Wrexham, Denbighshire LL12 7BP
Tel: 01352 707330
Fax: 0870 739 4239
DX: 702521 Mold 2

Courts and times
The Law Courts, Mold, Flintshire CH7 1AE
Court building open: 9:30am to 4:30pm (4pm Friday)

3238 YNYS MON/ANGLESEY LJA
Criminal Justice Centre, Llanberis Road, Caernarfon, Gwynedd LL55 2DF
Tel: 01286 669700
Fax: 0870 739 4384
DX: 744382 CAERNARFON 6
Email: nw-caernarfonmcenq@hmcts.gsi.gov.uk

Courts and times
The Law Courts, Holyhead
Court building open for court hearings only

SOUTH EAST WALES

3348 CARDIFF LJA
combined with **3349 VALE OF GLAMORGAN LJA** to form **3251 CARDIFF AND THE VALE OF GLAMORGAN LJA**

3251 CARDIFF AND THE VALE OF GLAMORGAN LJA
    7251 (YC)
The Magistrates' Court, Fitzalan Place, Cardiff CF24 0RZ
Tel: 029 2046 3040
Fax: 0870 324 0236
Email: sw-cardiffmcenq@hmcts.gsi.gov.uk
Courts and times
Magistrates' Court, Cardiff
Court building open: 9am to 4:30pm

3262 CYNON VALLEY
combined with **3264 MERTHYR TYDFIL LJA** and **3265 MISKIN LJA** to form **3270 GLAMORGAN VALLEYS LJA**

3270 GLAMORGAN VALLEYS LJA
    7270 (YC)
Magistrates' Court, Law Courts, Glebeland Place, Merthyr Tydfil CF47 8BH
Tel: 01685 727600
Fax: 0870 3240338
DX: 99582 Merthyr Tydfil 2
Email: sw-merthyrmcenq@hmcts.gsi.gov.uk
Courts and times
Law Courts, Merthyr Tydfil
Court building open: Monday to Friday 9am to 5pm; Court counter open: 10am to 2pm

3211 GWENT LJA
Gwent Magistrates' Court, The Law Courts, Faulkner Road, Newport, Gwent NP20 4PR
Tel: 01633 261300
Fax: 0870 739 4319
DX: 311301 NEWPORT (GWENT) 19
Email: gw-adminenq@hmcts.gsi.gov.uk
Courts and times
Magistrates' Court, Tudor Road, Cwmbran
Court building open for court hearings only

3264 MERTHYR TYDFIL LJA
combined with **3262 CYNON VALLEY LJA** and **3265 MISKIN LJA** to form **GLAMORGAN VALLEYS LJA**

3265 MISKIN LJA
combined with **3262 CYNON VALLEY LJA** and **3264 MERTHYR TYDFIL LJA** to form **3270 GLAMORGAN VALLEYS LJA**

3266 NEWCASTLE AND OGMORE LJA
The Magistrates' Court, The Law Courts, Sunnyside, Bridgend CF31 4AJ
Tel: 01656 673800
Fax: 01656 668981
DX: 99750 Bridgend 2
Courts and times
Magistrates' Court, Sunnyside, Bridgend
Court open: 9am to 4pm

3349 VALE OF GLAMORGAN LJA
combined with **3348 CARDIFF LJA** to form **3251 CARDIFF AND THE VALE OF GLAMORGAN LJA**

NUMERICAL INDEX TO COURT CODES OF COURTS SUMMARY JURISDICTION IN ENGLAND AND WALES

ENGLAND

1012 BATH DIVISION
combined with 1018 WANSDYKE DIVISION to form **1022 BATH AND WANSDYKE DIVISION**

1013 BRISTOL LJA
see **AVON, SOMERSET AND GLOUCESTERSHIRE** .... p. 137

1014 LAWFORD'S GATE DIVISION
combined with 1016 SODBURY DIVISION to form **1020 AVON NORTH DIVISION**

1015 LONG ASHTON DIVISION
combined with 1019 WESTON-SUPER-MARE DIVISION to form **1023 WOODSPRING DIVISION**

1016 SODBURY DIVISION
combined with 1014 LAWFORD'S GATE DIVISION to form **1020 AVON NORTH DIVISION**

1017 THORNBURY DIVISION
combined with 1020 AVON NORTH DIVISION to form **1021 NORTH AVON DIVISION**

1018 WANSDYKE DIVISION
combined with 1012 BATH DIVISION to form **1022 BATH AND WANSDYKE DIVISION**

1019 WESTON-SUPER-MARE DIVISION
combined with 1015 LONG ASHTON DIVISION to form **1023 WOODSPRING DIVISION**

1020 AVON NORTH DIVISION
combined with 1017 THORNBURY DIVISION to form **1021 NORTH AVON DIVISION**

1021 NORTH AVON LJA
see **AVON, SOMERSET AND GLOUCESTERSHIRE** ....p. 137

1022 BATH AND WANSDYKE LJA
see **1022 SOMERSET LJA**

1023 NORTH SOMERSET LJA
see **1022 SOMERSET LJA**

1022 SOMERSET LJA
see **AVON, SOMERSET AND GLOUCESTERSHIRE** . . . p. 137

1050 AMPTHILL DIVISION
combined with 124 BEDFORD DIVISION, 1052 BIGGLESWADE DIVISION, 1053 DUNSTABLE DIVISION (Part) and 1054 LEIGHTON BUZZARD DIVISION (Part) to form **124 BEDFORD AND MID BEDFORDSHIRE DIVISION**

124 BEDFORD DIVISION
(formerly North Bedfordshire Division) combined with 1050 AMPTHILL DIVISION, 1052 BIGGLESWADE DIVISION, 1053 DUNSTABLE DIVISION (Part) and 1054 LEIGHTON BUZZARD DIVISION (Part) to form **124 *BEDFORD AND MID* BEDFORDSHIRE DIVISION**

124 BEDFORD AND MID BEDFORDSHIRE LJA
see **BEDFORDSHIRE AND HERTFORDSHIRE** ....p. 128

1052 BIGGLESWADE DIVISION
combined with 1050 AMPTHILL DIVISION, 124 BEDFORD DIVISION, 1053 DUNSTABLE DIVISION (Part) and 1054 LEIGHTON BUZZARD DIVISION (Part) to form **124 BEDFORD AND MID BEDFORDSHIRE DIVISION**

1053 DUNSTABLE DIVISION
Parish of Harlington combined 1050 AMPTHILL DIVISION, 124 BEDFORD DIVISION, 1052 BIGGLESWADE DIVISION and 1054 LEIGHTON BUZZARD DIVISION (Part) to form **124 BEDFORD AND MID BEDFORDSHIRE DIVISION**. *Remaining parishes combined with 1054 LEIGHTON BUZZARD (Part) and 1055 LUTON DIVISION to form* **1055 LUTON AND SOUTH BEDFORDSHIRE DIVISION**

1054 LEIGHTON BUZZARD DIVISION
Part combined with 1050 AMPTHILL DIVISION, 124 BEDFORD DIVISION, 1052 BIGGLESWADE DIVISION, 1053 DUNSTABLE DIVISION (Parish of Harlington) to form **124 BEDFORD AND BEDFORDSHIRE DIVISION**. *Remainder combined with 1053 DUNSTABLE DIVISION (except Harlington) and 1055 LUTON DIVISION to form* **1055 LUTON AND SOUTH BEDFORDSHIRE DIVISION**

1055 LUTON DIVISION
combined with 1053 DUNSTABLE DIVISION, (except Harlington), and 1054 LEIGHTON BUZZARD DIVISION to form **1055 LUTON AND SOUTH BEDFORDSHIRE DIVISION**

1055 LUTON AND SOUTH BEDFORDSHIRE LJA
see **BEDFORDSHIRE AND HERTFORDSHIRE** ....p. 128

1065 BRADFIELD AND SONNING DIVISION
combined with 1071 READING DIVISION to form **1076 READING AND SONNING DIVISION**

1066 FOREST DIVISION
combined with 1068 MAIDENHEAD DIVISION, 1072 SLOUGH DIVISION and 1074 WINDSOR DIVISION to form **072 EAST BERKSHIRE DIVISION**

1067 HUNGERFORD AND LAMBOURN DIVISION
combined with 1069 NEWBURY DIVISION to form **1075 WEST BERKSHIRE DIVISION**

1068 MAIDENHEAD DIVISION
combined with 1066 FOREST DIVISION, 1072 SLOUGH DIVISION and 1074 WINDSOR DIVISION to form **1072 EAST BERKSHIRE DIVISION**

1069 NEWBURY DIVISION
combined with 1067 HUNGERFORD AND LAMBOURN DIVISION to form **1075 WEST BERKSHIRE DIVISION**

1070 NEW WINDSOR DIVISION
combined with 1073 WINDSOR COUNTY DIVISION to form **1074 WINDSOR DIVISION**

1071 READING DIVISION
combined with 1065 BRADFIELD AND SONNING DIVISION to form **1076 READING AND SONNING DIVISION**

1072 SLOUGH DIVISION
combined with 1066 FOREST DIVISION, 1068 MAIDENHEAD DIVISION and 1074 WINDSOR DIVISION to form **1072 EAST BERKSHIRE DIVISION**

1072 EAST BERKSHIRE LJA
combined with 1075 WEST BERKSHIRE LJA and 1076 READING LJA to form **1076 BERKSHIRE LJA**

1073 WINDSOR COUNTY DIVISION
combined with 1070 NEW WINDSOR DIVISION to form **1074 WINDSOR DIVISION**

1074 WINDSOR DIVISION
combined with 1066 FOREST DIVISION, 1068 MAIDENHEAD DIVISION and 1072 SLOUGH DIVISION to form **1072 EAST BERKSHIRE DIVISION**

1075 WEST BERKSHIRE LJA
combined with 1072 EAST BERKSHIRE LJA and 1076 READING LJA to form **1076 BERKSHIRE LJA**

1076 READING AND SONNING DIVISION
renamed **1076 READING PSA**

1076 READING LJA
combined with 1072 EAST BERKSHIRE LJA and 1075 WEST BERKSHIRE LJA to form **1076 BERKSHIRE LJA**

1110 AMERSHAM DIVISION
combined with 1115 CHESHAM DIVISION to form **1128 CHILTERN DIVISION**

1111 AYLESBURY DIVISION
combined with 1112 BRILL DIVISION and 1118 LINSLADE DIVISION to form **1125 AYLESBURY DIVISION**

1112 BRILL DIVISION
combined with 1111 AYLESBURY DIVISION and 1118 LINSLADE DIVISION to form **1125 AYLESBURY DIVISION**

1113 BUCKINGHAM DIVISION
combined with 1122 WINSLOW DIVISION to form **126 BUCKINGHAM DIVISION**

1114 BURNHAM DIVISION
combined with 1127 WYCOMBE DIVISION to form **1130 WYCOMBE AND BEACONSFIELD DIVISION**

1115 CHESHAM DIVISION
combined with 1110 AMERSHAM DIVISION to form **1128 CHILTERN DIVISION**

1116 FENNY STRATFORD DIVISION
combined with 1120 NEWPORT PAGNELL DIVISION and 1121 STONY STRATFORD DIVISION to form **1124 MILTON KEYNES DIVISION**

1117 HIGH WYCOMBE DIVISION
combined with 1119 MARLOW DIVISION and 1123 WYCOMBE (COUNTY) DIVISION to form **1127 WYCOMBE DIVISION**

1118 LINSLADE DIVISION
combined with 1111 AYLESBURY DIVISION and 1112 BRILL DIVISION to form **1125 AYLESBURY DIVISION**

1119 MARLOW DIVISION
combined with 1117 HIGH WYCOMBE DIVISION and 1123 WYCOMBE (COUNTY) DIVISION to form **1127 WYCOMBE DIVISION**

1120 NEWPORT PAGNELL DIVISION
combined with 1116 FENNY STRATFORD DIVISION and 1121 STONY STRATFORD DIVISION to form **1124 MILTON KEYNES DIVISION**

1121 STONY STRATFORD DIVISION
combined with 1116 FENNY STRATFORD DIVISION and 1120 NEWPORT PAGNELL DIVISION to form **1124 MILTON KEYNES DIVISION**

1122 WINSLOW DIVISION
combined with 1113 BUCKINGHAM DIVISION to form **1126 BUCKINGHAM DIVISION**

1123 WYCOMBE (COUNTY) DIVISION
combined with 1117 HIGH WYCOMBE DIVISION and 1119 MARLOW DIVISION to form **1127 WYCOMBE DIVISION**

1124 MILTON KEYNES LJA
combined with 1129 CENTRAL BUCKINGHAMSHIRE LJA and 1130 WYCOMBE & BEACONSFIELD LJA to form **1124 BUCKINGHAMSHIRE LJA**

1125 AYLESBURY DIVISION
combined with 1126 BUCKINGHAM DIVISION and 1128 CHILTERN DIVISION to form **1129 CENTRAL BUCKINGHAMSHIRE DIVISION**

1126 BUCKINGHAM DIVISION
combined with 1125 AYLESBURY DIVISION and 1128 CHILTERN DIVISIION to form **1129 CENTRAL BUCKINGHAMSHIRE DIVISION**

1127 WYCOMBE DIVISION
combined with 1114 BURNHAM DIVISION to form **1130 WYCOMBE AND BEACONSFIELD DIVISION**

1128 CHILTERN DIVISION
combined with 1125 AYLESBURY DIVISION and 1126 BUCKINGHAM DIVISION to form **1129 CENTRAL BUCKINGHAMSHIRE DIVISION**

1129 CENTRAL BUCKINGHAMSHIRE LJA
combined with 1125 MILTON KEYNES LJA and 1130 WYCOMBE & BEACONSFIELD LJA to form **1124 BUCKINGHAMSHIRE LJA**

1130 WYCOMBE AND BEACONSFIELD LJA
combined with 1124 MILTON KEYNES LJA and 1129 CENTRAL BUCKINGHAMSHIRE LJA to form **1124 BUCKINGHAMSHIRE LJA**

1133 ARRINGTON AND MELBOURN DIVISION
combined with 1134 BOTTISHAM DIVISION, 1159 CAXTON DIVISION and 1141 LINTON DIVISION to form **1163 SOUTH CAMBRIDGESHIRE DIVISION**

1134 BOTTISHAM DIVISION
combined with 1133 ARRINGTON AND MELBOURN DIVISION, 1141 LINTON DIVISION and 1159 CAXTON DIVISION to form **1163 SOUTH CAMBRIDGESHIRE DIVISION**

1135 CAMBRIDGE DIVISION
combined with 1137 CAXTON DIVISION to form **1159 CAXTON DIVISION**

1136 CAMBRIDGE CITY DIVISION
combined with 1163 SOUTH CAMBRIDGESHIRE DIVISION to form **1165 CAMBRIDGE DIVISION**

1137 CAXTON DIVISION
combined with 1135 CAMBRIDGE DIVISION to form **1159 CAXTON DIVISION**

1138 ELY DIVISION
combined with 1164 NEWMARKET DIVISION to form **1166 EAST CAMBRIDGESHIRE DIVISION**

1140 HURSTINGSTONE DIVISION
combined with 1157 HUNTINGDON AND NORMAN CROSS DIVISION and 1145 RAMSEY DIVISION to form **1161 HUNTINGDON DIVISION**

1141 LINTON DIVISION
combined with 1133 ARRINGTON AND MELBOURN DIVISION, 1134 BOTTISHAM DIVISION and 1159 CAXTON DIVISION to form **1163 SOUTH CAMBRIDGESHIRE DIVISION**

1142 NEWMARKET DIVISION
combined with part of 1134 BOTTISHAM DIVISION to form **1164 NEWMARKET (CAMBS) DIVISION**

1143 NORMAN CROSS DIVISION
see **1157 HUNTINGDON AND NORMAN CROSS**

1144 NORTH WITCHFORD DIVISION
combined with 1160 WISBECH DIVISION to form **1167 FENLAND DIVISION**

1145 RAMSEY DIVISION
combined with 1157 HUNTINGDON AND NORMAN CROSS DIVISION and 1140 HURSTINGSTONE DIVISION to form **1161 HUNTINGDON DIVISION**

1147 TOSELAND DIVISION
combined with 1161 HUNTINGDON DIVISION to form **1168 HUNTINGDONSHIRE DIVISION**

1148 WHITTLESEY DIVISION
combined with 1158 SOKE OF PETERBOROUGH DIVISION to form **1162 PETERBOROUGH DIVISION**

1149 WISBECH (BOROUGH) DIVISION
combined with 1150 WISBECH (ISLE) DIVISION to form **1160 WISBECH DIVISION**

1150 WISBECH (ISLE) DIVISION
combined with 1149 WISBECH (BOROUGH) DIVISION to form **1160 WISBECH DIVISION**

1157 HUNTINGDON AND NORMAN CROSS DIVISION
combined with 1140 HURSTINGSTONE DIVISION and 1145 RAMSEY DIVISION to form **1161 HUNTINGDON DIVISION**

1158 SOKE OF PETERBOROUGH DIVISION
combined with 1148 WHITTLESEY DIVISION **to form 1162 PETERBOROUGH DIVISION**

1159 CAXTON DIVISION
combined with 1133 ARRINGTON AND MELBOURN DIVISION, 1134 BOTTISHAM DIVISION AND 1141 LINTON DIVISION to form **1163 SOUTH CAMBRIDGESHIRE DIVISION**

1160 WISBECH DIVISION
combined with 1144 NORTH WITCHFORD DIVISION to form **1167 FENLAND DIVISION**

1161 HUNTINGDON DIVISION
combined with 1147 TOSELAND DIVISION to form **1168 HUNTINGDONSHIRE DIVISION**

1162 PETERBOROUGH LJA
combined with 1167 FENLAND LJA to form **NORTH CAMBRIDGESHIRE LJA** *– wef 1/1/12*

1163 SOUTH CAMBRIDGESHIRE DIVISION
combined with 1136 CAMBRIDGE CITY DIVISION to form **1166 EAST CAMBRIDGESHIRE DIVISION**

1164 NEWMARKET (CAMBS) DIVISION
combined with 1138 ELY DIVISION to form **1166 EAST CAMBRIDGESHIRE DIVISION**

1165 CAMBRIDGE LJA
combined with 1166 EAST CAMBRIDGESHIRE LJA to form **SOUTH CAMBRIDGESHIRE LJA** *– wef 1/1/12*

1166 EAST CAMBRIDGESHIRE LJA
combined with 1165 CAMBRIDGE LJA to form **SOUTH CAMBRIDGESHIRE LJA** *– wef 1/1/12*

1167 FENLAND LJA
combined with 1162 PETERBOROUGH LJA to form **NORTH CAMBRIDGESHIRE LJA**

1168 HUNTINGDONSHIRE LJA
see **CAMBRIDGESHIRE, ESSEX, NORFOLK AND SUFFOLK** ....p. 129

1173 CHESTER PSA
combined with 1176 ELLESMERE PORT AND NESTON PSA to form **1188 CHESTER, ELLESMERE PORT AND NESTON PSA**

1174 CONGLETON DIVISION
combined with 1175 CREWE AND NANTWICH DIVISION to form **1187 SOUTH CHESHIRE DIVISION**

1175 CREWE AND NANTWICH DIVISION
combined with 1174 CONGLETON DIVISION to form **1187 SOUTH CHESHIRE DIVISION**

1176 ELLESMERE PORT AND NESTON PSA
combined with 1173 CHESTER PSA to form **1188 CHESTER, ELLESMERE PORT AND NESTON PSA**

1177 HALTON LJA
combined with 1180 WARRINGTON LJA to form **1722 NORTH CHESHIRE LJA**

1178 MACCLESFIELD LJA
see **CHESHIRE AND MERSEYSIDE** ....p. 121

1179 VALE ROYAL LJA
CLOSED wef 9/11

1180 WARRINGTON LJA
combined with 1177 HALTON LJA to form **1722 NORTH CHESHIRE LJA**

1187 SOUTH CHESHIRE LJA
see **CHESHIRE AND MERSEYSIDE** ....p. 121

1188 CHESTER, ELLESMERE PORT AND NESTON LJA
see **1729 WEST CHESHIRE LJA**

1247 HARTLEPOOL LJA
see **CLEVELAND AND DURHAM** ....p. 114

1248 LANGBAURGH EAST LJA
CLOSED wef 1/12

1249 TEESSIDE LJA
see **CLEVELAND AND DURHAM** ....p. 114

1260 BODMIN AND TRIGG DIVISION
combined with 1269 LESNEWTH DIVISION, 1273 POWDER TYWARDREATH DIVISION and 1278 WADEBRIDGE DIVISION to form **1279 BODMIN DIVISION**

1261 DUNHEVED DIVISION
combined with 1276 STRATTON DIVISION to form **1284 DUNHEVED AND STRATTON DIVISION**

1262 EAST MIDDLE DIVISION
combined with 1265 EAST SOUTH DIVISION and 1270 LISKERRETT DIVISION to form **1280 SOUTH EAST CORNWALL DIVISION**

1263 EAST PENWITH PSA
combined with 1268 ISLES OF SCILLY PSA, PENWITH PSA, FALMOUTH AND KERRIER PSA, 1282 TRURO AND SOUTH POWDER PSA and the parishes of Cubert and St Newlyn East in 1274 PYDAR PSA to form **1288 WEST CORNWALL PSA**

1264 EAST POWDER PSA
combined with 1274 PYDAR PSA (except the parishes of Cubert and St Newlyn East), 1279 BODMIN PSA, 1284 DUNHEVED AND STRATTON., and 1280 SOUTH EAST CORNWALL to form **1289 EAST CORNWALL PSA**

1265 EAST SOUTH DIVISION
combined with 1262 EAST MIDDLE DIVISION and 1270 LISKERRETT DIVISION to form **1280 SOUTH EAST CORNWALL DIVISION**

1266 FALMOUTH DIVISION
combined with 1271 PENRYN DIVISION to form **1281 FALMOUTH-PENRYN DIVISION**

1267 HELSTON AND KERRIER DIVISION
combined with 1281 FALMOUTH-PENRYN DIVISION to form **1283 FALMOUTH AND KERRIER DIVISION**

1268 ISLES OF SCILLY PSA
combined with 1272 PENWITH PSA, 1283 FALMOUTH AND KERRIER PSA, 1282 TRURO AND SOUTH POWDER PSA, and the Parishes of Cuber and St Newlyn East in 1274 PYDAR PSA to form **1288 WEST CORNWALL PSA**

1269 LESNEWTH DIVISION
combined with 1260 BODMIN AND TRIGG DIVISION, 1273 POWDER TYWARDREATH DIVISION and 1278 WADEBRIDGE DIVISION to form **1279 BODMIN DIVISION**

1270 LISKERRETT DIVISION
combined with 1262 EAST MIDDLE DIVISION and 1265 EAST SOUTH DIVISION to form **1280 EAST CORNWALL DIVISION**

1271 PENRYN DIVISION
combined with 1266 FALMOUTH DIVISION to form **1281 FALMOUTH-PENRYN DIVISION**

1272 PENWITH PSA
combined with 1268 ISLES OF SCILLY PSA, 1263 EAST PENWITH PSA, 1283 FALMOUTH AND KERRIER PSA, 1282 TRURO AND SOUTH POWDER PSA and the Parishes of Cubert and St Newlyn East in 1274 PYDAR PSA to form **1288 WEST CORNWALL DIVISION**

1273 POWDER TYWARDREATH DIVISION
combined with 1260 BODMIN AND TRIGG DIVISION, 1269 LESNEWTH DIVISION and 1278 WADEBRIDGE DIVISION to form **1279 BODMIN DIVISION**

1274 PYDAR PSA
Parishes of Cubert and St Newlyn East combined with 1268 ISLES OF SCILLY PSA, 1272 PENWITH PSA, 1263 EAST PENWITH PSA, 1283 FALMOUTH AND KERRIER PSA and 1282 TRURO AND SOUTH POWDER PSA to form **1288 WEST CORNWALL PSA** *.Remainder combined with 1279 BODMIN PSA, 1264 EAST POWDER PSA 1284 DUNHEVED AND STRATTON PSA, and 1280 SOUTH EAST CORNWALL PSA to form* **1289 EAST CORNWALL PSA**

1275 SOUTH POWDER DIVISION
combined with 1277 TRURO AND WEST POWDER DIVISION to form **1282 TRURO AND SOUTH POWDER DIVISION**

1276 STRATTON DIVISION
combined with 1261 DUNHEVED DIVISION to form **1284 DUNHEVED AND STRATTON DIVISION**

1277 TRURO AND WEST POWDER DIVISION
combined with 1275 SOUTH POWDER DIVISION to form **1282 TRURO AND SOUTH POWDER DIVISION**

1278 WADEBRIDGE DIVISION
combined with 1260 BODMIN AND TRIGG DIVISION, 1269 LESNEWTH DIVISION and 1273 POWDER TYWARDREATH DIVISION to form **1279 BODMIN DIVISION**

1279 BODMIN P.S.A.
combined with 1274 PYDAR PSA (except the parishes of Cubert and St Newlyn East) 1264 EAST POWDER PSA, 1284 DUNHEVED AND STRATTON PSA and 1280 SOUTH EAST CORNWALL to form **1289 EAST CORNWALL**

1280 SOUTH EAST CORNWALL PSA
combined with 1274 PYDAR PSA (except the parishes of Cubert and St Newlyn East), 1279 BODMIN PSA, 1264 EAST POWDER PSA and 1284 DUNHEVED AND STRATTON PSA to form **1289 EAST CORNWALL PSA**

1281 FALMOUTH-PENRYN DIVISION
combined with 1267 HELSTON AND KERRIER DIVISION to form **1283 FALMOUTH AND KERRIER DIVISION**

1282 TRURO AND SOUTH POWDER PSA
combined with 1268 ISLES OF SCILLY PSA, 1272 PENWITH PSA, 1263 EAST PENWITH PSA, 1283 FALMOUTH AND KERRIER PSA and the Parishes of Cubert and St Newlyn East in 1274 PYDAR PSA to form **1288 WEST CORNWALL PSA**

1283 FALMOUTH AND KERRIER PSA
combined with 1268 ISLES OF SCILLY PSA, 1272 PENWITH PSA, 1263 EAST PENWITH PSA, 1282 TRURO AND SOUTH POWDER PSA and the Parishes of Cuber and St Newlyn East in 1274 PYDAR PSA to form **1288 WEST CORNWALL PSA**

1284 DUNHEVED AND STRATTON PSA
combined with 1274 PYDAR PSA (except the parishes of Cubert and St Newlyn East) 1279 BODMIN PSA, 1263 EAST POWDER PSA and 1280 SOUTH EAST CORNWALL PSA to form **1289 EAST CORNWALL PSA**

1288 WEST CORNWALL LJA
combined with 1289 East Cornwall LJA to form **1301 CORNWALL LJA**

1289 EAST CORNWALL LJA
combined with 1288 West Cornwall LJA to form **1301 CORNWALL LJA**

1290 PLYMOUTH DISTRICT LJA
see **DEVON, CORNWALL AND DORSET** ....p. 138

1291 NORTH DEVON LJA
combined with 1292 Central Devon LJA to form **1292 NORTH AND EAST DEVON LJA**

1292 NORTH AND EAST DEVON LJA
see **DEVON, CORNWALL AND DORSET** ....p. 138

1292 CENTRAL DEVON LJA
combined with 1291 North Devon LJA to form **1292 NORTH AND EAST DEVON LJA**

1302 SOUTH DEVON LJA
see **DEVON, CORNWALL AND DORSET** ....p. 138

1301 CORNWALL LJA
see **DEVON, CORNWALL AND DORSET LJA** . . . p. 138

1304 WEST HAMPSHIRE LJA
see **HAMPSHIRE, ISLE OF WIGHT AND WILTSHIRE** . . . p. 140

1305 NORTH HAMPSHIRE LJA (ADULT)
see **HAMPSHIRE, ISLE OF WIGHT AND WILTSHIRE** ....p. 140

1322 CARLISLE AND DISTRICT LJA
see **1727 NORTH CUMBRIA LJA**

1398 SOUTH LAKELAND LJA
see **CUMBRIA AND LANCASHIRE** ....p. 123

1324 EDEN LJA
CLOSED wef 1/12

1325 WEST ALLERDALE AND KESWICK LJA
see **1726 WEST CUMBRIA LJA**

1360 ALSTON DIVISION
combined with 1373 PENRITH DIVISION to form **1378 PENRITH AND ALSTON DIVISION**

1361 AMBLESIDE AND WINDERMERE DIVISION
combined with 1367 HAWKSHEAD DIVISION to form **1381 SOUTH LAKES DIVISION**

1362 BARROW-IN-FURNESS DIVISION
combined with 1363 BOOTLE DIVISION to form **1380 BARROW WITH BOOTLE DIVISION**

1363 BOOTLE DIVISION
combined with 1362 BARROW-IN-FURNESS DIVISION to form **1380 BARROW WITH BOOTLE DIVISION**

1364 CARLISLE PSA
combined with 1376 WIGTON PSA to form **1322 CARLISLE AND DISTRICT PSA**

1365 COCKERMOUTH DIVISION
combined with 1371 MARYPORT DIVISION and 1377 WORKINGTON DIVISION to form **1379 WEST ALLERDALE DIVISION**

1366 EAST WARD DIVISION
combined with portions of 1374 WEST WARD DIVISION to form **1383 APPLEBY DIVISION**

1367 HAWKSHEAD DIVISION
combined with 1361 AMBLESIDE AND WINDERMERE DIVISION to form **1381 SOUTH LAKES DIVISION**

1368 KENDAL DIVISION
combined with 1370 LONSDALE WARD DIVISION to form **1382 KENDAL AND LONSDALE DIVISION**

1369 KESWICK PSA
(except for the Parish of Threlkeld) combined with 1379 WEST ALLERDALE PSA to form **1325 WEST ALLERDALE AND KESWICK PSA**

1370 LONSDALE WARD DIVISION
combined with 1368 KENDAL DIVISION to form **1382 KENDAL AND LONSDALE DIVISION**

1371 MARYPORT DIVISION
combined with 1365 COCKERMOUTH DIVISION and 1377 WORKINGTON DIVISION to form **1379 WEST ALLERDALE DIVISION**

1372 NORTH LONSDALE DIVISION
combined with 1380 BARROW WITH BOOTLE DIVISION to form **1398 FURNESS AND DISTRICT DIVISION**

1373 PENRITH DIVISION
combined with 1360 ALSTON DIVISION to form **1378 PENRITH AND ALSTON DIVISION**

1374 WEST WARD DIVISION
abolished – part absorbed into **1383 APPLEBY DIVISION** *and remainder into* **1384 PENRITH AND ALSTON DIVISION**

1375 WHITEHAVEN LJA
CLOSED wef 6/11 – see **1726 WEST CUMBRIA LJA**

1376 WIGTON PSA
combined with 1364 CARLISLE PSA to form **1322 CARLISLE AND DISTRICT PSA**

1377 WORKINGTON DIVISION
combined with 1365 COCKERMOUTH DIVISION and 1371 MARYPORT DIVISION to form **1379 WEST ALLERDALE DIVISION**

1378 PENRITH AND ALSTON DIVISION
combined with portions of 1374 WEST WARD DIVISION to form **1384 PENRITH AND ALSTON DIVISION**

1379 WEST ALLERDALE PSA
combined with 1369 KESWICK PSA (except for the Parish of Threlkeld) to form **1325 WEST ALLERDALE AND KESWICK PSA**

1380 BARROW WITH BOOTLE DIVISION
combined with portions of 1372 NORTH LONSDLAE DIVISION to form **1398 FURNESS AND DISTRICT DIVISION**

1381 SOUTH LAKES PSA
combined with 1382 KENDAL AND LONSDALE PSA to form **1398 SOUTH LAKELAND PSA**

1382 KENDAL AND LONSDALE PSA
combined with 1381 SOUTH LAKES PSA to form **1398 SOUTH LAKELAND PSA**

1383 APPLEBY PSA
combined with 1384 PENRITH AND ALSTON PSA and the Parish of Threlkeld in 1369 KESWICK PSA to form **1324 EDEN PSA**

1384 PENRITH AND ALSTON PSA
combined with 1383 APPLEBY PSA and the Parish of Threlkeld in 1369 KESWICK PSA to form **1324 EDEN PSA**

1385 NORWICH DIVISION
subjected to boundary adjustments and renumbered **1445 NORWICH DIVISION**

1386 DOWNHAM MARKET DIVISION
combined with 1389 FAKENHAM DIVISION, 1394 HUNSTANTON DIVISION and 1392 KING'S LYNN DIVISION to form (after boundary adjustment) **1447 WEST NORFOLK DIVISION**

1387 DISS DIVISION
combined with 1396 THETFORD DIVISION to form **1446 SOUTH NORFOLK DIVISION**

1388 EAST DEREHAM DIVISION
combined with 1395 SWAFFHAM DIVISION and 1390 WYMONDHAM DIVISION to form **1442 CENTAL NORFOLK DIVISION**

1389 FAKENHAM DIVISION
combined with 1386 DOWNHAM MARKET DIVISION, 1394 HUNSTANTON DIVISION and 1392 KING'S LYNN DIVISION to form (after boundary adjustment) **1447 WEST NORFOLK DIVISION**

1390 WYMONDHAM DIVISION
combined with 1388 EAST DEREHAM DIVISION and 1395 SWAFFHAM DIVISION to form **1442 CENTRAL NORFOLK DIVISION**

1391 GREAT YARMOUTH DIVISION
subjected to boundary adjustments and renumbered **1443 GREAT YARMOUTH DIVISION**

1392 KING'S LYNN DIVISION
combined with 1386 DOWNHAM MARKET DIVISION, 1398 FAKENHAM DIVISION and 1394 HUNSTANTON DIVISION to form (after boundary adjustment) **1447 WEST NORFOLK DIVISION**

1393 CROMER DIVISION
combined with 1397 NORTH WALSHAM DIVISION to form (after boundary adjustment) **1444 NORTH NORFOLK DIVISION**

1394 HUNSTANTON DIVISION
combined with 1386 DOWNHAM MARKET DIVISION, 1389 FAKENHAM DIVISION and 1392 KING'S LYNN DIVISION to form (after boundary adjustment) **1447 WEST NORFOLK DIVISION**

1395 SWAFFHAM DIVISION
combined with 1388 EAST DEREHAM DIVISION and 1390 WYMONDHAM DIVISION to form **1442 CENTRAL NORFOLK DIVISION**

1396 THETFORD DIVISION
combined with 1387 DISS DIVISION to form **1446 SOUTH NORFOLK DIVISION**

1397 NORTH WALSHAM DIVISION
combined with 1393 CROMER DIVISION to form (after boundary adjustment) **1444 NORTH NORFOLK DIVISION**

1398 FURNESS AND DISTRICT LJA
see **CUMBRIA AND LANCASHIRE** ....p. 123

1414 ALFRETON DIVISION
combined with 1417 BELPER DIVISION to form (after boundary adjustments) **1426 ALFRETON AND BELPER DIVISION**

1415 ASHBOURNE DIVISION
combined with 1416 BAKEWELL DIVISION and 1424 MATLOCK DIVISION to form (after boundary adjustments) **1428 WEST DERBYSHIRE DIVISION**

1416 BAKEWELL DIVISION
combined with 1415 ASHBOURNE DIVISION and 1424 MATLOCK DIVISION to form (after boundary adjustments) **1428 WEST DERBYSHIRE DIVISION**

1417 BELPER DIVISION
combined with 1414 ALFRETON DIVISION to form (after boundary adjustments) **1426 ALFRETON AND BELPER DIVISION**

1418 CHESTERFIELD PSA
combined with Part of 1420 WEST DERBYSHIRE to form **1432 NORTH EAST DERBYSHIRE AND DALES PSA**

1419 DERBY DIVISION
combined with 1420 DERBY COUNTY AND APPLETREE DIVISION and 1425 SOUTH DERBYSHIRE DIVISION to form (after boundary adjustments) **1427 DERBY AND SOUTH DERBYSHIRE DIVISION**

1420 DERBY COUNTY AND APPLETREE DIVISION
combined with 1419 DERBY DIVISION and 1425 SOUTH DERBYSHIRE DIVISION to form (after boundary adjustments) **1427 DERBY AND SOUTH DERBYSHIRE DIVISION**

1421 GLOSSOP PSA
combined with 1422 HIGH PEAK PSA to form **HIGH PEAK PSA**

1422 HIGH PEAK PSA
combined with 1421 GLOSSOP PSA to form **HIGH PEAK PSA**

1423 ILKESTON DIVISION
combined with 1426 ALFRETON AND BELPER DIVISION to form **1429 EAST DERBYSHIRE DIVISION**

1424 MATLOCK DIVISION
combined with 1415 ASHBOURNE DIVISION and 1416 BAKEWELL DIVISION to form (after boundary adjustments) **1428 WEST DERBYSHIRE DIVISION**

1425 SOUTH DERBYSHIRE DIVISION
combined with 1419 DERBY DIVISION and 1420 DERBY COUNTY AND APPLETREE DIVISION to form (after boundary adjustments) **1427 DERBY AND SOUTH DERBYSHIRE DIVISION**

1426 ALFRETON AND BELPER DIVISION
combined with 1423 ILKESTON DIVISION to form **1429 EAST DERBYSHIRE DIVISION**

1427 DERBY AND SOUTH DERBYSHIRE PSA
combined with Part of 1428 WEST DERBYSHIRE PSA to form **1431 DERBY AND SOUTH DERBYSHIRE PSA**

1428 SOUTHERN DERBYSHIRE LJA
see **DERBYSHIRE AND NOTTINGHAMSHIRE** ....p. 107

1429 EAST DERBYSHIRE PSA
combined with 1431 DERBY AND SOUTH DERBYSHIRE PSA to form **1431 SOUTHERN DERBYSHIRE PSA**

1430 HIGH PEAK LJA
see **DERBYSHIRE AND NOTTINGHAMSHIRE** ....p. 107

1431 DERBY AND SOUTH DERBYSHIRE PSA
combined with 1429 EAST DERBYSHIRE PSA to form **1428 SOUTHERN DERBYSHIRE PSA**

1432 NORTH EAST DERBYSHIRE AND DALES LJA
see **DERBYSHIRE AND NOTTINGHAMSHIRE** ....p. 107

1442 CENTRAL NORFOLK LJA
combined with 1443, 1444, 1445, 1446, 1447 to form **1972 NORFOLK LJA**

1443 GREAT YARMOUTH LJA
combined with 1442, 1444, 1445, 1446, 1447 to form **1972 NORFOLK LJA**

1444 NORTH NORFOLK LJA
combined with 1442, 1443, 1445, 1446, 1447 to form **1972 NORFOLK LJA**

1445 NORWICH LJA
combined with 1442, 1443, 1444, 1446, 1447 to form **1972 NORFOLK LJA**

1446 SOUTH NORFOLK LJA
combined with 1442, 1443, 1444, 1445, 1447 to form **1972 NORFOLK LJA**

1447 WEST NORFOLK LJA
combined with 1442, 1443, 1444, 1445, 1446 to form **1972 NORFOLK LJA**

1475 AXMINSTER DIVISION
combined with 1481 HONITON DIVISION to form **1493 AXMINSTER AND HONITON DIVISION**

1476 BARNSTAPLE DIVISION
combined with 1486 SOUTH MOLTON DIVISION to form **1494 BARNSTAPLE AND SOUTH MOLTON DIVISION**

1477 BIDEFORD AND GREAT TORRINGTON PSA
combined with part of 1495 WEST DEVON PSA and 1494 BARNSTAPLE AND SOUTH MOLTON PSA (except Chawleigh, Eggesford and Thelbridge) to form **1291 NORTH DEVON PSA**

1478 CULLOMPTON PSA
combined with Chawleigh, Eggesford and Thelbridge in 1494 BARNSTAPLE AND SOUTH MOLTON, Part of 1495 WEST DEVON PSA, 1493 AXMINSTER AND HONITON PSA, 1478 CULLOMPTON PSA, 1489 TIVERTON PSA, 1497 EXETER AND WONFORD PSA and 1480 EXMOUTH PSA to form **1292 CENTRAL DEVON PSA**

1479 EXETER DIVISION
combined with 1492 WONFORD DIVISION to form **1497 EXETER AND WONFORD DIVISION**

1480 EXMOUTH PSA
combined with Chawleigh, Eggesford and Thelbridge in 1494 BARNSTAPLE AND SOUTH MOLTON PSA, Part of 1495 WEST DEVON PSA, 1493 AXMINSTER AND HONITON PSA, 1478 CULLOMPTON PSA, 1489 TIVERTON PSA, and 1497 EXETER AND WONFORD PSA to form **1292 CENTRAL DEVON PSA**

1481 HONITON DIVISION
combined with 1475 AXMINSTER DIVISION to form **1493 AXMINSTER AND HONITON DIVISION**

1482 KINGSBRIDGE DIVISION
combined with 1485 PLYMPTON DIVISION and 1491 TOTNES DIVISION to form **1496 SOUTH HAMS DIVISION**

1483 OKEHAMPTON DIVISION
combined with 1487 TAVISTOCK DIVISION to form **1495 WEST DEVON DIVISION**

1484 PLYMOUTH PSA
combined with part of 1495 WEST DEVON PSA to form **1290 PLYMOUTH DISTRICT PSA**

1485 PLYMPTON DIVISION
combined with 1482 KINGSBRIDGE DIVISION and 1491 TOTNES DIVISION to form **1496 SOUTH HAMS DIVISION**

1486 SOUTH MOLTON DIVISION
combined with 1476 BARNSTAPLE DIVISION to form **1494 BARNSTAPLE AND SOUTH MOLTON DIVISION**

1487 TAVISTOCK DIVISION
combined with 1476 OKEHAMPTON DIVISION to form **1495 WEST DEVON DIVISION**

1488 TEIGNBRIDGE PSA
combined with 1496 SOUTH HAMS PSA and 1490 TORBAY PSA to form **1302 SOUTH DEVON PSA**

1489 TIVERTON PSA
combined with Chawleigh, Eggesford and Thelbridge in 1494 BARNSTAPLE AND SOUTH MOLTON PSA, Part of 1495 WEST DEVON PSA 1493 AXMINSTER AND HONITON PSA, 1478 CULLOMPTON PSA, 1497 EXETER AND WOMFORD PSA and 1480 EXMOUTH PSA to form **1292 CENTRAL DEVON PSA**

1490 TORBAY PSA
combined with 1488 TEIGNBRIDGE PSA and 1496 SOUTH HANTS PSA to form **1302 SOUTH DEVON PSA**

1491 TOTNES DIVISION
combined with 1482 KINGSBRIDGE DIVISION and 1485 PLYMPTON DIVISION to form **1496 SOUTH HAMS DIVISION**

1492 WONFORD DIVISION
combined with 1479 EXETER DIVISION to form **1497 EXETER AND WONFORD DIVISION**

1493 AXMINSTER AND HONITON PSA
combined with Chawleigh, Eggesford and Thelbridge in 1494 BARNSTAPLE AND SOUTH MOLTON PSA, Part of 1495 WEST DEVON PSA, 1478 CULLOMPTON PSA, 1489 TIVERTON PSA, 1497 EXETER AND WONFORD PSA to form **1292 CENTRAL DEVON PSA**

1494 BARNSTAPLE AND SOUTH MOLTON PSA
(except Chawleigh, Eggesford and Thelbridge) combined with 1477 BIDEFORD AND GREAT TORRINGTON PSA and Part of 1495 WEST DEVON PSA to form **1291 NORTH DEVON PSA** *Chawleigh, Eggesford and Thelbridge combined with part of 1495 WEST DEVON PSA and 1493 AXMINSTER AND HONNINGTON PSA, 1478 CULLOMPTON PSA, 1489 TIVERTON PSA, 1497 EXETER AND WONFORD PSA and 1480 EXMOUTH PSA to form* **1292 CENTRAL DEVON PSA**

1495 WEST DEVON PSA
Part combined with 1484 PLYMOUTH PSA to form **1290 PLYMOUTH PSA** *Part combined with 1477 BIDEFORD AND GREAT TORRINGTON PSA and 1494 BARNSTAPLE AND SOUTH MOLTON PSA (except Chawleigh, Eggesford and Thelbridge) to form* **1291 NORTH DEVON PSA**, *and remaining part combined with Chawleigh, Eggesford and Thelbridgein 1494 BARNSTAPLE AND SOUTH MOLTON PSA together with 1493 AXMINSTER AND HONITON PSA, 1478 CULLOMPTON PSA, 1489 TIVERTON PSA, 1479 EXETER AND WONFORD PSA and* **1480 EXMOUTH** *PSA to form* **1292 CENTRAL DEVON**

1496 SOUTH HAMS PSA
combined with 1488 TEIGNBRIDGE PSA and 1490 TORBAY PSA to form **1302 SOUTH DEVON PSA**

1497 EXETER AND WONFORD PSA
combined with Chawleigh, Eggesford and Thelbridge in 1494 BARNSTAPLE AND SOUTH MOLTON PSA, Part of 1495 WEST DEVON PSA, 1493 AXMINSTER AND HONITON PSA, 1478 CULLOMPTON PSA, 1489 TIVERTON PSA, 1497 EXETER AND WONFORD PSA and EXMOUTH PSA to form **1292 CENTRAL DEVON PSA**

1500 BLANDFORD DIVISION
combined with 1508 STURMINSTER DIVISION to form (after boundary adjustments) **1512 BLANDFORD AND STURMINSTER DIVISION**

1501 BOURNEMOUTH DIVISION
combined with 1503 CHRISTCHURCH DIVISION to form **1514 BOURNEMOUTH AND CHRISTCHURCH DIVISION**

1502 BRIDPORT DIVISION
combined with 1504 DORCHESTER DIVISION and 1507 SHERBORNE DIVISION to form **1516 WEST DORSET DIVISION**

1503 CHRISTCHURCH DIVISION
combined with 1501 BOURNEMOUTH DIVISION to form **1514 BOURNEMOUTH AND CHRISTCHURCH DIVISION**

1504 DORCHESTER DIVISION
combined with 1502 BRIDPORT DIVISION and 1507 SHERBORNE DIVISION to form **1516 WEST DORSET DIVISION**

1505 POOLE PSA
combined with 1514 BOURNEMOUTH AND CHRISTCHURCH PSA and 1515 CENTRAL DORSET PSA (except for the area of the North Dorset District Council) to form **1522 EAST DORSET PSA**

1506 SHAFTESBURY DIVISION
combined with 1508 STURMINSTER DIVISION to form **1513 SHAFTESBURY DIVISION**

1507 SHERBORNE DIVISION
combined with 1502 BRIDPORT DIVISION and 1504 DORCHESTER DIVISION to form **1516 WEST DORSET DIVISION**

1508 STURMINSTER DIVISION
abolished – majority absorbed into **1512 BLANDFORD AND STURMINSTER DIVISION** *and remainder into* **1513 SHAFTESBURY DIVISION**

1509 WAREHAM DIVISION
combined with 1512 BLANDFORD AND STURMINSTER DIVISION, 1513 SHAFTESBURY DIVISION and 1511 WIMBORNE DIVISION to form **1515 CENTRAL DORSET DIVISION**

1510 WEYMOUTH AND PORTLAND PSA
combined with 1516 WEST DORSET DIVISION and the area of the North Dorset District Council within 1515 CENTRAL DORSET PSA **to form 1510 WEST DORSET PSA**

1511 WIMBORNE DIVISION
combined with 1512 BLANDFORD AND STURMINSTER DIVISION, 1513 SHAFTESBURY DIVISION and 1509 WAREHAM DIVISION to form **1515 CENTRAL DORSET DIVISION**

1512 BLANDFORD AND STURMINSTER DIVISION
combined with 1513 SHAFTESBURY DIVISION, 1509 WAREHAM DIVISION and 1511 WIMBORNE DIVISION to form **1515 CENTRAL DORSET DIVISION**

1513 SHAFTESBURY DIVISION
combined with 1512 BLANDFORD AND STURMINSTER DIVISION, 1509 WAREHAM DIVISION and 1511 WIMBORNE DIVISION to form **1515 CENTRAL DORSET DIVISION**

1514 BOURNEMOUTH AND CHRISTCHURCH PSA
combined with 1505 POOLE PSA and 1515 CENTRAL DORSET PSA (except for the area of North Dorset District Council) to form **1522 EAST DORSET PSA**

1515 CENTRAL DORSET PSA
(Except for the area of the North Dorset District Council) combined with 1514 BOURNEMOUTH AND CHRISTCHURCH PSA and 1505 POOLE PSA to form **1522 EAST DORSET PSA** *– The area of the North Dorset District Council combined with 1516 WEST DORSET PSA and 1510 WEYMOUTH AND PORTLAND PSA to form* **1510 WEST DORSET PSA**

1516 WEST DORSET PSA
combined with 1510 WEYMOUTH AND PORTLAND PSA and the area of the North Dorset District Council within 1515 CENTRAL DORSET PSA to form **1510 WEST DORSET PSA**

1522 EAST DORSET LJA
see **DEVON, CORNWALL AND DORSET** ....p. 138

1510 WEST DORSET LJA
see **DEVON, CORNWALL AND DORSET** ....p. 138

1576 CHESTER-LE-STREET PSA
combined with 1579 DURHAM PSA, 1576 DERWENTSIDE PSA and 1580 EASINGTON PSA to form **1583 NORTH DURHAM PSA**

1577 DARLINGTON PSA
combined with 1581 SEDGEFIELD PSA and 1582 TEESDALE AND WEAR VALLEY to form **1584 SOUTH DURHAM PSA**

1578 DERWENTSIDE PSA
combined with 1579 DURHAM PSA, 1576 CHESTER-LE-STREET PSA and 1580 EASINGTON PSA to form **1583 NORTH DURHAM PSA**

1579 DURHAM PSA
combined with 1578 DERWENTSIDE PSA, 1576 CHESTER-LE-STREET PSA and 1580 EASINGTON PSA to form **1583 NORTH DURHAM PSA**

1580 EASINGTON PSA
combined with 1579 DURHAM PSA, 1578 DERWENTSIDE PSA and 1576 CHESTER-LE-STREET PSA to form **1583 NORTH DURHAM PSA**

1581 SEDGEFIELD PSA
combined with 1577 DARLINGTON PSA and 1582 TEESDALE AND WEAR VALLEY PSA to form **1584 SOUTH DURHAM PSA**

1582 TEESDALE AND WEAR VALLEY PSA
combined with 1581 SEDGFIELD PSA and 1577 DARLINGTON PSA to form **1584 SOUTH DURHAM PSA**

1583 NORTH DURHAM LJA
combined with 1584 South Durham LJA to form **1585/5585 COUNTY DURHAM AND DARLINGTON LJA**

1584 SOUTH DURHAM LJA
combined with 1583 North Durham LJA to form **1585/5585 COUNTY DURHAM AND DARLINGTON LJA**

1585 COUNTY DURHAM AND DARLINGTON LJA
see **CLEVELAND AND DURHAM** ....p. 114

1595 BATTLE AND RYE DIVISION
combined with 1596 BEXHILL DIVISION and 1601 HASTINGS DIVISION to form **1606 HASTINGS AND ROTHER DIVISION**

1596 BEXHILL DIVISION
combined with 1595 BATTLE AND RYE DIVISION and 1601 HASTINGS DIVISION to form **1606 HASTINGS AND ROTHER DIVISION**

1597 BRIGHTON DIVISION
combined with 1602 HOVE DIVISION to form **1604 BRIGHTON AND HOVE DIVISION**

1598 CROWBOROUGH DIVISION
combined with 1603 LEWES DIVISION to form **1607 LEWES AND CROWBOROUGH DIVISION**

1599 EASTBOURNE DIVISION
combined with 1600 HAILSHAM DIVISION to form **1605 EASTBOURNE AND HAILSHAM DIVISION**

1600 HAILSHAM DIVISION
combined with 1599 EASTBOURNE DIVISION to form **1605 EASTBOURNE AND HAILSHAM DIVISION**

1601 HASTINGS DIVISION
combined with 1595 BATTLE AND RYE DIVISION and 1596 BEXHILL DIVISION to form **1606 HASTINGS AND ROTHER DIVISION**

1602 HOVE DIVISION
combined with 1597 BRIGHTON DIVISION to form **1604 BRIGHTON AND HOVE DIVISION**

1603 LEWES DIVISION
combined with 1596 CROWBOROUGH DIVISION to form **1607 LEWES AND CROWBOROUGH DIVISION**

1604 BRIGHTON AND HOVE PSA
combined with 1607 LEWES AND CROWBOROUGH PSA to form **2950 SUSSEX (CENTRAL) PSA**

1605 EASTBOURNE AND HAILSHAM PSA
combined with 1606 HASTINGS AND ROTHER PSA to form **2948 SUSSEX (EASTERN) PSA**

1606 HASTINGS AND ROTHER PSA
combined with 1605 EASTBOURNE AND HAILSHAM PSA to form **2948 SUSSEX (EASTERN) PSA**

1607 LEWES AND CROWBOROUGH PSA
combined with 1604 BRIGHTON AND HOVE PSA to **form 2950 SUSSEX (CENTRAL) PSA**

1610 BASILDON DIVISION
(formerly Billericay Division) – *renamed* **MID-SOUTH ESSEX DIVISION**

1610 MID-SOUTH ESSEX LJA
combined with 1629 SOUTH-EAST ESSEX LJA and 1626 SOUTH-WEST LJA to form **1971 SOUTH ESSEX LJA**

1611 BRENTWOOD DIVISION
combined with 1626 THURROCK DIVISION to form **1626 SOUTH-WEST ESSEX DIVISION**

1612 CHELMSFORD DIVISION
combined with 1630 MALDON AND WITHAM DIVISION and (after boundary adjustment) 1631 BRAINTREE AND HALSTEAD DIVISION to form **1612 MID-NORTH ESSEX DIVISION**

1612 MID-NORTH ESSEX LJA
combined with 1613 NORTH-EAST ESSEX LJA and 1619 NORTH-WEST ESSEX LJA to form **1970 NORTH ESSEX LJA**

1613 COLCHESTER DIVISION
combined with 1620 HARWICH DIVISION, 1625 TENDRING DIVISION and part of 1631 BRAINTREE AND HALSTEAD DIVISION to form **1613 NORTH-EAST ESSEX DIVISION**

1613 NORTH-EAST ESSEX LJA
combined with 1612 MID-NORTH ESSEX LJA and 1619 NORTH-WEST ESSEX LJA to form **1970 NORTH ESSEX LJA**

1614 DENGIE AND MALDON DIVISION
combined with 1627 WITHAM DIVISION to form **1630 MALDON AND WITHAM DIVISION**

1615 DUNMOW DIVISION
combined with 1623 SAFFRON WALDEN DIVISION to form **1632 DUNMOW AND SAFFRON WALDEN DIVISION**

1616 EPPING AND ONGAR DIVISION
combined with 1632 DUNMOW AND SAFFRON WALDEN DIVISION and 1619 HARLOW DIVISION to form **1619 NORTH-WEST ESSEX DIVISION**

1617 FRESHWELL AND SOUTH HINCKFORD DIVISION
combined with 1628 HALSTEAD AND HEDINGHAM DIVISION to form **1631 BRAINTREE AND HALSTEAD DIVISION**

1618 HALSTEAD DIVISION
combined with 1621 NORTH HINCKFORD DIVISION to form **1628 HALSTEAD AND HEDINGHAM DIVISION**

1619 HARLOW DIVISION
combined with 1616 EPPING AND ONGAR DIVISION and 1632 DUNMOW AND SAFFRON WALDEN DIVISION to form **1619 NORTH-WEST ESSEX DIVISION**

1619 NORTH-WEST ESSEX LJA
combined with 1612 MID-NORTH ESSEX LJA and 1613 NORTH-EAST ESSEX LJA to form **1970 NORTH ESSEX LJA**

1620 HARWICH DIVISION
combined with 1613 COLCHESTER DIVISION, 1625 TENDRING DIVISION and part of 1631 BRAINTREE AND HALSTEAD DIVISION to form **1613 NORTH-EAST ESSEX DIVISION**

1621 NORTH HINCKFORD DIVISION
combined with 1618 HALSTEAD DIVISION to form **1628 HALSTEAD AND HEDINGHAM DIVISION**

1622 ROCHFORD DIVISION
combined with 1624 SOUTHEND-ON-SEA DIVISION to form **1629 ROCHFORD AND SOUTHEND-ON-SEA DIVISION**

1623 SAFFRON WALDEN DIVISION
combined with 1615 DUNMOW DIVISION to form **1632 DUNMOW AND SAFFRON WALDEN DIVISION**

1624 SOUTHEND-ON-SEA DIVISION
combined with 1622 ROCHFORD DIVISION to form **1629 ROCHFORD AND SOUTHEND-ON-SEA DIVISION**

1625 TENDRING DIVISION
combined with 1613 COLCHESTER DIVISION, 1620 HARWICH DIVISION and part of BRAINTREE AND HALSTEAD DIVISION to form **1613 NORTH-EAST ESSEX DIVISION**

1626 THURROCK DIVISION
combined with 1611 BRENTWOOD DIVISION to form **1626 SOUTH-WEST ESSEX DIVISION**

1626 SOUTH-WEST ESSEX LJA
combined with 1610 MID-SOUTH ESSEX LJA and 1629 SOUTH-EAST ESSEX LJA to form **1971 SOUTH ESSEX LJA**

1627 WITHAM DIVISION
combined with DENGIE AND MALDON DIVISION to form **1630 MALDON AND WITHAM DIVISION**

1628 HALSTEAD AND HEDINGHAM DIVISION
combined with 1617 FRESHWELL AND SOUTH HINCKFORD DIVISION to form **1631 BRAINTREE AND HALSTEAD DIVISION**

1629 ROCHFORD AND SOUTHEND-ON-SEA DIVISION
renamed **SOUTH-EAST ESSEX DIVISION**

1629 SOUTH-EAST ESSEX LJA
combined with 1610 MID-SOUTH ESSEX LJA and 1626 SOUTH-WEST ESSEX LJA to form **1971 SOUTH ESSEX LJA**

1630 MALDON AND WITHAM DIVISION
combined with 1612 CHELMSFORD DIVISION and (after boundary adjustment) 1631 BRAINTREE AND HALSTEAD DIVISION to form **1612 MID-NORTH ESSEX DIVISION**

1631 BRAINTREE AND HALSTEAD DIVISION
combined (after boundary adjustment) with 1612 CHELMSFORD DIVISION AND 1630 MALDON AND WITHAM DIVISION to form **1612 MID-NORTH ESSEX DIVISION**

1632 DUNMOW AND SAFFRON WALDEN DIVISION
combined with 1616 EPPING AND ONGAR DIVISION and 1619 HARLOW DIVISION to form **1619 NORTH-WEST ESSEX DIVISION**

1670 BERKELEY DIVISION
combined with 1675 DURSLEY DIVISION to form **1691 BERKELEY AND DURSLEY DIVISION**

1671 CAMPDEN DIVISION
combined with 1682 NORTHLEACH DIVISION, 1983 STOW-ON-THE-WOLD DIVISION and 1688 WINCHCOMBE DIVISION to form **1694 NORTH COTSWOLD DIVISION**

1672 CHELTENHAM DIVISION
combined with 1694 NORTH COTSWOLD DIVISION and 1686 TEWKSBURY DIVISION to form **1696 NORTH GLOUCESTERSHIRE DIVISION**

1673 CIRENCESTER DIVISION
combined with 1676 FAIRFORD DIVISION and 1685 TETBURY DIVISION to form **1689 CIRENCESTER, FAIRFORD AND TETBURY DIVISION**

1674 COLEFORD DIVISION
combined with 1679 LYDNEY DIVISION and 1681 NEWNHAM DIVISION to form **1695 FOREST OF DEAN DIVISION**

1675 DURSLEY DIVISION
combined with 1670 BERKELEY DIVISION to form **1691 BERKELEY AND DURSLEY DIVISION**

1676 FAIRFORD DIVISION
combined with 1673 CIRENCESTER DIVISION and 1685 TETBURY DIVISION to form **1689 CIRENCESTER, FAIRFORD AND TETBURY DIVISION**

1677 GLOUCESTER (CITY) DIVISION
combined with 1690 GLOUCESTER COUNTY DIVISION to form **1692 GLOUCESTER DIVISION**

1678 GLOUCESTER (COUNTY) DIVISION
combined with 1680 NEWENT DIVISION to form **1690 GLOUCESTER COUNTY DIVISION**

1679 LYDNEY DIVISION
combined with 1674 COLEFORD DIVISION and 1681 NEWNHAM DIVISION to form **1695 FOREST OF DEAN DIVISION**

1680 NEWENT DIVISION
combined with 1678 GLOUCESTER (COUNTY) DIVISION to form **1690 GLOUCESTER COUNTY DIVISION**

1681 NEWNHAM DIVISION
combined with 1674 COLEFORD DIVISION and 1679 LYDNEY DIVISION to form **1695 FOREST OF DEAN DIVISION**

1682 NORTHLEACH DIVISION
combined with 1671 CAMPDEN DIVISION, 1683 STOW-ON-THE-WOLD DIVISION and 1688 WINCHCOMBE DIVISION to form **1694 NORTH COTSWOLD DIVISION**

1683 STOW-ON-THE-WOLD DIVISION
combined with 1671 CAMPDEN DIVISION, 1682 NORTHLEACH DIVISION and 1688 WINCHCOMBE
DIVISION to form **1694 NORTH COTSWOLD DIVISION**

1684 STROUD DIVISION
combined with 1691 BERKELEY AND DURSLEY DIVISION and 1687 WHITMINSTER DIVISION to
form **1693 SOUTH GLOUCESTERSHIRE DIVISION**

1685 TETBURY DIVISION
combined with 1673 CIRENCESTER DIVISION and 1676 FAIRFORD DIVISION to form **1689**
CIRENCESTER, FAIRFORD AND TETBURY DIVISION

1686 TEWKSBURY DIVISION
combined with 1672 CHELTENHAM DIVISION and 1694 NORTH COTSWOLD DIVISION to form
1696 NORTH GLOUCESTERSHIRE DIVISION

1687 WHITMINSTER DIVISION
combined with 1691 BERKELEY AND DURSLEY DIVISION and 1684 STROUD DIVISION to form
1693 SOUTH GLOUCESTERSHIRE DIVISION

1688 WINCHCOMBE DIVISION
combined with 1671 CAMPDEN DIVISION, 1682 NORTHLEACH DIVISION and 1683
STOW-ON-THE-WOLD DIVISION to form **1694 NORTH COTSWOLD DIVISION**

1689 CIRENCESTER, FAIRFORD AND TETBURY PSA
renamed and renumbered **1698 CIRENCESTER LJA**

1690 GLOUCESTER COUNTY DIVISION
combined with 1677 GLOUCESTER (CITY) DIVISION to form **1692 GLOUCESTER DIVISION**

1691 BERKELEY AND DURSLEY DIVISION
combined with 1684 STROUD DIVISION and 1687 WHITMINSTER DIVISION to form **1693 SOUTH**
GLOUCESTERSHIRE DIVISION

1692 GLOUCESTER PSA
renamed and renumbered **1692 GLOUCESTERSHIRE LJA**

1693 SOUTH GLOUCESTERSHIRE PSA
renamed and renumbered **1698 STROUD LJA**

1694 NORTH COTSWOLD DIVISION
combined with 1672 CHELTENHAM DIVISION and 1686 TEWKSBURY DIVISION to form **1696**
NORTH GLOUCESTERSHIRE DIVISION

1695 FOREST OF DEAN PSA
renamed and renumbered **1698 CIRENCESTER LJA**

1696 NORTH GLOUCESTERSHIRE PSA
renamed and renumbered **1692 GLOUCESTERSHIRE LJA**

1692 GLOUCESTERSHIRE LJA
see **AVON, SOMERSET AND GLOUCESTERSHIRE** ....p. 137

1722 NORTH CHESHIRE LJA
see **CHESHIRE AND MERSEYSIDE** . . . p. 121

1733 MANCHESTER AND SALFORD LJA
see **GREATER MANCHESTER** ....p. 126

1724 BURY AND ROCHDALE LJA
see **GREATER MANCHESTER** ....p. 126

1725 EAST LANCASHIRE LJA
see **CUMBRIA AND LANCASHIRE** ....p. 123

1726 WEST CUMBRIA LJA
see **CUMBRIA AND LANCASHIRE** ....p. 123

1727 NORTH CUMBRIA LJA
see **CUMBRIA AND LANCASHIRE** ....p. 123

1728 SEFTON LJA
see **CHESHIRE AND MERSEYSIDE** ....p. 121

1729 WEST CHESHIRE LJA
see **CHESHIRE AND MERSEYSIDE** ....p. 121

1731 BOLTON LJA
see **GREATER MANCHESTER** ....p. 126

1732 BURY LJA
see **1724 BURY AND ROCHDALE LJA**

1733 MANCHESTER CITY LJA
see **1733 MANCHESTER AND SALFORD LJA**

1734 OLDHAM LJA
see **GREATER MANCHESTER** ....p. 126

1735 MIDDLETON AND HEYWOOD DIVISION
combined with 1736 ROCHDALE DIVISION to form **1750 ROCHDALE, MIDDLETON AND HEYWOOD DIVISION**

1736 ROCHDALE DIVISION
combined with 1735 MIDDLETON AND HEYWOOD DIVISION to form **1750 ROCHDALE, MIDDLETON AND HEYWOOD DIVISION**

1737 ECCLES DIVISION
combined with 1738 SALFORD DIVISION to form **1747 CITY OF SALFORD DIVISION**

1738 SALFORD DIVISION
combined with 1737 ECCLES DIVISION to form **1747 CITY OF SALFORD DIVISION**

547 STOCKPORT LJA
see **GREATER MANCHESTER** ....p. 126

1740 ASHTON-UNDER-LYNE DIVISION
combined with 1741 SOUTH TAMESIDE DIVISION to form **1748 TAMESIDE DIVISION**

1741 SOUTH TAMESIDE DIVISION
combined with 1740 ASHTON-UNDER-LYNE DIVISION to form **1748 TAMESIDE DIVISION**

1742 TRAFFORD LJA
see **GREATER MANCHESTER** ....p. 126

1743 LEIGH PSA
combined with 1746 WIGAN PSA to form **1749 WIGAN AND LEIGH PSA**

1744 MAKERFIELD DIVISION
combined with 1745 WIGAN DIVISION to form **1746 WIGAN DIVISION**

1745 WIGAN DIVISION
combined with 1744 MAKERFIELD DIVISION to form **1746 WIGAN DIVISION**

1746 WIGAN PSA
combined with 1743 LEIGH PSA to form **1749 WIGAN AND LEIGH PSA**

1747 CITY OF SALFORD LJA
CLOSED wef 12/11

1748 TAMESIDE LJA
see **GREATER MANCHESTER** ....p. 126

1749 WIGAN AND LEIGH LJA
see **GREATER MANCHESTER** ....p. 126

1750 ROCHDALE, MIDDLETON AND HEYWOOD LJA
CLOSED wef 12/11 see **1724 BURY AND ROCHDALE LJA**

1760 ALTON DIVISION
combined with 1771 PETERSFIELD DIVISION to form **1778 ALTON AND PETERSFIELD DIVISION**

1761 ANDOVER DIVISION
combined with 1762 BASINGSTOKE DIVISION and 1777 WINCHESTER DIVISION to form **1781 NORTH WEST HAMPSHIRE DIVISION**

1762 BASINGSTOKE DIVISION
combined with 1761 ANDOVER DIVISION and 1777 WINCHESTER DIVISION to form **1781 NORTH WEST HAMPSHIRE DIVISION**

1763 DROXFORD DIVISION
combined with 1764 EASTLEIGH DIVISION, 1765 FAREHAM DIVISION and 1766 GOSPORT DIVISION to form **1783 SOUTH HAMPSHIRE DIVISION**

1764 EASTLEIGH DIVISION
combined with 1763 DROXFORD DIVISION, 1765 FAREHAM DIVISION and 1766 GOSPORT DIVISION to form **1783 SOUTH HAMPSHIRE DIVISION**

1765 FAREHAM DIVISION
combined with 1763 DROXFORD DIVISION, 1764 EASTLEIGH DIVISION and 1766 GOSPORT DIVISION to form **1783 SOUTH HAMPSHIRE DIVISION**

1766 GOSPORT DIVISION
combined with 1763 DROXFORD DIVISION, 1764 EASTLEIGH DIVISION and 1765 FAREHAM DIVISION to form **1783 SOUTH HAMPSHIRE DIVISION**

1767 HAVANT DIVISION
combined with 1772 PORTSMOUTH DIVISION to form **1782 EAST HAMPSHIRE DIVISION**

1768 HYTHE DIVISION
combined with 1769 LYMINGTON DIVISION, 1773 RINGWOOD DIVISION, 1774 ROMSEY DIVISION and 1776 TOTTON AND NEW FOREST DIVISION to form **1779 NEW FOREST DIVISION**

1769 LYMINGTON DIVISION
combined with 1768 HYTHE DIVISION, 1773 RINGWOOD DIVISION, 1774 ROMSEY DIVISION and 1776 TOTTON AND NEW FOREST DIVISION to form **1779 NEW FOREST DIVISION**

1770 ODIHAM DIVISION
combined with 1778 ALTON AND PETERSFIELD DIVISION to form **1780 NORTH EAST HAMPSHIRE DIVISION**

1771 PETERSFIELD DIVISION
combined with 1760 ALTON DIVISION to form **1778 ALTON AND PETERSFIELD DIVISION**

1772 PORTSMOUTH DIVISION
combined with 1767 HAVANT DIVISION to form **1782 SOUTH EAST HAMPSHIRE DIVISION**

1773 RINGWOOD DIVISION
combined with 1768 HYTHE DIVISION, 1769 LYMINGTON DIVISION, 1774 ROMSEY DIVISION and 1776 TOTTON AND NEW FOREST DIVISION to form **1779 NEW FOREST DIVISION**

1774 ROMSEY DIVISION
combined with 1768 HYTHE DIVISION, 1769 LYMINGTON DIVISION, 1773 RINGWOOD DIVISION and 1776 TOTTON AND NEW FOREST DIVISION to form **1779 NEW FOREST DIVISION**

1775 SOUTHAMPTON LJA
see **1304 WEST HAMPSHIRE LJA**

1776 TOTTON AND NEW FOREST DIVISION
TOTTON AND NEW FOREST DIVISION – combined with 1768 HYTHE DIVISION, 1769 LYMINGTON DIVISION, 1773 RINGWOOD DIVISION and 1774 ROMSEY DIVISION to form **1779 NEW FOREST DIVISION**

1777 WINCHESTER DIVISION
combined with 1761 ANDOVER DIVISION and 1762 BASINGSTOKE DIVISION to form **1781 NORTH WEST HAMPSHIRE DIVISION**

1778 ALTON AND PETERSFIELD DIVISION
combined with 1770 ODIHAM DIVISION to form **1780 NORTH EAST HAMPSHIRE DIVISION**

1779 NEW FOREST LJA
CLOSED wef 1/04/11

1780 NORTH EAST HAMPSHIRE LJA
combined with 1781 NORTH WEST HAMPSHIRE LJA to form **1305/5305 NORTH HAMPSHIRE LJA**

1781 NORTH WEST HAMPSHIRE LJA
combined with 1780 NORTH EAST HAMPSHIRE LJA to form **1305/5305 NORTH HAMPSHIRE LJA**

1782 SOUTH EAST HAMPSHIRE LJA
see **HAMPSHIRE, ISLE OF WIGHT AND WILTSHIRE** ....p. 140

1783 SOUTH HAMPSHIRE LJA
see **HAMPSHIRE, ISLE OF WIGHT AND WILTSHIRE** ....p. 140

1837 HAVERING MAGISTRATES' COURT
see **2573/6573 NORTH EAST LONDON LJA** ....p. 103

1840 BROMSGROVE AND REDDITCH LJA
see **STAFFORDSHIRE AND WEST MERCIA** ....p. 111

1841 HEREFORDSHIRE LJA
see **STAFFORDSHIRE AND WEST MERCIA** ....p. 111

1842 SEVERNMINSTER PSA
renamed **1842 KIDDERMINSTER PSA**

1842 KIDDERMINSTER LJA
see **STAFFORDSHIRE AND WEST MERCIA** ....p. 111

1843 SOUTH WORCESTERSHIRE LJA
see **STAFFORDSHIRE AND WEST MERCIA** ....p. 111

1845 BEWDLEY BOROUGH DIVISION
combined with 1862 STOURPORT DIVISION to form (after boundary adjustment) **1871 BEWDLEY AND STOURPORT DIVISION**

1846 BROMSGROVE DIVISION
(after boundary adjustment) combined with 1860 REDDITCH DIVISION to form **1840 BROMSGROVE AND REDDITCH DIVISION**

1847 BROMYARD DIVISION
abolished wef 1/1/88: Majority absorbed into 1868 NORTH HEREFORDSHIRE DIVISION and remainder into **1869 SOUTH HEREFORDSHIRE DIVISION**

1848 DORE AND BREDWARDINE DIVISION
abolished wef 1/1/88 and absorbed into **1869 SOUTH HEREFORDSHIRE DIVISION**

1849 DROITWICH DIVISION
combined with 1853 HUNDRED HOUSE DIVISION and 1866 WORCESTER (COUNTY) DIVISION to form (after boundary adjustment) **1872 MID-WORCESTER DIVISION**

1850 EVESHAM DIVISION
combined with 1859 PERSHORE DIVISION to form (after boundary adjustment) **1873 VALE OF EVESHAM DIVISION**

1851 CITY OF HEREFORD DIVISION
combined with 1868 NORTH HEREFORDSHIRE DIVISION and 1869 SOUTH HEREFORDSHIRE DIVISION to form **1841 HEREFORDSHIRE DIVISION**

1852 HEREFORD (COUNTY) DIVISION
abolished wef 1/1/88. Majority absorbed into **1869 SOUTH HEREFORDSHIRE DIVISION** *and remainder into* **1868 NORTH HEREFORDSHIRE DIVISION**

1853 HUNDRED HOUSE DIVISION
combined with 1849 DROITWICH DIVISION and 1866 WORCESTER (COUNTY) DIVISION to form (after boundary adjustment) **1872 MID-WORCESTERSHIRE DIVISION**

1854 KIDDERMINSTER DIVISION
combined with 1871 BEWDLEY AND STOURPORT DIVISION to form **1842 SEVERNMINSTER DIVISION**

1855 KINGTON DIVISION
absorbed into **1868 NORTH HEREFORDSHIRE DIVISION**

1856 LEDBURY DIVISION
absorbed into **1869 SOUTH HEREFORDSHIRE DIVISION**

1857 LEOMINSTER AND WIGMORE DIVISION
absorbed into **1868 NORTH HEREFORDSHIRE DIVISION**

1858 MALVERN DIVISION
combined with 1864 UPTON-ON-SEVERN DISTRICT to form (after boundary adjustment) **1870 MALVERN HILLS DIVISION**

1859 PERSHORE DIVISION
combined with 1850 EVESHAM DIVISION to form (after boundary adjustment) **1873 VALE OF EVESHAM DIVISION**

1860 REDDITCH DIVISION
combined with 1846 BROMSGROVE DIVISION (after boundary adjustment) to form **1840 BROMSGROVE AND REDDITCH DIVISION**

1861 ROSS DIVISION
absorbed into **1869 SOUTH HEREFORDSHIRE DIVISION**

1862 STOURPORT DIVISION
combined with 1845 BEWDLEY BOROUGH DIVISION to form (after boundary adjustment) **1871 BEWDLEY AND STOURPORT DIVISION**

1863 TENBURY DIVISION
absorbed into **1868 NORTH HEREFORDSHIRE DIVISION**

1864 UPTON-ON-SEVERN DIVISION
combined with 1858 MALVERN DIVISION to form (after boundary adjustment **1870 MALVERN HILLS DIVISION**

1865 CITY OF WORCESTER DIVISION
boundary with 1866 WORCESTER (COUNTY) DIVISION adjusted to form **1874 CITY OF WORCESTER DIVISION**

1866 WORCESTER (COUNTY) DIVISION
combined with 1849 DROITWICH DIVISION and 1853 HUNDRED HOUSE DIVISION to form (after boundary adjustment) **1872 MID-WORCESTERSHIRE DIVISION**

1867 WORCESTER (COUNTY) DIVISION (MOTORWAY)
abolished

1868 NORTH HEREFORDSHIRE DIVISION
combined with 1851 CITY OF HEREFORD DIVISION and 1869 SOUTH HEREFORDSHIRE DIVISION to form **1841 HEREFORDSHIRE DIVISION**

1869 SOUTH HEREFORDSHIRE DIVISION
combined with 1851 CITY OF HEREFORD DIVISION and 1868 HEREFORDSHIRE DIVISION to form **1841 HEREFORDSHIRE DIVISION**

1870 MALVERN HILLS DIVISION
combined with 1872 MID-WORCESTERSHIRE DIVISION (after boundary adjustment), 1873 VALE OF EVESHAM DIVISION and 1874 CITY OF WORCESTER DIVISION to form **1843 SOUTH WORCESTERSHIRE DIVISION**

1871 BEWDLEY AND STOURPORT DIVISION
combined with 1854 KIDDERMINSTER DIVISION to form **1842 SEVERNMINSTER DIVISION**

1872 MID-WORCESTERSHIRE DIVISION
(after boundary adjustment) combined with 1870 MALVERN HILLS DIVISION, 1873 VALE OF EVESHAM DIVISION and 1874 CITY OF WORCESTER DIVISION to form **1843 SOUTH WORCESTERSHIRE DIVISION**

1873 VALE OF EVESHAM DIVISION
combined with 1870 MALVERN HILLS DIVISION, 1872 MID-WORCESTERSHIRE DIVISION (after boundary adjustment) and CITY OF WORCESTER DIVISION to form **1843 SOUTH WORCESTERSHIRE DIVISION**

1874 CITY OF WORCESTER DIVISION
combined with 1870 MALVERN HILLS DIVISION, 1872 MID-WORCESTERSHIRE DIVISION (after boundary adjustment) and 1873 VALE OF EVESHAM DIVISION to form **1843 SOUTH WORCESTERSHIRE DIVISION**

1875 BISHOP'S STORTFORD DIVISION
combined with 1877 CHESHUNT DIVISION and 1888 HERTFORD AND WARE DIVISION to form **1888 EAST HERTFORDSHIRE DIVISION**

1876 BUNTINGFORD DIVISION
combined with 1888 HERTFORD AND WARE

1877 CHESHUNT DIVISION
combined with 1875 BISHOP'S STORTFORD DIVISION and 1888 HERTFORD AND WARE DIVISION to form **1888 EAST HERFORDSHIRE DIVISION**

1878 DACORUM PSA
combined with 1886 WATFORD PSA to form **1893 WEST HERTFORDSHIRE PSA**

1879 HATFIELD DIVISION
combined with 1887 WELWYN DIVISION to form **1890 MID HERTFORDSHIRE DIVISION**

1879 HATFIELD MAGISTRATES' COURT
see **BEDFORDSHIRE AND HERTFORDSHIRE** ....p. 128

p. 128

1881 HITCHIN DIVISION
combined with 1882 ODSEY DIVISION to form **1889 NORTH HERTFORDSHIRE DIVISION**

1882 ODSEY DIVISION
combined with HITCHIN DIVISION to form **1889 NORTH HERTFORDSHIRE DIVISION**

1883 ST ALBAN'S PSA
combined with 1890 MID HERTFORDSHIRE PSA to form **1892 CENTRAL HERTFORDSHIRE PSA**

1884 SOUTH MIMMS DIVISION
abolished wef 3/9/93 and absorbed into **1877 CHESHUNT DIVISION and 1886 WATFORD DIVISION**

1885 STEVENAGE DIVISION
combined with 1889 North Hertfordshire Division to form one new division to be known as the **NORTH HERTFORDSHIRE DIVISION**

1886 WATFORD PSA
after boundary adjustment) combined with 1878 DACORUM PSA to form **1893 WEST HERTFORDSHIRE PSA**

1887 WELWYN DIVISION
combined with 1879 HATFIELD DIVISION to form **1890 MID HERTFORDSHIRE DIVISION**

1888 HERTFORD AND WARE DIVISION
combined with 1875 BISHOP'S STORTFORD DIVISION and 1877 CHESHUNT DIVISION to form **1888 EAST HERTFORDSHIRE DIVISION** *(retaining existing Court Code No.)*

1888 EAST HERTFORDSHIRE LJA
combined with 1889 NORTH HERTFORDSHIRE LJA to form **1889 NORTH AND EAST HERTFORDSHIRE LJA**

1889 NORTH HERTFORDSHIRE LJA
combined with 1888 EAST HERTFORDSHIRE LJA to form **1889 NORTH AND EAST HERFORDSHIRE LJA**

1890 MID HERTFORDSHIRE PSA
combined with 1883 ST ALBANS PSA to form **1892 CENTRAL HERTFORDESHIRE PSA**

1892 CENTRAL HERTFORDSHIRE LJA
combined with 1893 WEST HERTFORDSHIRE LJA to form **1910 WEST AND CENTRAL HERTFORDSHIRE LJA**

1893 WEST HERTFORDSHIRE LJA
combined with 1892 CENTRAL HERTFORDSHIRE LJA to form **1910 WEST AND CENTRAL HERTFORDSHIRE LJA**

1901 SOUTH HUNSLEY BEACON AND HOWDENSHIRE DIVISION
Part combined with part of 1928 EPWORTH AND GOOLE DIVISION to form **1928 GOOLE AND HOWDENSHIRE DIVISION** *and remainder becomin* **1901 SOUTH HUNSLEY BEACON DIVISION**

1901 SOUTH HUNSLEY BEACON PSA
combined with 1925 BEVERLEY PSA, parts of 1905 BAINTON, WILTON AND HOLME BEACON PSA and parts of DICKERING AND NORTH HOLDERNESS PSA to form **1942 BEVERLEY AND THE WOLDS PSA**

1902 SOUTH AND MIDDLE HOLDERNESS PSA
combined with 1933 KINGSTON UPON HULL PSA to form **1943 HULL AND HOLDERNESS PSA**

1903 SCUNTHORPE, BRIGG AND BARTON DIVISION
combined with part of 1928 EPWORTH AND GOOLE DIVISION to form **319 NORTH LINCOLNSHIRE DIVISION**

319   NORTH LINCOLNSHIRE LJA
see **HUMBER AND SOUTH YORKSHIRE** p. 115

1904 DICKERING AND NORTH HOLDERNESS PSA
Part combined with 1901 SOUTH HUNSLEY BEACON, 1925 BEVERLEY PSA and part of 1905 BAINTON, WILTON AND HOLME BEACON PSA to form **1942 BEVERLEY AND THE WOLDS PSA**
Remainder combined with remaining part of 1905 BAINTON WILTON AND HOLME PSA to form
1941 BRIDLINGTON PSA

1905 BAINTON, WILTON AND HOLME BEACON PSA
Part combined with 1901 SOUTH HUNSLEY BEACON PSA, 1925 BEVERLEY PSA and part of 1904 DICKERING AND NORTH HOLDERNESS PSA to form **1942 BEVERLEY AND THE WOLDS PSA.**
Remainder combined with the remainder of DICKERING AND NORTH HOLDERNESS to form **1941 BRIDLINGTON PSA**

1910 WEST AND CENTRAL HERTFORDSHIRE LJA
see **BEDFORDSHIRE AND HERTFORDSHIRE** ....p. 128

1889 NORTH AND EAST HERTFORDSHIRE LJA
see **BEDFORDSHIRE AND HERTFORDSHIRE** ....p. 128

1076 BERKSHIRE LJA
see **THAMES VALLEY** ....p. 135

1124 BUCKINGHAMSHIRE LJA
see **THAMES VALLEY** ....p. 135

2777 OXFORDSHIRE LJA
see **THAMES VALLEY** ....p. 135

1923 BAINTON BEACON DIVISION
combined with 1939 WILTON BEACON DIVISION and 1931 HOLME BEACON DIVISION to form
1905 BAINTON, WILTON AND HOLME BEACON DIVISION

1924 BARTON-UPON-HUMBER DIVISION
combined with 1936 SCUNTHORPE DIVISION and 1926 BRIGG DIVISION to form **319 SCUNTHORPE, BRIGG AND BARTON DIVISION**

1925 BEVERLEY PSA
combined with 1901 SOUTH HUNSLEY BEACON PSA, part of 1905 BAINTON, WILTON AND HOLME BEACON PSA and part of 1904 DICKERING AND NORTH HOLDERNESS PSA to form **1942 BEVERLEY AND THE WOLDS PSA**

1926 BRIGG DIVISION
combined with 1936 SCUNTHORPE DIVISION and 1924 BARTON-UPON-HUMBER DIVISION to form **319 SCUNTHORPE, BRIGG AND BARTON DIVISION**

1927 DICKERING DIVISION
combined with 1935 NORTH HOLDERNESS DIVISION to form **1904 DICKERING AND NORTH HOLDERNESS DIVISION**

1928 EPWORTH AND GOOLE DIVISION
Part combined with 319 SCUNTHORPE, BRIGG AND BARTON DIVISION to form **1903 NORTH LINCOLNSHIRE DIVISION**; *Part combined with part of 1901 SOUTH HUNSLEY BEACON AND HOWDENSHIRE DIVISION to form* **1928 GOOLE AND HOWDENSHIRE DIVISION**

1928 GOOLE AND HOWDENSHIRE LJA
CLOSED wef 12/11

1929 GRIMSBY (BOROUGH) DIVISION
combined with 1930 CLEETHORPES DIVISION to form **1940 GRIMSBY AND CLEETHORPES DIVISION**

1930 GRIMSBY (COUNTY) DIVISION
renamed **CLEETHORPES DIVISION**, *see below*

1930 CLEETHORPES DIVISION
combined with 1929 GRIMSBY (BOROUGH) DIVISION to form **1940 GRIMSBY AND CLEETHORPES DIVISION**

1931 HOLME BEACON DIVISION
combined with 1923 BAINTON BEACON DIVISION and 1939 WILTON BEACON DIVISION to form
1905 BAINTON, WILTON AND HOLME BEACON DIVISION

1932 HOWDENSHIRE DIVISION
combined with 1938 SOUTH HUNSLEY BEACON DIVISION to form **1901 SOUTH HUNSLEY BEACON AND HOWDENSHIRE DIVISION**

1933 KINGSTON UPON HULL PSA
combined with 1902 SOUTH AND MIDDLE HOLDERNESS PSA to form **1943 HULL AND HOLDERNESS PSA**

1934 MIDDLE HOLDERNESS DIVISION
combined with 1937 SOUTH HOLDERNESS DIVISION to form **1902 SOUTH AND MIDDLE HOLDERNESS DIVISION**

1935 NORTH HOLDERNESS DIVISION
combined with 1927 DICKERING DIVISION to form **1904 DICKERING AND NORTH HOLDERNESS DIVISION**

1936 SCUNTHORPE DIVISION
combined with 1926 BRIGG DIVISION and 1924 BARTON-UPON-HUMBER DIVISION to form **319 SCUNTHORPE, BRIGG AND BARTON DIVISION**

1937 SOUTH HOLDERNESS DIVISION
combined with 1934 MIDDLE HOLDERNESS DIVISION to form **1902 SOUTH AND MIDDLE HOLDERNESS DIVISION**

1938 SOUTH HUNSLEY BEACON DIVISION
combined with 1932 HOWDENSHIRE DIVISION to form **1901 SOUTH HUNSLEY BEACON AND HOWDENSHIRE DIVISION**

1939 WILTON BEACON DIVISION
combined with 1923 BAINTON BEACON DIVISION and 1931 HOLME BEACON DIVISION to form
1905 BAINTON, WILTON AND HOLME BEACON DIVISION

1940 GRIMSBY AND CLEETHORPES LJA
see **HUMBER AND SOUTH YORKSHIRE** ....p. 115

1941 BRIDLINGTON LJA
combined with 1942 BEVERLEY AND THE WOLDS LJA to form 2353 **EAST YORKSHIRE LJA**

1942 BEVERLEY AND THE WOLDS LJA
combined with 1941 BRIDLINGTON LJA to form 2353 **EAST YORKSHIRE LJA**

1943 HULL AND HOLDERNESS LJA
see **HUMBER AND SOUTH YORKSHIRE** ....p. 115

1945 ISLE OF WIGHT LJA
see **HAMPSHIRE, ISLE OF WIGHT AND WILTSHIRE** ....p. 140

1952 ASHFORD AND TENTERDEN DIVISION
combined with 1955 DOVER AND EAST KENT DIVISION and 1957 FOLKESTONE AND HYTHE DIVISION to form **1957 CHANNEL DIVISION**

1953 CANTERBURY LJA
combined with 1957 CHANNEL LJA and 1968 THANET LJA to form **1957 EAST KENT LJA**

1954 DARTFORD DIVISION
part combined with 1963 SEVENOAKS DIVISION, 1966 TUNBRIDGE WELLS AND CRANBROOK DIVISION and 1965 TONBRIDGE AND MALLING DIVISION (Part) to form **1963 WEST KENT DIVISION** – *balance remains under existing Court Code of 1954*

1954 DARTFORD DIVISION
combined with 1958 GRAVESHAM DIVISION to form **1969 DARTFORD AND GRAVESHAM DIVISION**

1955 DOVER AND EAST KENT DIVISION
combined with 1952 ASHFORD AND TENTERDEN DIVISION and 1957 FOLKESTONE AND HYTHE DIVISION to form **1957 CHANNEL DIVISION**

1956 FAVERSHAM DIVISION
combined with 1964 SITTINGBOURNE DIVISION to form **1967 FAVERSHAM AND SITTINGBOURNE DIVISION**

1957 FOLKESTONE AND HYTHE DIVISION
combined with 1952 ASHFORD AND TENTERDEN DIVISION and 1955 DOVER AND EAST KENT DIVISION to form **1957 CHANNEL DIVISION**

1957 CHANNEL LJA
combined with 1953 CANTERBURY LJA and 1968 THANET LJA to form **1957 EAST KENT LJA**

1957 EAST KENT LJA
see **KENT** ....p. 131

1958 GRAVESHAM DIVISION
combined with 1954 DARTFORD DIVISION to form **1969 DARTFORD AND GRAVESHAM DIVISION**

1959 MAIDSTONE DIVISION
combined with 1965 TONBRIDGE AND MALLING DIVISION (Part) to form **1959 MID KENT DIVISION**

1959 MID KENT
abolished and absorbed into **1959 CENTRAL KENT LJA**

1960 MARGATE DIVISION
combined with 1962 RAMSGATE DIVISION to form **1968 THANET DIVISION**

1959 CENTRAL KENT LJA
see **KENT** ....p. 131

1961 MEDWAY
combined with 1969 DARTFORD AND GRAVESHAM PSA to form **1966 NORTH KENT LJA**

1962 RAMSGATE DIVISION
combined with 1962 MARGATE DIVISION to form **1968 THANET DIVISION**

1963 SEVENOAKS DIVISION
combined with 1965 TONBRIDGE AND MALLING DIVISION (Part), 1966 TUNBRIDGE WELLS AND CRANBROOK DIVISION and 1954 DARTFORD DIVISION (Part) to form **1963 WEST KENT DIVISION**

1963 WEST KENT
abolished and absorbed into **1959 CENTRAL KENT LJA**

1964 SITTINGBOURNE DIVISION
combined with 1956 FAVERSHAM DIVISION to form **1967 FAVERSHAM AND SITTINGBOURNE DIVISION**

1965 TONBRIDGE AND MALLING DIVISION
part combined with 1959 MAIDSTONE DIVISION to form **1959 MID KENT DIVISION**: *part combined with 1966 TUNBRIDGE WELLS AND CRANBROOK DIVISION, 1963 SEVENOAKS DIVISION and 1954 DARTFORD DIVISION (Part) to form* **1963 WEST KENT DIVISION**

1955 EAST KENT LJA
see **KENT** ....p. 131

1966 TUNBRIDGE WELLS AND CRANBROOK DIVISION
combined with 1963 SEVENOAKS DIVISION, 1965 TONBRIDGE AND MALLING DIVISION (Part) and 1954 DARTFORD DIVISION (Part) to form **1963 WEST KENT DIVISION**

1966 NORTH KENT LJA (DARTFORD AND MEDWAY)
see **KENT** ....p. 131

1967 FAVERSHAM AND SITTINGBOURNE
abolished and absorbed into **1959 CENTRAL KENT LJA**

1968 THANET LJA
combined with 1953 CANTERBURY LJA and 1957 CHANNEL LJA to form **1957 EAST KENT LJA**

1969 DARTFORD AND GRAVESHAM PSA
combined with 1961 MEDWAY PSA to form **1966 NORTH KENT LJA**

1970 NORTH ESSEX LJA
see **CAMBRIDGESHIRE AND ESSEX** ....p. 129

1971 SOUTH ESSEX LJA
see **CAMBRIDGESHIRE AND ESSEX** ....p. 129

1972 NORFOLK LJA
see **NORFOLK AND SUFFOLK** ....p. 132

1992 FYLDE COAST LJA
see **CUMBRIA AND LANCASHIRE** ....p. 123

1994 ACCRINGTON DIVISION
combined with 1999 CHURCH DIVISION to form **2010 HYNDBURN DIVISION**

1995 BLACKBURN DIVISION
combined with 2000 DARWEN DIVISION and major part of 2008 RIBBLE VALLEY DIVISION to form
2012 BLACKBURN, DARWEN AND RIBBLE VALLEY DIVISION

1996 BLACKPOOL DIVISION
combined with 2001 FYLDE DIVISION to form **1996 BLACKPOOL AND FYLDE DIVISION**

1996 BLACKPOOL AND FYLDE PSA
combined with 2009 WYRE PSA to form **1992 FLYDE COAST PSA**

1997 BURNLEY DIVISION
combined with 2004 PENDLE DIVISION and part of 2008 RIBBLE VALLEY DIVISION to form **2011
BURNLEY AND PENDLE DIVISION**

1998 CHORLEY LJA
see **CUMBRIA AND LANCASHIRE** ....p. 123

1999 CHURCH DIVISION
combined with 1994 ACCRINGTON DIVISION to form **2010 HYNDBURN DIVISION**

2000 DARWEN DIVISION
combined with 1925 BLACKBURN DIVISION and major part of 2008 RIBBLE VALLEY DIVISION to
form **2012 BLACKBURN, DARWEN AND RIBBLE VALLEY DIVISION**

2001 FYLDE DIVISION
combined with 1996 BLACKPOOL DIVISION to form **1996 BLACKPOOL AND FYLDE DIVISION**

2002 LANCASTER LJA
see **CUMBRIA AND LANCASHIRE** ....p. 123

2003 ORMSKIRK LJA
see **CUMBRIA AND LANCASHIRE** ....p. 123

2004 PENDLE DIVISION
combined with 1997 BURNLEY DIVISION and part of 2008 RIBBLE VALLEY DIVISION to form **2011
BURNLEY AND PENDLE DIVISION**

2005 PRESTON LJA
see **CUMBRIA AND LANCASHIRE** ....p. 123

2006 ROSSENDALE PSA
combined with 2011 BURNLEY AND PENDLE PSA to form **2014 BURNLEY, PENDLE AND
ROSSENDALE PSA**

2007 SOUTH RIBBLE LJA
see **CUMBRIA AND LANCASHIRE** ....p. 123

2008 RIBBLE VALLEY DIVISION
abolished and absorbed into **2012 BLACKBURN, DARWEN AND RIBBLE VALLEY DIVISION, 2011
BURNLEY AND PENDLE DIVISION and 2005 PRESTON DIVISION**

2009 WYRE PSA
combined with 1996 BLACKPOOL AND FLYDE PSA to form **1992 FLYDE COAST PSA**

2010 HYNDBURN LJA
see **1725 EAST LANCASHIRE LJA**

2011 BURNLEY AND PENDLE PSA
combined with 2006 ROSSENDALE PSA to form **2014 BURNLEY, PENDLE AND ROSSENDALE PSA**

2012 BLACKBURN, DARWEN AND RIBBLE VALLEY LJA
see **1725 EAST LANCASHIRE LJA**

2014 BURNLEY, PENDLE AND ROSSENDALE LJA
see **CUMBRIA AND LANCASHIRE** ....p. 123

2038 ASHBY-DE-LA-ZOUCH DIVISION
subjected to boundary adjustment and renumbered **2047 ASHBY-DE-LA-ZOUCH DIVISION**

2039 LEICESTER (CITY) DIVISION
combined with 2040 LEICESTER (COUNTY) DIVISION to form (after boundary adjustment) **2089 LEICESTER DIVISION**

2040 LEICESTER (COUNTY) DIVISION
combined with 2039 LEICESTER (CITY) DIVISION to form (after boundary adjustment) **2089 LEICESTER DIVISION**

2041 LOUGHBOROUGH DIVISION
subjected to boundary adjustment and renumbered **2090 LOUGHBOROUGH DIVISION**

2042 LUTTERWORTH DIVISION
combined with 2044 MARKET HARBOROUGH DIVISION to form (after boundary adjustment **2051 MARKET HARBOROUGH AND LUTTERWORTH DIVISION**

2043 MARKET BOSWORTH DIVISION
subjected to boundary adjustment and renumbered **2050 MARKET BOSWORTH DIVISION**

2044 MARKET HARBOROUGH DIVISION
combined with 2042 LUTTERWORTH DIVISION to form (after boundary adjustment) **2051 MARKET HARBOROUGH AND LUTTERWORTH DIVISION**

2045 MELTON AND BELVOIR DIVISION
combined with 2046 RUTLAND DIVISION to form **2045 MELTON, BELVOIR AND RUTLAND DIVISION**

2045 MELTON, BELVOIR AND RUTLAND LJA
CLOSED wef 31/7/11

2046 RUTLAND DIVISION
combined with 2045 MELTON AND BELVOIR DIVISION to form **2045 MELTON, BELVOIR AND RUTLAND DIVISION**

2047 ASHBY-DE-LA-ZOUCH LJA
CLOSED wef 7/11

2089 LEICESTER LJA
see **LEICESTERSHIRE, RUTLAND, LINCOLNSHIRE, NORTHAMPTONSHIRE** ....p. 109

2090 LOUGHBOROUGH LJA
see **LEICESTERSHIRE, RUTLAND, LINCOLNSHIRE, NORTHAMPTONSHIRE** ....p. 109

2050 MARKET BOSWORTH LJA
see **LEICESTERSHIRE, RUTLAND, LINCOLNSHIRE, NORTHAMPTONSHIRE** ....p. 109

2051 MARKET HARBOROUGH AND LUTTERWORTH LJA
CLOSED wef 31/7/11

2053 ALFORD DIVISION
combined with 2064 LOUTH DIVISION and 2067 SPILSBY DIVISION to form **2070 LOUTH DIVISION and 2071 SPILSBY AND SKEGNESS DIVISION**

2054 BOSTON DIVISION
subjected to boundary adjustments and renumbered **2073 BOSTON DIVISION**

2055 BOURNE DIVISION
combined with 2068 STAMFORD DIVISION to form **2074 BOURNE AND STAMFORD DIVISION**

2056 CAISTOR DIVISION
*combined with 2079 LINCOLN DISTRICT DIVISION and 2081 MARKET RASEN DIVISION to form
new* **2079 LINCOLN DISTRICT DIVISION**

2057 EAST ELLOE DIVISION
combined with 2069 WEST ELLOE DIVISION to form (after boundary adjustment) **2076 ELLOES
DIVISION**

2058 GAINSBOROUGH DIVISION
subjected to boundary adjustments and renumbered **2075 GAINSBOROUGH DIVISION**

2059 GRANTHAM DIVISION
subjected to boundary adjustments and renumbered **2077 GRANTHAM DIVISION**

2060 HORNCASTLE DIVISION
combined with 2070 LOUTH DIVISION to form (after boundary adjustments) **2078 WOLDS DIVISION**

2061 LINCOLN (CITY) DIVISION
combined with 2072 LINCOLN (COUNTY) DIVISION to form (after boundary adjustments) **2079
LINCOLN DISTRICT DIVISION**

2062 LINCOLN (KESTEVEN) DIVISION
combined with 2063 LINDSEY (LINCOLN AND WRAGBY) DIVISION to form **2072 LINCOLN
(COUNTY) DIVISION**

2063 LINDSEY (LINCOLN AND WRAGBY) DIVISION
*combined with 2062 LINCOLN (KESTEVEN) DIVISION to **form** 2072 LINCOLN (COUNTY) DIVISION*

2064 LOUTH DIVISION
combined with 2053 ALFORD DIVISION and 2067 SPILSBY DIVISION to form **2070 LOUTH
DIVISION** *and* **2071 SPILSBY AND SKEGNESS DIVISION**

2065 MARKET RASEN DIVISION
subjected to boundary adjustments and renumbered **2081 MARKET RASEN DIVISION**

2066 SLEAFORD DIVISION
subjected to boundary adjustments and renumbered **2080 SLEAFORD DIVISION**

2067 SPILSBY DIVISION
combined with 2053 ALFORD DIVISION and 2064 LOUTH DIVISION to form **2070 LOUTH DIVISION**
and **2071 SPILSBY AND SKEGNESS DIVISION**

2068 STAMFORD DIVISION
combined with 2055 BOURNE DIVISION to form **2074 BOURNE AND STAMFORD** DIVISION

2069 WEST ELLOE DIVISION
combined with 2057 EAST ELLOE DIVISION to form (after boundary adjustments) **2076 ELLOES
DIVISION**

2070 LOUTH DIVISION
combined with 2060 HORNCASTLE DIVISION to form (after boundary adjustments) **2079 WOLDS
DIVISION**

2071 SPILSBY AND SKEGNESS DIVISION
subjected to boundary adjustments and renumbered **2082 SPILSBY AND SKEGNESS DIVISION**

2072 LINCOLN (COUNTY) DIVISION
combined with 2061 LINCOLN (CITY) DIVISION to form (after boundary adjustments) **2079 LINCOLN
DISTRICT DIVISION**

2073 BOSTON LJA
combined with 2082 SKEGNESS LJA to form **2085 EAST LINCOLNSHIRE LJA**

2074 BOURNE AND STAMFORD LJA
combined with ELLOES LJA to form **2076 ELLOES, BOURNE AND STAMFORD LJA**

2075 GAINSBOROUGH LJA
closed wef 31/7/11

2076 ELLOES, BOURNE AND STAMFORD LJA
combined with 2077 GRANTHAM AND SLEAFORD LJA to form **2105 SOUTH LINCOLNSHIRE LJA**

2077 GRANTHAM AND SLEAFORD LJA
combined with 2076 ELLOES, BOURNE AND STAMFORD LJA to form **2105 SOUTH LINCOLNSHIRE LJA**

2078 WOLDS DIVISION
combined with part of 2079 LINCOLN DISTRICT DIVISION to form enlarged **2078 WOLDS DIVISION**

2078 WOLDS LJA
abolished

2079 LINCOLN DISTRICT DIVISION
part combined with 2078 WOLDS DIVISION to form enlarged 2078 WOLDS DIVISION; remainder combined with 2056 CAISTOR DIVISION and 2081 MARKET RASEN DIVISION to form new **2079 LINCOLN DISTRICT DIVISON**

2079 LINCOLN DISTRICT LJA
now **2083 NORTH WEST LINCOLNSHIRE LJA**

2080 SLEAFORD LJA
combined with GRANTHAM LJA to form **2077 GRANTHAM AND SLEAFORD LJA**

2081 MARKET RASEN DIVISION
combined with 2056 CAISTOR DIVISION and 2079 LINCOLN DISTRICT DIVISION to form new **2079 LINCOLN DISTRICT DIVISION**

2082 SPILSBY AND SKEGNESS DIVISION
renamed **SKEGNESS DIVISION** *– see* **EAST MIDLANDS**

2082 SKEGNESS LJA
combined with 2073 BOSTON LJA to form **2085 EAST LINCOLNSHIRE LJA**

2083 NORTH WEST LINCOLNSHIRE LJA
see **LEICESTERSHIRE, RUTLAND, LINCOLNSHIRE, NORTHAMPTONSHIRE** ....p. 109

2105 SOUTH LINCOLNSHIRE LJA
see **LEICESTERSHIRE, RUTLAND, LINCOLNSHIRE, NORTHAMPTONSHIRE** ....p. 109

2085 EAST LINCOLNSHIRE LJA
see **LEICESTERSHIRE, RUTLAND, LINCOLNSHIRE, NORTHAMPTONSHIRE** ....p. 109

2266 KNOWSLEY LJA
CLOSED wef 12/11

2267 LIVERPOOL LJA
see **1730 LIVERPOOL AND KNOWSLEY LJA**

2268 ST HELENS LJA
see **CHESHIRE AND MERSEYSIDE** ....p. 121

2269 NORTH SEFTON DISTRICT LJA
CLOSED wef 9/11

2270 SOUTH SEFTON DISTRICT LJA
see **1728 SEFTON LJA**

2271 WIRRAL LJA
see **CHESHIRE AND MERSEYSIDE** ....p. 121

2320 BRACKLEY DIVISION
now amalgamated with **2327 TOWCESTER DIVISION**

2321 CORBY LJA
see **LEICESTERSHIRE, RUTLAND, LINCOLNSHIRE, NORTHAMPTONSHIRE** ....p. 109

2322 DAVENTRY LJA
CLOSED wef 31/3/11

2323 KETTERING LJA
see **LEICESTERSHIRE, RUTLAND, LINCOLNSHIRE, NORTHAMPTONSHIRE** ....p. 109

2324 MID NORTHANTS DIVISION
part amalgamated with **2322 DAVENTRY DIVISION**: *– part amalgamated with* 2327 **TOWCESTER DIVISION**

2325 NORTHAMPTON LJA
see LEICESTERSHIRE, RUTLAND, LINCOLNSHIRE, NORTHAMPTONSHIRE ....p. 109

2326 OUNDLE AND THRAPSTON DIVISION
part amalgamated with **2321 CORBY DIVISION**: – *part amalgamated with* **2323 KETTERING DIVISION**: – *part amalgamated with* **2328 WELLINGBOROUGH DIVISION**

2327 TOWCESTER LJA
CLOSED wef 31/3/11

2328 WELLINGBOROUGH LJA
see LEICESTERSHIRE, RUTLAND, LINCOLNSHIRE, NORTHAMPTONSHIRE ....p. 109

2335 BAMBURGH WARD DIVISION
combined with **2339 EAST COQUETDALE WARD DIVISION** *to form* **2345 BAMBURGH AND EAST COQUETDALE DIVISION**

2336 BELLINGHAM DIVISION
combined with **2341 HEXHAM DIVISION** *to form* **2346 TYNEDALE DIVISION**

2337 BERWICK-UPON-TWEED DIVISION
combined with **2340 GLENDALE WARD DIVISION** *to form* **2348 BERWICK-UPON-TWEED DIVISION**

2338 BLYTH VALLEY DIVISION
combined with **2342 MORPETH WARD DIVISION** *and* **2343 WANSBECK DIVISION** *to form* **2352 SOUTH EAST NORTHUMBERLAND DIVISION**

2339 EAST COQUETDALE WARD DIVISION
combined with **2335 BAMBURGH WARD DIVISION** *to form* **2345 BAMBURGH AND EAST COQUETDALE DIVISION**

2340 GLENDALE WARD DIVISION
combined with **2337 BERWICK-UPON-TWEED DIVISION** *to form* **2348 BERWICK-UPON-TWEED DIVISION**

2341 HEXHAM DIVISION
combined with **2336 BELLINGHAM DIVISION** *to form* **2346 TYNEDALE DIVISION**

2342 MORPETH WARD DIVISION
combined with **2338 BLYTH VALLEY DIVISION** *and* **2343 WANSBECK DIVISION** *to form* **2352 SOUTH EAST NORTHUMBERLAND DIVISION**

2343 WANSBECK DIVISION
combined with **2338 BLYTH VALLEY DIVISION** *and* **2342 MORPETH WARD DIVISION** *to form* **2352 SOUTH EAST NORTHUMBERLAND DIVISION**

2344 WEST COQUETDALE WARD DIVISION
combined with **2345 BAMBURGH AND EAST COQUETDALE DIVISION** *to form* **2347 COQUETDALE DIVISION**

2345 BAMBURGH AND EAST COQUETDALE DIVISION
combined with **2344 WEST COQUETDALE WARD DIVISION** *to form* **2347 COQUETDALE DIVISION**

2346 TYNEDALE LJA
CLOSED wef 31/3/11

2347 ALNWICK LJA
CLOSED wef 31/3/11

2348 BERWICK-UPON-TWEED LJA
see NORTHUMBRIA ....p. 119

2352 SOUTH EAST NORTHUMBERLAND LJA
see NORTHUMBRIA ....p. 119

2353 SOUTH EAST YORKSHIRE LJA
see HUMBER AND SOUTH YORKSHIRE ....p. 115

2522 ALLERTONSHIRE DIVISION
combined with 2523 BIRDFORTH DIVISION, 2528 GILLING EAST DIVISION (part), 2529 HALLIKELD DIVISION, 2530 HANG EAST DIVISION (part) and 2539 STOKESLEY DIVISION to form **2543 NORTHALLERTON DIVISION**

2523 BIRDFORTH DIVISION
combined with 2522 ALLERTONSHIRE DIVISION, 2528 GILLING EAST DIVISION (part), 2529 HALLIKELD DIVISION, 2530 HANG EAST DIVISION (part) and 2539 STOKESLEY DIVISION to form **2543 NORTHALLERTON DIVISION**

2524 BUCKROSE DIVISION
combined with 2542 MALTON DIVISION

2525 BULMER EAST DIVISION
combined with 2526 BULMER WEST DIVISION to form **2544 EASINGWOLD DIVISION**

2526 BULMER WEST DIVISION
combined with 2525 BULMER EAST DIVISION to form **2544 EASINGWOLD DIVISION**

2527 CLARO DIVISION
abolished wef 1/1/97 and, after adjustment of boundaries with 2357 YORK division, reformed without change of Court Code Number.

2527 CLARO DIVISION
combined with 2534 RIPON LIBERTY DIVISION, 2534 NORTHALLERTON DIVISION (part) and 2537 SELBY DIVISION (Parish of Wighill only) to form **2358 HARROGATE DIVISION**

2358 HARROGATE AND SKIPTON LJA
see **NORTH AND WEST YORKSHIRE** ....p. 117

2528 GILLING EAST DIVISION
part combined with 2522 ALLERTONSHIRE DIVISION, 2523 BIRDFORTH DIVISION, 2529 HALLIKELD DIVISION, 2530 HANG EAST DIVISION (part) and 2539 STOKESLEY DIVISION to form **2543 NORTHALLERTON DIVISION**: – part combined with 2530 HANG EAST DIVISION (part), 2531 HANG WEST DIVISION and 2533 RICHMOND AND GILLING WEST DIVISION to form **2545 RICHMOND DIVISION**

2529 HALLIKELD DIVISION
combined with 2522 ALLERTONSHIRE DIVISION, 2523 BIRDFORTH DIVISION, 2528 GILLING EAST DIVISION (part), 2530 HANG EAST DIVISION (part) and 2539 STOKESLEY DIVISION to form **2543 NORTHALLERTON DIVISION**

2530 HANG EAST DIVISION
part combined with 2522 ALLERTONSHIRE DIVISION, 2523 BIRDFORTH DIVISION, 2528 GILLING EAST DIVISION (part), 2529 HALLIKELD DIVISION and 2539 STOKESLEY DIVISION to form **2543 NORTHALLERTON DIVISION**: – part combined with 2528 GILLING EAST DIVISION (part), 2531 HANG WEST DIVISION and 2533 RICHMOND AND GILLING WEST DIVISION to form **2545 RICHMOND DIVISION**

2531 HANG WEST DIVISION
combined with 2528 GILLING EAST DIVISION (part), 2530 HANG EAST DIVISION (part), and 2533 RICHMOND AND GILLING WEST DIVISION to form **2545 RICHMOND DIVISION**

2533 RICHMOND AND GILLING WEST DIVISION
combined with 2528 GILLING EAST DIVISION (part), 2530 HANG EAST DIVISION (part), and 2531 HANG WEST DIVISION to form **2545 RICHMOND DIVISION**

2534 RIPON LIBERTY DIVISION
combined with 2527 CLARO DIVISION, 2543 NORTHALLERTON DIVISION (part) and 2537 SELBY DIVISION (Parish of Wighill only) to form **2358 HARROGATE DIVISION**

2535 RYEDALE DIVISION
combined with 2542 MALTON DIVISION to form **2546 RYEDALE DIVISION**

2536 SCARBOROUGH DIVISION
combined with 2540 WHITBY STRAND DIVISION, 2546 RYEDALE DIVISION and 2543 NORTHALLERTON DIVISION (part) to form **2536 SCARBOROUGH DIVISION**

2536 SCARBOROUGH LJA
see **NORTH AND WEST YORKSHIRE** ....p. 117

2537 SELBY DIVISION
abolished wef 1/1/97 and, after adjustment of boundaries with 2357 YORK DIVISION, reformed without change of Court Code Number

2537 SELBY LJA
closed wef March 2013, see **2357 YORK AND SELBY LJA**

2538 SKIPTON LJA
see **2358 HARROGATE AND SKIPTON LJA**

2539 STOKESLEY DIVISION
combined with 2522 ALLERTONSHIRE DIVISION, 2523 BIRDFORTH DIVISION, 2528 GILLING EAST DIVISION (part), 2529 HALLIKELD DIVISION and 2530 HANG EAST DIVISION (part) to form **2543 NORTHALLERTON DIVISION**

2540 WHITBY STRAND DIVISION
combined with 2536 SCARBOROUGH DIVISION, 2546 RYEDALE DIVISION and 2543 NORTHALLERTON DIVISION (part) to form **2536 SCARBOROUGH DIVISION**

2357 YORK DIVISION
abolished wef 1/1/97 and, after adjustment of boundaries with 2527 CLARO DIVISION and 2537 SELBY DIVISION and absorbing part of 2544 EASINGWOLD DIVISION, reformed without change to Court Code Number

2541 YORK LJA
see **NORTH AND WEST YORKSHIRE** ....p. 117

2542 MALTON DIVISION
combined with 2535 RYEDALE DIVISION to form **2546 RYEDALE DIVISION**

2543 NORTHALLERTON DIVISION
abolished wef 1/1/97 and reformed to include part of 2544 EASINGWOLD DIVISION, without change of Court Code Number

2543 NORTHALLERTON DIVISION
part combined with 2527 CLARO DIVISION and 2534 RIPON DIVISION and 2537 SELBY DIVISION (part) to form **2358 HARROGATE DIVISION**: *– part combined with 2536 SCARBOROUGH DIVISION, 2540 WHITBY STRAND DIVISION AND 2546 RYESDALE DIVISION to form* **2536 SCARBOROUGH DIVISION**: *– remainder combined with 2545 RICHMOND DIVISION to form* **2543 NORTHALLERTON AND RICHMOND DIVISION.**

2543 NORTHALLERTON AND RICHMOND LJA
see **NORTH AND WEST YORKSHIRE** ....p. 117

2544 EASINGWOLD DIVISION
abolished wef 1/1/97 – part combined with 2543 NORTHALLERTON DIVISION, part with 2546 RYEDALE DIVISION and part with 2357 YORK DIVISION

2545 RICHMOND DIVISION
combined with 2543 NORTHALLERTON DIVISION (part) to form **2543 NORTHALLERTON AND RICHMOND DIVISION**

2546 RYEDALE DIVISION
abolished wef 1/1/97 and reformed to include part of 2544 EASINGWOLD DIVISION, without change of Court Code Number

2546 RYEDALE DIVISION
combined with 2536 SCARBOROUGH DIVISION, 2540 WHITBY STRAND DIVISION and 2543 NORTHALLERTON DIVISION (part) to form **2536 SCARBOROUGH DIVISION**

2552 BINGHAM DIVISION
combined with 2557 NOTTINGHAM (CITY) DIVISION and 2558 NOTTINGHAM (COUNTY) DIVISION to form (after boundary adjustments) **2086 NOTTINGHAM DIVISION**

2553 EAST RETFORD PSA
combined with 2560 WORKSOP PSA to form **2087 WORKSOP AND RETFORD PSA**

2554 MANSFIELD (BOROUGH) DIVISION
combined with 2555 MANSFIELD (COUNTY) DIVISION to form **2087 MANSFIELD DIVISION**

2555 MANSFIELD (COUNTY) DIVISION
combined with 2554 MANSFIELD (BOROUGH) DIVISION to form **2087 MANSFIELD DIVISION**

2556 NEWARK DIVISION
combined with 2559 SOUTHWELL DIVISION to form **2567 NEWARK AND SOUTHWELL DIVISION**

2557 NOTTINGHAM (CITY) DIVISION
combined with 2552 BINGHAM DIVISION and 2558 NOTTINGHAM (COUNTY) DIVISION to form (after boundary adjustments) **2086 NOTTINGHAM DIVISION**

2558 NOTTINGHAM (COUNTY) DIVISION
combined with 2552 BINGHAM DIVISION and 2557 NOTTINGHAM (CITY) DIVISION to form (after boundary adjustments) **2086 NOTTINGHAM DIVISION**

2559 SOUTHWELL DIVISION
combined with 2556 NEWARK DIVISION to form **2567 NEWARK AND SOUTHWELL DIVISION**

2560 WORKSOP PSA
combined with 2553 EAST RETFORD PSA to form **2087 WORKSOP AND RETFORD PSA**

2087 MANSFIELD LJA
see **DERBYSHIRE AND NOTTINGHAMSHIRE** ....p. 107

2567 NEWARK AND SOUTHWELL LJA
CLOSED wef 30/9/11

2086 NOTTINGHAM LJA
see **DERBYSHIRE AND NOTTINGHAMSHIRE** ....p. 107

2087 WORKSOP AND RETFORD LJA
see **DERBYSHIRE AND NOTTINGHAMSHIRE** ....p. 107

2570 CENTRAL LONDON LJA (ADULT)
see **LONDON – CENTRAL AND SOUTH (CRIME)** ....p. 99

2571 NORTH WEST LONDON LJA (ADULT)
see **LONDON – NORTH AND WEST (CRIME)** ....p. 102

2572 NORTH LONDON LJA (ADULT)
see **LONDON – NORTH AND WEST (CRIME)** ....p. 102

2573 NORTH EAST LONDON LJA (ADULT)
see **LONDON – NORTH AND WEST (CRIME)** ....p. 102

2574 EAST LONDON LJA (ADULT)
see **LONDON – NORTH AND WEST (CRIME)** ....p. 102

2575 SOUTH EAST LONDON LJA (ADULT)
see **LONDON – CENTRAL AND SOUTH (CRIME)** ....p. 99

2576 SOUTH LONDON LJA (ADULT)
see **LONDON – CENTRAL AND SOUTH (CRIME)** ....p. 99

2577 SOUTH WEST LONDON LJA (ADULT)
see **LONDON – CENTRAL AND SOUTH (CRIME)** ....p. 99

2578 WEST LONDON LJA (ADULT)
see **LONDON – NORTH AND WEST (CRIME)** ....p. 102

2631 CITY OF LONDON MAGISTRATES' COURT
see **2570/6570 CENTRAL LONDON LJA**

2641 BOW STREET MAGISTRATES' COURT
CLOSED

2642 CLERKENWELL MAGISTRATES' COURT
CLOSED

2643 GREENWICH MAGISTRATES' COURT
see **2575/6575 SOUTH EAST LONDON LJA**

2643 WOOLWICH MAGISTRATES' COURT
CLOSED wef 1/7/11

2644 MARLBOROUGH STREET MAGISTRATES' COURT
CLOSED

2646 MARYLEBONE MAGISTRATES' COURT
CLOSED

2648 OLD STREET MAGISTRATES' COURT
CLOSED

2649 SOUTH WESTERN MAGISTRATES' COURT
see **2577/6577 SOUTH WEST LONDON LJA**

2650 THAMES MAGISTRATES' COURT
see **2574/6574 EAST LONDON LJA**

2651 TOWER BRIDGE MAGISTRATES' COURT
CLOSED wef 2013

2652 WEST LONDON M.C.
combined with 2657 WALTON STREET M.C. to form **2658 WEST LONDON M.C.**

2653 WOOLWICH MAGISTRATES' COURT
renumbered 2643 see **GREATER LONDON**

2655 WELLS STREET MAGISTRATES' COURT
CLOSED

2656 CAMBERWELL GREEN MAGISTRATES' COURT
see **2576/6576 SOUTH LONDON LJA**

2657 WALTON STREET M.C.
combined with 2652 WEST LONDON M.C. to form **2658 WEST LONDON M.C.**

2658 WEST LONDON MAGISTRATES' COURT
see **2578/6578 WEST LONDON LJA**

2660 HORSEFERRY ROAD MAGISTRATES' COURT
renamed **CITY OF WESTMINSTER MAGISTRATES COURT**

2660 CITY OF WESTMINSTER MAGISTRATES' COURT
see **2570/6570 CENTRAL LONDON LJA**

2663 HIGHBURY CORNER MAGISTRATES' COURT
see **2572/6572 NORTH LONDON LJA**

2665 METROPOLITAN POLICE
(Fixed Penalty)

2667 ABINGDON (BOROUGH) DIVISION
combined with 2668 ABINGDON (COUNTY) DIVISION to form **2681 ABINGDON DIVISION**

2668 ABINGDON (COUNTY) DIVISION
combined with 2667 ABINGDON (BOROUGH) DIVISION to form **2681 ABINGDON DIVISION**

2669 BAMPTON EAST DIVISION
combined with 2670 BAMPTON WEST DIVISION to form **2703 WITNEY DIVISION**

2670 BAMPTON WEST DIVISION
combined with 2669 BAMPTON EAST DIVISION to form **2703 WITNEY DIVISION**

2671 BICESTER DIVISION
subjected to boundary adjustment and renumbered **2776 BICESTER DIVISION**

2672 BULLINGDON DIVISION
combined with 2680 WATLINGTON DIVISION to form **2717 EAST OXFORDSHIRE DIVISION**

2673 CHIPPING NORTON DIVISION
combined with 2677 NORTH OXFORDSHIRE DIVISION to form **2702 NORTH OXFORDSHIRE AND CHIPPING NORTON DIVISION**

2674 FARINGDON DIVISION
combined with 2679 WANTAGE DIVISION to form **2682 WANTAGE AND FARINGDON DIVISION**

2675 HENLEY DIVISION
combined with 2717 EAST OXFORDSHIRE DIVISION to form **2719 THAME AND HENLEY DIVISION**

2676 MORETON AND WALLINGFORD DIVISION
combined with 2682 WANTAGE AND FARINGDON DIVISION to form **2718 DIDCOT AND WANTAGE DIVISION**

2677 NORTH OXFORDSHIRE DIVISION
combined with 2673 CHIPPING NORTON DIVISION to form **2702 NORTH OXFORDSHIRE AND CHIPPING NORTON DIVISION**

2678 OXFORD DIVISION
subjected to boundary adjustment and renumbered **2777 OXFORD DIVISION**

2679 WANTAGE DIVISION
combined with 2674 FARINGDON DIVISION to form **2682 WANTAGE AND FARINGDON DIVISION**

2680 WATLINGTON DIVISION
combined with 2672 BULLINGDON DIVISION to form **2717 EAST OXFORDSHIRE DIVISION**

2681 ABINGDON DIVISION
combined with 2718 DIDCOT AND WANTAGE DIVISION to form (after boundary adjustment) **2774 ABINGDON, DIDCOT AND WANTAGE DIVISION**

2682 WANTAGE AND FARINGDON DIVISION
combined with 2676 MORETON AND WALLINGFORD DIVISION to form **2718 DIDCOT AND WANTAGE DIVISION**

2701 WOODSTOCK DIVISION
abolished and absorbed into **2775 BANBURY DIVISION, 2776 BICESTER DIVISION and 2779 WITNEY DIVISION**

2702 NORTH OXFORDSHIRE AND CHIPPING NORTON DIVISION
abolished and absorbed into **2779 WITNEY DIVISION and 2775 BANBURY DIVISION**

2703 WITNEY DIVISION
subjected to boundary adjustment and renumbered **2779 WITNEY DIVISION**

2704 FROME DIVISION
combined with 2707 SHEPTON MALLET DIVISION and 2710 WELLS DIVISION to form **2715 MENDIP DIVISION**

2705 ILMINSTER DIVISION
combined with 2708 SOMERTON DIVISION, 2712 WINCANTON DIVISION and 2713 YEOVIL DIVISION to form **2714 SOUTH SOMERSET DIVISION**

2706 SEDGEMOOR LJA
CLOSED wef April 2012

2707 SHEPTON MALLET DIVISION
combined with 2704 FROME DIVISION and 2710 WELLS DIVISION to form **2715 MENDIP DIVISION**

2708 SOMERTON DIVISION
combined with 2705 ILMINSTER DIVISION, 2712 WINCANTON DIVISION and 2713 YEOVIL DIVISION to form **2714 SOUTH SOMERSET DIVISION**

2709 TAUNTON DEANE PSA
renamed **2709 TAUNTON DEANE AND WEST SOMERSET PSA**

2709 TAUNTON DEANE AND WEST SOMERSET LJA
see **1022 SOMERSET lja**

2710 WELLS DIVISION
combined with 2704 FROME DIVISION and 2707 SHEPTON MALLET DIVISION to form **2713 MENDIP DIVISION**

2711 WEST SOMERSET PSA
absorbed into 2709 TAUNTON DEANE PSA and renamed **2709 TAUNTON DEANE AND WEST SOMERSET PSA**

2712 WINCANTON DIVISION
combined with 2705 ILMINSTER DIVISION, 2708 SOMERTON DIVISION and 2713 YEOVIL DIVISION to form **2714 SOUTH SOMERSET DIVISION**

2713 YEOVIL DIVISION
combined with 2705 ILMINSTER DIVISION, 2708 SOMERTON DIVISION and 2712 WINCANTON DIVISION to form **2714 SOUTH SOMERSET DIVISION**

2714 SOUTH SOMERSET LJA
combined with 2715 MENDIP LJA to form **2716 (now 1030) SOUTH SOMERSET AND MENDIP LJA**

2715 MENDIP LJA
combined with 2714 SOUTH SOMERSET LJA to form **2716 (now 1030) SOUTH SOMERSET AND MENDIP LJA**

2716 SOUTH SOMERSET AND MENDIP LJA
see **1022 SOMERSET LJA**

2717 EAST OXFORDSHIRE DIVISION
combined with 2675 HENLEY DIVISION to form **2719 THAME AND HENLEY DIVISION**

2718 DIDCOT AND WANTAGE DIVISION
combined with 2681 ABINGDON DIVISION to form (after boundary adjustment) **2774 ABINGDON, DIDCOT AND WANTAGE DIVISION**

2719 THAME AND HENLEY DIVISION
subjected to boundary adjustment and renumbered **2778 THAME AND HENLEY DIVISION**

2721 STRATFORD MAGISTRATES' COURT
see **2574/6574 EAST LONDON LJA**

2722 WEST HAM MAGISTRATES' COURT
CLOSED

2723 ACTON MAGISTRATES' COURT
CLOSED wef 4/2011

2725 BARNET MAGISTRATES' COURT
CLOSED

2726 BRENTFORD MAGISTRATES' COURT
renumbered 2769

2727 BROMLEY MAGISTRATES' COURT
see **2575/6575 SOUTH EAST LONDON LJA**

2728 BEXLEY MAGISTRATES' COURT
see **2575/6575 SOUTH EAST LONDON LJA**

2731 WALLINGTON MAGISTRATES' COURT
combined with 2756 SUTTON M.C. to form **2733 SUTTON MAGISTRATES' COURT**

2732 CROYDON MAGISTRATES' COURT
see **2576/6576 SOUTH LONDON LJA**

2733 SUTTON MAGISTRATES' COURT
CLOSED wef 6/2011

2734 EALING MAGISTRATES' COURT
see **2578/6578 WEST LONDON LJA**

2740 HAMPSTEAD MAGISTRATES' COURT
CLOSED

2741 HENDON MAGISTRATES' COURT
see **2571/6571 NORTH WEST LONDON LJA**

2742 HARINGEY MAGISTRATES' COURT
see **2572/6572 NORTH LONDON LJA**

2755 BEACONTREE MAGISTRATES' COURT
renamed and renumbered **2815 REDBRIDGE MAGISTRATES' COURT**

2756 SUTTON MAGISTRATES' COURT
combined with 2731 WALLINGTON M.C. to form **2733 SUTTON M.C.**

2757 ENFIELD MAGISTRATES' COURT
see **2572/6572 NORTH LONDON LJA**

2760 HARROW MAGISTRATES' COURT
CLOSED wef 6/2011

2762 BRENT MAGISTRATES' COURT
see **2578/6578 WEST LONDON LJA**

2763 WIMBLEDON MAGISTRATES' COURT
see **2577/6577 SOUTH WEST LONDON LJA**

2766 UXBRIDGE MAGISTRATES' COURT
see **2578/6578 WEST LONDON LJA**

2768 RICHMOND-UPON-THAMES MAGISTRATES' COURT
see **2577/6577 SOUTH WEST LONDON LJA**

2769 FELTHAM MAGISTRATES' COURT
see **2578/6578 WEST LONDON LJA**

2769 BRENTFORD MAGISTRATES' COURT
CLOSED wef 12/2011

2770 BARNSLEY LJA
see **HUMBER AND SOUTH YORKSHIRE** ....p. 115

2771 DONCASTER LJA
see **HUMBER AND SOUTH YORKSHIRE** ....p. 115

2772 ROTHERHAM LJA
see **HUMBER AND SOUTH YORKSHIRE** ....p. 115

2773 SHEFFIELD LJA
see **HUMBER AND SOUTH YORKSHIRE** ....p. 115

2774 ABINGDON, DIDCOT AND WANTAGE DIVISION
renamed **2774 SOUTHERN OXFORDSHIRE DIVISION**

2774 SOUTHERN OXFORDSHIRE LJA
combined with **2777** *OXFORD LJA and* **2775** *NORTHERN OXFORDSHIRE LJA to form* **2777 OXFORDSHIRE LJA**

2775 NORTHERN OXFORDSHIRE LJA
combined with **2777** *OXFORD LJA and* **2774** *SOUTHERN OXFORDSHIRE LJA to form* **2777 OXFORDSHIRE LJA**

2776 BICESTER DIVISION
combined with **2775** *BANBURY DIVISION and* **2779** *WITNEY DIVISION to form* **2775 NORTHERN OXFORDSHIRE DIVISION**

2777 OXFORD DIVISION
combined with **2778** *THAME AND HENLEY DIVISION to form* **2777 OXFORD PSA**

2777 OXFORD LJA
combined with **2775** *NORTHERN OXFORDSHIRE LJA and* **2774** *SOUTHERN OXFORDSHIRE LJA to form* **2777 OXFORDSHIRE LJA**

2778 THAME AND HENLEY DIVISION
combined with **2777** *OXFORD DIVISION to form* **2777 OXFORD DIVISION**

2779 WITNEY DIVISION
combined with **2775** *BANBURY DIVISION and* **2776** *BICESTER DIVISION to form* **2775 NORTHERN OXFORDSHIRE DIVISION**

2780 BURTON-UPON-TRENT PSA
combined with **2860** *LICHFIELD AND TAMWORTH PSA to form* **2799 SOUTH EAST STAFFORDSHIRE PSA**

2781 CANNOCK DIVISION
combined with **2789** *SEISDON DIVISION to form* **2859 CANNOCK AND SEISDON DIVISION**

2782 CHEADLE DIVISION
combined with 2784 LEEK DIVISION to form **2796 STAFFORDSHIRE MOORLANDS DIVISION**

2783 ECCLESHALL DIVISION
combined with 2790 STAFFORD DIVISION, 2792 STONE DIVISION and 2794 UTTOXETER DIVISION to form **2795 MID-STAFFORDSHIRE DIVISION**

2784 LEEK DIVISION
combined with 2782 CHEADLE DIVISION to form **2796 STAFFORDSHIRE MOORLANDS DIVISION**

2785 LICHFIELD DIVISION
combined with 2793 TAMWORTH DIVISION to form **2860 LICHFIELD AND TAMWORTH DIVISION**

2786 NEWCASTLE-UNDER-LYME DIVISION
combined with 2787 PIREHILL NORTH DIVISION to form **2797 NEWCASTLE-UNDER-LYME AND PIREHILL NORTH DIVISION**

2787 PIREHILL NORTH DIVISION
combined with 2786 NEWCASTLE-UNDER-LYME DIVISION to form **2797 NEWCASTLE-UNDER-LYME AND PIREHILL NORTH DIVISION**

2788 RUGELEY DIVISION
combined with 2795 MID STAFFORDSHIRE DIVISION to form **2799 MID STAFFORDSHIRE AND RUGELEY DIVISION**

2789 SEISDON DIVISION
combined with 2781 CANNOCK DIVISION to form **2859 CANNOCK AND SEISDON DIVISION**

2790 STAFFORD DIVISION
combined with 2792 STONE DIVISION, 2783 ECCLESHALL DIVISION and 2794 UTTOXETER DIVISION to form **2795 MID-STAFFORDSHIRE DIVISION**

2791 STOKE-ON-TRENT PSA
combined with 2798 NORTH STAFFORDSHIRE PSA to form **2786 NORTH STAFFORDSHIRE PSA**

2786 NORTH STAFFORDSHIRE LJA
see **STAFFORDSHIRE AND WEST MERCIA** p. 111

2792 STONE DIVISION
combined with 2790 STAFFORD DIVISION, 2783 ECCLESHALL DIVISION and 2794 UTTOXETER DIVISION to form **2795 MID-STAFFORDSHIRE DIVISION**

2793 TAMWORTH DIVISION
combined with 2785 LICHFIELD DIVISION to form **2860 LICHFIELD AND TAMWORTH DIVISON**

2794 UTTOXETER DIVISION
combined with 2790 STAFFORD DIVISION, 2792 STONE DIVISION and 2793 ECCLESHALL DIVISION to form **2795 MID-STAFFORDSHIRE DIVISION**

2795 MID-STAFFORDSHIRE DIVISION
combined with 2788 RUGELEY DIVISION to form **2799 MID STAFFORDSHIRE AND RUGELEY DIVISION**

2796 STAFFORDSHIRE MOORLANDS DIVISION
combined with 2797 NEWCASTLE-UNDER-LYME AND PIREHILL NORTH DIVISION to form **2798 NORTH STAFFORDSHIRE DIVISION**

2797 NEWCASTLE-UNDER-LYME AND PIREHILL NORTH DIVISION
combined with 2796 STAFFORDSHIRE MOORLANDS DIVISION to form **2798 NORTH STAFFORDSHIRE DIVISION**

2798 NORTH STAFFORDSHIRE PSA
combined with 2791 STOKE-ON-TRENT PSA to form **2786 NORTH STAFFORDSHIRE PSA**

2799 MID STAFFORDSHIRE AND RUGELEY PSA
combined with 2859 CANNOCK AND SEISDON PSA to form **2799 CENTRAL AND SOUTH WEST STAFFORDSHIRE PSA**

2799 CENTRAL AND SOUTH WEST STAFFORDSHIRE LJA
see **STAFFORDSHIRE AND WEST MERCIA** p. 111

2812 KINGSTON-UPON-THAMES MAGISTRATES' COURT
CLOSED wef 6/2011

2813 WALTHAM FOREST MAGISTRATES' COURT
see **2574/6574 EAST LONDON LJA**

2814 BARKING MAGISTRATES' COURT
CLOSED wef 9/2011

2815 REDBRIDGE MAGISTRATES' COURT
see **2573/6573 NORTH EAST LONDON LJA**

2816 BECCLES DIVISION
combined with 2822 LOWESTOFT DIVISION and 2831 SAXMUNDHAM DIVISION to form **2863 NORTH EAST SUFFOLK DIVISION**

2817 BLYTHING DIVISION
combined with portions of 2819 HARTISMERE DIVISION to form **2831 SAXMUNDHAM DIVISION**

2818 FELIXSTOWE DIVISION
combined with 2829 WOODBRIDGE DIVISION to form **2861 DEBEN DIVISION**

2819 HARTISMERE DIVISION
abolished – part absorbed into **2831 SAXMUNDHAM DIVISION,** *part into* **2832 ST EDMUNDSBURY DIVISION** *and remainder into* **2833 STOW DIVISION**

2820 IPSWICH DIVISION
combined with 2824 ORWELL DIVISION to form **2830 IPSWICH DIVISION**

2821 LACKFORD DIVISION
renamed **MILDENHALL DIVISION** *– see below*

2821 MILDENHALL DIVISION
combined with 2923 NEWMARKET DIVISION to form **2862 NORTH WEST SUFFOLK DIVISION**

2822 LOWESTOFT DIVISION
combined with 2816 BECCLES DIVISION and 2831 SAXMUNDHAM DIVISION to form **2863 NORTH EAST SUFFOLK DIVISION**

2823 NEWMARKET DIVISION
combined with 2021 MILDENHALL DIVISION to for **2862 NORTH WEST SUFFOLK DIVISION**

2824 ORWELL DIVISION
combined with 2820 IPSWICH DIVISION to form **2830 IPSWICH DIVISION**

2825 HAVERHILL DIVISION (FORMERLY RISBRIDGE DIVISION)
combined with 2828 SUDBURY DIVISION to form **2864 HAVERHILL AND SUDBURY DIVISION**

2826 ST EDMUNDSBURY DIVISION
combined with portions of 2819 HARTISMERE DIVISION to form **2832 ST EDMUNDSBURY DIVISION**

2827 STOW DIVISION
combined with portions of 2819 HARTISMERE DIVISION to form **2833 STOW DIVISION (now** *renamed* **STOWMARKET DIVISION)**

2828 SUDBURY DIVISION (FORMERLY SUDBURY AND COSFORD DIVISION)
combined with 2825 HAVERHILL DIVISION to form **2864 HAVERHILL AND SUDBURY DIVISION**

2829 WOODBRIDGE DIVISION
combined with 2818 FELIXSTOWE DIVISION to form **2861 DEBEN DIVISION**

2830 IPSWICH PSA
combined with 2861 DEBEN PSA to form **2866 SOUTH EAST SUFFOLK PSA**

2831 SAXMUNDHAM DIVISION
combined with 2816 BECCLES DIVISION and 2822 LOWESTOFT DIVISION to form **2863 NORTH EAST SUFFOLK DIVISION**

2832 ST EDMUNDSBURY DIVISION
combined with 2833 STOWMARKET DIVISION to form **2865 ST EDMUNDSBURY AND STOWMARKET DIVISION**

2833 STOWMARKET DIVISION (FORMERLY STOW DIVISION)
combined with 2932 ST EDMUNDSBURY DIVISION to form **2865 ST EDMUNDSBURY AND STOWMARKET DIVISION**

2835 CHERTSEY DIVISION
combined with 2844 WOKING DIVISION (after boundary adjustment and including parts of 2838 ESHER AND WALTON DIVISION and 2839 FARNHAM DIVISION) to form **2846 NORTH WEST SURREY DIVISION**

2836 DORKING DIVISION
combined with 2840 GODSTONE DIVISION and 2842 REIGATE DIVISION to form **2847 SOUTH EAST SURREY DIVISION**

2837 EPSOM DIVISION
combined with 2843 STAINES AND SUNBURY DIVISION and part of 2838 EASHER AND WALTON DIVISION to form **2845 NORTH AND EAST SURREY DIVISION**

2838 ESHER AND WALTON DIVISION
now absorbed into 2845 NORTH AND EAST SURREY DIVISION and **2846 NORTH WEST SURREY DIVISION**

2839 FARNHAM DIVISION
now absorbed into 2846 NORTH WEST SURREY DIVISION and **2856 SOUTH WEST SURREY DIVISION**

2840 GODSTONE DIVISION
combined with 2836 DORKING DIVISION and 2842 REIGATE DIVISION to form **2847 SOUTH EAST SURREY DIVISION**

2841 GUILDFORD DIVISION
boundary adjusted to include part of 2844 WOKING DIVISION and part of 2839 FARNHAM DIVISION to form **2856 SOUTH WEST SURREY DIVISION**

2842 REIGATE DIVISION
combined with 2836 DORKING DIVISION and 2840 GODSTONE DIVISION to form **2847 SOUTH EAST SURREY DIVISION**

2843 STAINES AND SUNBURY DIVISION
combined with 2837 EPSOM DIVISION and part of 2838 ESHER AND WALTON DIVISION to form **2845 NORTH AND EAST SURREY DIVISION**

2844 WOKING DIVISION
(after boundary adjustment and including parts of 2838 ESHER AND WALTON DIVISION and 2839 FARNHAM DIVISION) combined with 2835 CHERTSEY DIVISION to form **2846 NORTH WEST SURREY DIVISION**

2845 NORTH AND EAST SURREY DIVISION
boundary adjusted to include part of 2846 NORTH WEST SURREY TO FORM **2841 NORTH SURREY PSA**

2846 NORTH WEST SURREY DIVISION
boundary adjusted following absorption by NORTH SURREY of part of 2846 North West Surrey to form **2857 NORTH WEST SURREY PSA**

2847 SOUTH EAST SURREY DIVISION
boundary adjusted to include part of 2845 NORTH AND EAST SURREY to form **2856 SOUTH EAST SURREY PSA**

2853 SOUTH TYNESIDE DISTRICT LJA
see **NORTHUMBRIA** ....p. 119

2854 HOUGHTON-LE-SPRING LJA
CLOSED wef 31/3/11

2855 SUNDERLAND LJA
see **NORTHUMBRIA** ....p. 119

2856 SOUTH EAST SURREY LJA
see **SURREY AND SUSSEX** ....p. 133

2857 NORTH WEST SURREY LJA
CLOSED wef 31/12/11

2859 CANNOCK AND SEISDON PSA
combined with 2799 MID STAFFORDSHIRE AND RUGELEY PSA to form **2799 CENTRAL AND SOUTH WEST STAFFORDSHIRE PSA**

2860 LICHFIELD AND TAMWORTH PSA
combined with 2780 BURONT-UPON-TRENT PSA to form **2860 SOUTH EAST STAFFORDSHIRE PSA**

2799 SOUTH EAST STAFFORDSHIRE LJA
see **STAFFORDSHIRE AND WEST MERCIA** ....p. 111

2861 DEBEN PSA
combined with 2830 IPSWICH PSA to form **2866 SOUTH EAST SUFFOLK PSA**

2862 NORTH WEST SUFFOLK PSA
combined with 2864 HAVERHILL AND SUDBURY PSA and 2865 ST EDMUNDSBURY AND STOWMARKET PSA to form **2867 WEST SUFFOLK PSA**

2863 NORTH EAST SUFFOLK LJA
see **NORFOLK AND SUFFOLK** ....p. 132

2864 HAVERHILL AND SUDBURY PSA
combined with 2862 NORTH WEST SUFFOLK PSA and 2865 ST EDMUNDSBURY AND STOWMARKET PSA to form **2867 WEST SUFFOLK PSA**

2865 ST EDMUNDSBURY AND STOWMARKET PSA
combined with 2862 NORTH WEST SUFFOLK PSA and 2864 HAVERHILL AND SUDBURY PSA to form **2867 WEST SUFFOLK PSA**

2866 SOUTH EAST SUFFOLK LJA
see **NORFOLK AND SUFFOLK** ....p. 132

2867 WEST SUFFOLK LJA
see **NORFOLK AND SUFFOLK** ....p. 132

2893 ALCESTER DIVISION
combined with 2895 KINETON DIVISION, 2898 SHIPSTON-ON-STOUR DIVISION and 2900 STRATFORD-UPON-AVON DIVISION to form **2902 SOUTH WARWICKSHIRE DIVISION**

2894 ATHERSTONE AND COLESHILL PSA
combined with 2896 NENEATON PSA, 2897 RUGBY PSA, 2902 SOUTH WARWICKSHIRE PSA and 2903 MID-WARWICKSHIRE PSA to form **2905 WARWICKSHIRE PSA**

2895 KINETON DIVISION
combined with 2893 ALCESTER DIVISION, 2898 SHIPSTON-ON-STOUR DIVISION and 2900 STRATFORD-UPON-AVON DIVISION to form **2902 SOUTH WARWICKSHIRE DIVISION**

2896 NUNEATON PSA
combined with 2894 ATHERSTONE AND COLESHILL PSA, 2897 RUGBY PSA, 2902 SOUTH WARWICKSHIRE PSA and 2903 MID-WARWICKSHIRE PSA to form **2905 WARWICKSHIRE PSA**

2897 RUGBY PSA
combined with 2894 ATHERSTONE AND COLESHILL PSA, 2896 NUNEATON PSA, 2902 SOUTH WARWICKSHIRE PSA and 2903 MID-WARWICKSHIRE PSA to form **2905 WARWICKSHIRE PSA**

2898 SHIPSTON-ON-STOUR DIVISION
combined with 2893 ALCESTER DIVISION, 2895 KINETON DIVISION and 2900 STRATFORD-UPON-AVON DIVISION to form **2902 SOUTH WARWICKSHIRE DIVISION**

2899 SOUTHAM DIVISION
combined with 2901 WARWICK DIVISION to form **2903 MID-WARWICKSHIRE DIVISION**

2900 STRATFORD-UPON-AVON DIVISION
combined with 2893 ALCESTER DIVISION, 2895 KINETON DIVISION and 2898 SHIPSTON-ON-STOUR DIVISION to form **2902 SOUTH WARWICKSHIRE DIVISION**

2901 WARWICK DIVISION
combined with 2899 SOUTHAM DIVISION to form **2903 MID-WARWICKSHIRE DIVISION**

2902 SOUTH WARWICKSHIRE PSA
combined with 2894 ATHERSTONE AND COLESHILL PSA, 2896 NUNEATON PSA, 2897 RUGBY PSA and 2903 MID-WARWICKSHIRE PSA to form **2905 WARWICKSHIRE PSA**

2903 MID-WARWICKSHIRE PSA
combined with 2894 ATHERSTONE AND COLESHILL PSA, 2896 NUNEATON PSA, 2897 RUGBY PSA and 2902 SOUTH WARWICKSHIRE PSA to form **2905 WARWICKSHIRE PSA**

2905 WARWICKSHIRE LJA
see **WEST MIDLANDS AND WARWICKSHIRE** ....p. 112

2922 BIRMINGHAM LJA
see **WEST MIDLANDS AND WARWICKSHIRE** ....p. 112

2909 SUTTON COLDFIELD LJA
CLOSED wef 30/6/11

2910 COVENTRY DISTRICT LJA
see **WEST MIDLANDS AND WARWICKSHIRE** ....p. 112

2911 DUDLEY LJA
combined with 2912 STOURBRIDGE AND HALESOWEN LJA to form **2911 DUDLEY AND HALESOWEN LJA**

2912 HALESOWEN DIVISION
combined with 2913 STOURBRIDGE DIVISION to form **2912 STOURBRIDGE AND HALESOWEN DIVISION**

2912 STOURBRIDGE AND HALESOWEN LJA
combined with 2911 DUDLEY LJA to form **2911 DUDLEY AND HALESOWEN LJA**

2913 STOURBRIDGE DIVISION
combined with 2912 HALESOWEN DIVISION to form **2912 STOURBRIDGE AND HALESOWEN DIVISION**

2914 WARLEY LJA
combined with 2915 WEST BROMWICH LJA to form **2914 SANDWELL LJA**

2915 WEST BROMWICH LJA
combined with 2914 WARLEY LJA to form **2914 SANDWELL LJA**

2916 SOLIHULL LJA
see **WEST MIDLANDS AND WARWICKSHIRE** ....p. 112

2917 WALSALL AND ALDRIDGE LJA
see **WEST MIDLANDS AND WARWICKSHIRE** ....p. 112

2918 WALSALL LJA
combined with 2917 ALDRIDGE AND BROWNHILLS PSA to form **2917 WALSALL AND ALDRIDGE LJA**

2919 WOLVERHAMPTON LJA
see **WEST MIDLANDS AND WARWICKSHIRE** ....p. 112

2914 SANDWELL LJA
see **WEST MIDLANDS AND WARWICKSHIRE** ....p. 112

2911 DUDLEY AND HALESOWEN LJA
see **WEST MIDLANDS AND WARWICKSHIRE** ....p. 112

2927 ARUNDEL PSA
combined with 2937 WORTHING AND DISTRICT PSA and 2936 CHICHESTER AND DISTRICT PSA to form **2949 SUSSEX (WESTERN) PSA**

2928 CHICHESTER DIVISION
combined with 2931 MIDHURST DIVISION and 2933 PETWORTH DIVISION to form **2936 CHICHESTER AND DISTRICT DIVISION**

2929 CRAWLEY PSA
combined with 2930 HORSHAM PSA and 2932 MID-SUSSEX PSA to form **2947 SUSSEX (NORTHERN) PSA**

2930 HORSHAM PSA
combined with 2929 CRAWLEY PSA and 2932 MID-SUSSEX PSA to form **2947 SUSSEX (NORTHERN) PSA**

2931 MIDHURST DIVISION
combined with 2928 CRAWLEY PSA and 2930 HORSHAM DIVISION to form **2947 SUSSEX (NORTHERN) PSA**

2932 MID-SUSSEX PSA
combined with 2929 CRAWLEY PSA and 2930 HORSHAM DIVISION to form **2947 SUSSEX (NORTHERN) PSA**

2933 PETWORTH DIVISION
combined with 2928 CHICHESTER DIVISION and 2931 MIDHURST DIVISION to form **2936 CHICHESTER AND DISTRICT DIVISION**

2934 STEYNING DIVISION
abolished w.e.f. 1 April 1996 and absorbed into **2930 HORSHAM DIVISION and 2937 WORTHING AND DISTRICT DIVISION**

2935 WORTHING DIVISION
abolished w.e.f. 1 April 1996 and after adjustment of boundaries reconstituted as **2937 WORTHING AND DISTRICT DIVISION**

2936 CHICHESTER AND DISTRICT PSA
combined with 2927 ARUNDEL PSA and 2937 WORTHING AND DISTRICT PSA to form **2949 SUSSEX (WESTERN) PSA**

2937 WORTHING AND DISTRICT PSA
combined with 2927 ARUNDEL PSA and 2936 CHICHESTER AND DISTRICT PSA to form **2949 SUSSEX (WESTERN) PSA**

2947 SUSSEX (NORTHERN) LJA
see **SURREY AND SUSSEX** ....p. 133

2948 SUSSEX (EASTERN) LJA
see **SURREY AND SUSSEX** ....p. 133

2949 SUSSEX (WESTERN) LJA
see **SURREY AND SUSSEX** ....p. 133

2950 SUSSEX (CENTRAL) LJA
see **SURREY AND SUSSEX** ....p. 133

2354 BRADFORD AND KEIGHLEY LJA
see **NORTH AND WEST YORKSHIRE** ....p. 117

2979 KEIGHLEY LJA
CLOSED wef 4/12

2980 BRIGHOUSE DIVISION
combined with 2984 CALDER DIVISION and 2983 TODMORDEN DIVISION to form **2997 CALDERDALE DIVISION**

2981 CALDER DIVISION
combined with 2982 HALIFAX DIVISION to form **2984 CALDERDALE DIVISION**

2982 HALIFAX DIVISION
combined with 2981 CALDER DIVISION to form **2984 CALDER DIVISION**

2983 TODMORDEN DIVISION
combined with 2980 BRIGHOUSE DIVISION and 2984 CALDER DIVISION to form **2997 CALDERDALE DIVISION**

2984 CALDER DIVISION
combined with 2980 BRIGHOUSE DIVISION and 2983 TODMORDEN DIVISION to form **2997 CALDERDALE DIVISION**

2985 BATLEY DIVISION
combined with 2986 DEWSBURY DIVISION to form **2996 BATLEY AND DEWSBURY DIVISION**

2986 DEWSBURY DIVISION
combined with 2985 BATLEY DIVISION to form **2996 BATLEY AND DEWSBURY DIVISION**

2987 KIRKLEES LJA
see **NORTH AND WEST YORKSHIRE** ....p. 117

2988 LEEDS PSA
combined with 2989 MORLEY PSA, 2990 PUDSEY AND OTLEY PSA and 2991 SKYRACK AND WETHERBY PSA to form **2992 LEEDS DISTRICT PSA**

2989 MORLEY PSA
combined with 2988 LEEDS PSA, 2990 PUDSEY AND OTLEY PSA, and 2991 SKYRACK AND WETHERBY PSA to form **2992 LEEDS DISTRICT PSA**

2990 PUDSEY AND OTLEY PSA
combined with 2988 LEEDS PSA, 2989 MORLEY PSA and 2991 SKYRACK AND WETHERBY PSA to form **2992 LEEDS DISTRICT PSA**

2991 SKYRACK AND WETHERBY PSA
combined with 2988 LEEDS PSA, 2989 MORLEY PSA, 2990 PUDSEY AND OTLEY PSA to form **2992 LEEDS DISTRICT PSA**

2992 LEEDS DISTRICT LJA
see **NORTH AND WEST YORKSHIRE** ....p. 117

2994 PONTEFRACT LJA
closed wef March 2013, see **2355 WAKEFIELD AND PONTEFRACT LJA** ....p. 118

2355 WAKEFIELD AND PONTEFRACT LJA
see **NORTH AND WEST YORKSHIRE** ....p. 117

2996 BATLEY AND DEWSBURY LJA
CLOSED wef 4/12

2997 CALDERDALE LJA
see **NORTH AND WEST YORKSHIRE** p. 117

3005 BRADFORD-ON-AVON DIVISION
combined with 3013 MELKSHAM DIVISION, 3017 TROWBRIDGE DIVISION, 3018 WARMINSTER DIVISION (most), 3019 WESTBURY DIVISION and 3020 WHORWELLSDOWN DIVISION to form **3024 WEST WILTSHIRE DIVISION**

3006 CALNE DIVISION
combined with 3007 CHIPPENHAM DIVISION, 3008 CRICKLADE DIVISION and 3011 MALMESBURY DIVISION to form **3022 NORTH WILTSHIRE DIVISION**

3007 CHIPPENHAM DIVISION
combined with 3006 CALNE DIVISION, 3008 CRICKLADE DIVISION and 3011 MALMESBURY DIVISION to form **3022 NORTH WILTSHIRE DIVISION**

3008 CRICKLADE DIVISION
combined with 3006 CALNE DIVISION, 3007 CHIPPENHAM DIVISION and 3011 MALMESBURY DIVISION to form **3022 NORTH WILTSHIRE DIVISION**

3009 DEVIZES DIVISION
(most) combined with 3010 EVERLEY AND PEWSEY DIVISION (most) and 3011 MARLBOROUGH DIVISION to form **3025 KENNET DIVISION**

3010 EVERLEY AND PEWSEY DIVISION
(most) combined with 3009 DEVIZES DIVISION (most) and 3011 MARLBOROUGH DIVISION to form **3025 KENNET DIVISION**

3011 MALMESBURY DIVISION
combined with 3006 CALNE DIVISION, 3007 CHIPPENHAM DIVISION and 3008 CRICKLADE DIVISION to form **3022 WILTSHIRE DIVISION**

3012 MARLBOROUGH DIVISION
combined with 3009 DEVIZES DIVISION (most) and 3010 EVERLEY AND PEWSEY DIVISION (most) to form **3025 KENNET DIVISION**

3013 MELKSHAM DIVISION
combined with 3005 BRADFORD-ON-AVON DIVISION, 3017 TROWBRIDGE DIVISION, 3016 WARMINSTER DIVISION (most), 3019 WESTBURY DIVISION and 3020 WHORWELLSDOWN DIVISION to form **3024 WEST WILTSHIRE DIVISION**

3014 SALISBURY DIVISION
combined with 3018 TISBURY AND MERE DIVISION and parts of 3009 DEVIZES DIVISION, 3010 EVERLEY AND PEWSEY DIVISION and 3018 WARMINSTER DIVISION to form **3023 SALISBURY DIVISION**

3015 SWINDON LJA
see **3015 WILTSHIRE** ....p. 141

3016 TISBURY AND MERE DIVISION
combined with 3014 SALISBURY DIVISION and parts of 3009 DEVIZES DIVISION, 3010 EVERLEY AND PEWSEY DIVISION and 3018 WARMINSTER DIVISION to form **3023 SALISBURY DIVISION**

3017 TROWBRIDGE DIVISION
combined with 3005 BRADFORD-ON-AVON DIVISION, 3013 MELKSHAM DIVISION, 3018 WARMINSTER DIVISION (most), 3019 WESTBURY DIVISION and 3020 WHORWELLSDOWN DIVISION to form **3024 WEST WILTSHIRE DIVISION**

3018 WARMINSTER DIVISION
combined with 3005 BRADFORD-ON-AVON DIVISION, 3013 MELKSHAM DIVISION, 3017 TROWBRIDGE DIVISION, 3019 WESTBURY DIVISION and 3020 WHORWELLSDOWN DIVISION to form **3024 WEST WILTSHIRE DIVISION**

3019 WESTBURY DIVISION
combined with 3005 BRADFORD-ON-AVON DIVISION, 3013 MELKSHAM DIVISION, 3017 TROWBRIDGE DIVISION, 3018 WARMINSTER DIVISION (most) and 3020 WHORWELLSDOWN DIVISION to form **3024 WEST WILTSHIRE DIVISION**

3020 WHORWELLSDOWN DIVISION
combined with 3005 BRADFORD-ON-AVON DIVISION, 3013 MELKSHAM DIVISION, 3017 TROWBRIDGE DIVISION 3018 WARMINSTER DIVISION (most) and 3019 WESTBURY DIVISION to form **3024 WEST WILTSHIRE DIVISION**

3015 WILTSHIRE LJA
see **HAMPSHIRE, ISLE OF WIGHT AND WILTSHIRE** ....p. 140

3022 NORTH WILTSHIRE DIVISION
combined with 3024 WEST WILTSHIRE DIVISION to form **3026 NORTH WEST WILTSHIRE DIVISION**

3023 SALISBURY DIVISION
combined with 3025 KENNET DIVISION to form **3027 SOUTH EAST WILTSHIRE DIVISION**

3024 WEST WILTSHIRE DIVISION
combined with 3022 NORTH WILTSHIRE DIVISION to form **3026 NORTH WEST WILTSHIRE DIVISION**

3025 KENNET DIVISION
combined with 3023 SALISBURY DIVISION to form **3027 SOUTH EAST WILTSHIRE DIVISION**

3026 NORTH WEST WILTSHIRE LJA
see **3015 WILTSHIRE** ....p. 141

3027 SOUTH EAST WILTSHIRE LJA
see **3015 WILTSHIRE** ....p. 141

3282 TELFORD AND SOUTH SHROPSHIRE LJA
see **STAFFORDSHIRE AND WEST MERCIA** ....p. 111

WALES

3051 BERWYN DIVISION
abolished – functions transferred to 3052 COLWYN DIVISION, 3061 DENBIGHSHIRE DIVISION or
3058 WREXHAM MAELOR DIVISION

3052 COLWYN PSA
combined with 3237 ABERCONWY PSA to form **3062 CONWY PSA**

3053 DYFFRYN CLWYD DIVISION
part transferred to 3052 COLWYN DIVISION, remainder combined with 3057 RHUDDLAN DIVISION,
3051 BERWYN DIVISION (Part) and 3052 COLWYN DIVISION (Part) to form **3061 DENBIGHSHIRE**
DIVISION

3054 FLINT DIVISION
combined with 3055 HAWARDEN DIVISION, and 3056 MOLD DIVISION to form (after boundary
adjustment) **3059 FLINTSHIRE DIVISION**

3055 HAWARDEN DIVISION
combined with 3054 FLINT DIVISION and 3056 MOLD DIVISION to form (after boundary adjustment)
3059 FLINTSHIRE DIVISION

3056 MOLD DIVISION
combined with 3054 FLINT DIVISION, and 3055 HAWARDEN DIVISION to form (after boundary
adjustment) **3059 FLINTSHIRE DIVISION**

3057 RHUDDLAN DIVISION
combined with 3053 DYFFRYN CLWYD DIVISION (Part), 3051 BERWYN DIVISION (Part) and 3052
COLWYN DIVISION (Part) to form **3061 DENBIGHSHIRE DIVISION**

3058 WREXHAM MAELOR LJA
see **NORTH WALES** ....p. 144

3059 FLINTSHIRE LJA
see **NORTH WALES** ....p. 144

3060 ARFON PSA
combined with 3236 DWYFOR PSA and 3239 MEIRIONNYDD PSA to form **3244 GWYNEDD PSA**

3061 DENBIGHSHIRE LJA
see **NORTH WALES** p.144

3062 CONWY LJA
see **NORTH WALES** ....p. 144

3109 ABERAERON DIVISION
combined with 3118 LAMPETER DIVISION and 3121 LLANDYSSUL DIVISION to form **3134**
CEREDIGION GANOL DIVISION

3110 ABERYSTWYTH DIVISION
combined with 3131 TREGARON DIVISION to form **3135 GOGLEDD CEREDIGION DIVISION**

3111 AMMAN VALLEY DIVISION
combined with 3119 LLANDEILO DIVISION and 3120 LLANDOVERY DIVISION (part) to form **3140 DINEFWR DIVISION**

3112 CARDIGAN DIVISION
combined with 3128 RHYDLEWIS DIVISION to form **3136 DE CEREDIGION DIVISION**

3113 CARMARTHEN DIVISION
combined with 3129 ST CLEARS DIVISION and 3132 WHITLAND DIVISION to form **3138 CARMARTHEN SOUTH DIVISION**

3114 CEMAES DIVISION
combined with 3116 FISHGUARD DIVISION to form **3141 GOGLEDD PRESELI DIVISION**

3115 DEWSLAND DIVISION
combined with 3117 HAVERFORDWEST DIVISION to form **3133 DEWSLAND-HAVERFORDWEST DIVISION**

3116 FISHGUARD DIVISION
combined with 3114 CEMAES DIVISION to form **3141 GOGLEDD PRESELI DIVISION**

3117 HAVERFORDWEST DIVISION
combined with 3115 DEWSLAND DIVISION to form **3133 DEWSLAND-HAVERFORDWEST DIVISION**

3118 LAMPETER DIVISION
combined with 3109 ABERAERON DIVISION and 3121 LLANDYSSUL DIVISION to form **3134 CEREDIGION GANOL DIVISION**

3119 LLANDEILO DIVISION
combined with 3111 AMMAN VALLEY DIVISION and 3120 LLANDOVERY DIVISION (part) to form **3140 DINEFWR DIVISION**

3120 LLANDOVERY DIVISION
part combined with 3111 AMMAN VALLEY DIVISION and 3119 LLANDEILO DIVISION to form 3140 DINEFWR DIVISION and part combined with 3125 NEWCASTLE EMLYN DIVISION and PENCADER DIVISION to form **3137 CARMARTHEN NORTH DIVISION**

3121 LLANDYSSUL DIVISION
combined with 3109 ABERAERON DIVISION and 3118 LAMPETER DIVISION to form **3134 CEREDIGION DIVISION**

3122 LLANELLI LJA
combined with CARMARTHEN AND DINEFWR to form **3252 CARMARTHENSHIRE LJA**

3123 MILFORD HAVEN DIVISION
combined with 3133 DEWSLAND-HAVERFORDWEST DIVISION to form **3139 CLEDDAU DIVISION**

3124 NARBERTH DIVISION
combined with 3126 PEMBROKE DIVISION and 3130 TENBY DIVISION to form **3142 SOUTH PEMBROKESHIRE DIVISION**

3125 NEWCASTLE EMLYN DIVISION
combined with 3120 LLANDOVERY DIVISION (part) and 3127 PENCADER DIVISION to form **3137 CARMARTHEN NORTH DIVISION**

3126 PEMBROKE DIVISION
combined with 3124 NARBERTH DIVISION and 3130 TENBY DIVISION to form **3142 SOUTH PEMBROKESHIRE DIVISION**

3127 PENCADER DIVISION
combined with 3120 LLANDOVERY DIVISION (part) and 3125 NEWCASTLE EMLYN DIVISION to form **3137 CARMARTHEN NORTH DIVISION**

3128 RHYDLEWIS DIVISION
combined with 3112 CARDIGAN DIVISION to form **3136 DE CEREDIGION DIVISION**

3129 ST CLEARS DIVISION
combined with 3113 CARMARTHEN DIVISION and 3132 WHITLAND DIVISION to form **3138 CARMARTHEN SOUTH DIVISION**

3130 TENBY DIVISION
combined with 3124 NARBERTH DIVISION and 3126 PEMBROKE DIVISION to form **3142 PEMBROKESHIRE DIVISION**

3131 TREGARON DIVISION
combined with 3110 ABERYSTWYTH DIVISION to form **3135 GOGLEDD CEREDIGION DIVISION**

3132 WHITLAND DIVISION
combined with 3113 CARMARTHEN DIVISION and 3129 ST CLEARS DIVISION to form **3138 CARMARTHEN SOUTH DIVISION**

3133 DEWSLAND-HAVERFORDWEST DIVISION
combined with 3123 MILFORD HAVEN DIVISION to form **3139 CLEDDAU DIVISION**

3134 CEREDIGION GANOL DIVISION
combined with 3135 GOGLEDD CEREDIGION DIVISION and 3136 DE CEREDIGION DIVISION to form **3135 CEREDIGION DIVISION**

3135 GOGLEDD CEREDIGION DIVISION
combined with 3134 CEREDIGION GANOL DIVISION and 3136 DE CEREDIGION DIVISION to form **3135 CEREDIGION DIVISION**

3135 CEREDIGION LJA
combined with 3356 PEMBROKESHIRE LJA to form **3253 CEREDIGION AND PEMBROKESHIRE LJA**

3136 DE CEREDIGION DIVISION
combined with 3134 CEREDIGION GANOL DIVISION and 3135 GOGLEDD CEREDIGION DIVISION to form **3135 CEREDIGION DIVISION**

3137 CARMARTHEN NORTH DIVISION
combined with 3138 CARMARTHEN SOUTH DIVISION to form **3138 CARMARTHEN DIVISION**

3138 CARMARTHEN SOUTH DIVISION
combined with 3137 CARMARTHEN NORTH DIVISION to form **3138 CARMARTHEN DIVISION**

3138 CARMARTHEN LJA
combined with 3140 DINEFWR and LLANELLI to form **3252 CARMARTHENSHIRE LJA**

3139 CLEDDAU DIVISION
combined with 3141 GOGLEDD PRESELI DIVISION to form **3139 NORTH PEMBROKESHIRE DIVISION**

3139 NORTH PEMBROKESHIRE LJA
Combined with 3142 SOUTH PEMBROKESHIRE to form **3356 PEMBROKESHIRE LJA**

3140 DINEFWR LJA
combined with 3138 CARMARTHEN and 3122 LLANELLI to form **3252 CARMARTHENSHIRE LJA**

3141 GOGLEDD PRESELI DIVISION
combined with 3139 CLEDDAU DIVISION to form **3139 NORTH PEMBROKESHIRE DIVISION**

3142 SOUTH PEMBROKESHIRE LJA
combined with 3139 NORTH PEMBROKESHIRE to form **3356 PEMBROKESHIRE LJA**

3200 ABERGAVENNY DIVISION
combined with 3202 CWMBRAN DIVISION, 3203 CHEPSTOW DIVISION, 3204 MONMOUTH DIVISION, 3206 PONTYPOOL DIVISION and 3207 USK DIVISION to form **3208 EAST GWENT DIVISION**

3201 BEDWELLTY PSA (EXCEPT LLANELLY HILL)
combined with 3263 LOWER RHYMNEY VALLEY PSA and 3267 UPPER RHYMNEY VALLEY PSA to form **3209 NORTH WEST GWENT PSA**

3202 CWMBRAN DIVISION
combined with 3200 ABERGAVENNY DIVISION, 3203 CHEPSTOW DIVISION, 3204 MONMOUTH DIVISION, 3206 PONTYPOOL DIVISION and 3207 USK DIVISION to form **3208 EAST GWENT DIVISION**

3203 CHEPSTOW DIVISION
combined with 3200 ABERGAVENNY DIVISION, 3202 CWMBRAN DIVISION, 3204 MONMOUTH DIVISION, 3206 PONTYPOOL DIVISION and 3207 USK DIVISION to form **3208 EAST GWENT DIVISION**

3204 MONMOUTH DIVISION
combined with 3200 ABERGAVENNY DIVISION, 3202 CWMBRAN DIVISION, 3203 CHEPSTOW DIVISION, 3206 PONTYPOOL DIVISION and 3207 USK DIVISION to form **3208 EAST GWENT DIVISION**

3205 NEWPORT PSA
combined with 3208 EAST GWENT PSA (including Llanelly Hill) to form **3210 SOUTH EAST GWENT PSA**

3206 PONTYPOOL DIVISION
combined with 3200 ABERGAVENNY DIVISION, 3202 CWMBRAN DIVISION, 3203 CHEPSTOW DIVISION, 3204 MONMOUTH DIVISION and 3207 USK DIVISION to form **3208 EAST GWENT DIVISION**

3207 USK DIVISION
combined with 3200 ABERGAVENNY DIVISION, 3202 CWMBRAN DIVISION, 3203 CHEPSTOW DIVISION, 3204 MONMOUTH DIVISION AND 3206 PONTYPOOL DIVISION to form **3208 EAST GWENT DIVISION**

3208 EAST GWENT PSA (INCLUDING LLANELLY HILL)
combined with 3205 NEWPORT PSA to form **3210 SOUTH EAST GWENT PSA**

3209 NORTH WEST GWENT
combined with 3210 SOUTH EAST GWENT to form **3211 GWENT LJA**

3210 SOUTH EAST GWENT
combined with 3209 NORTH WEST GWENT to form **3211 GWENT LJA**

3211 GWENT LJA
see **SOUTH EAST WALES** ....p. 145

3220 ARDUDWY-IS-ARTRO DIVISION
combined with 3226 ESTIMANER DIVISION, 3230 PENLLYN DIVISION and 3233 TALYBONT DIVISION to form **3235 SOUTH MEIRIONNYDD DIVISION**

3221 NORTH MEIRIONNYDD DIVISION (FORMERLY ARDUDWY-UWCH-ARTRO DIVISION)
combined with 3235 SOUTH MEIRIONNYDD DIVISION to form **3239 MEIRIONNYDD DIVISION**

3222 BANGOR DIVISION
combined with 3234 CAERNARFON DIVISION to form (after boundary adjustment) **3060 ARDON DIVISION**

3223 CAERNARVON DIVISION
combined with 3227 GWYRFAI DIVISION to form **3234 CAERNARFON AND GWYRFAI DIVISION**

3224 CONWY AND LLANDUDNO DIVISION
combined with 3228 NANT CONWY DIVISION to form **3237 ABERCONWY DIVISION**

3225 EIFIONYDD DIVISION
combined with 3231 PWLLHELI DIVISION to form **3236 EIFIONYDD AND PWLLHELI DIVISION**

3226 ESTIMANER DIVISION
combined with 3220 ARDUDWY-IS-ARTRO DIVISION, 3230 PENLLYN DIVISION and 3233 TALYBONT DIVISION to form **3235 SOUTH MEIRIONNYDD DIVISION**

3227 GWYRFAI DIVISION
combined with 3223 CAERNARVON DIVISION to form **3234 CAERNARFON AND GWYRFAI DIVISION**

3228 NANT CONWY DIVISION
combined with 3224 CONWY AND LLANDUDNO DIVISION to form **3237 ABERCONWY DIVISION**

3229 NORTH ANGLESEY DIVISION
combined with 3232 SOUTH ANGLESEY DIVISION to form **3238 YNYS MON/ANGLESEY DIVISION**

3230 PENLLYN DIVISION
combined with 3220 *ARDUDWY-IS-ARTRO DIVISION, 3226 ESTIMANER DIVISION and 3233 TALYBONT DIVISION to form* **3235 SOUTH MEIRIONNYDD DIVISION**

3231 PWLLHELI DIVISION
combined with 3225 *EIFIONYDD DIVISION to form* **3236 EIFIONYDD AND PWLLHELI DIVISION**

3232 SOUTH ANGLESEY DIVISION
combined with 3229 *NORTH ANGLESEY DIVISION to form* **3238 YNYS MON/ANGLESEY DIVISION**

3233 TALYBONT DIVISION
combined with 3220 *ARDUDWY-IS-ARTRO DIVISION, 3226 ESTIMANER DIVISION and 3230 PENLLYN DIVISION to form* **3235 SOUTH MEIRIONNYDD DIVISION**

3234 CAERNARFON AND GWYRFAI DIVISION
combined with 3222 *BANGOR DIVISION to form (after boundary adjustment)* **3060 ARFON DIVISION**

3235 SOUTH MEIRIONNYDD DIVISION
combined with 3221 *NORTH MEIRIONNYDD DIVISION to form* **3239 MEIRIONNYDD DIVISION**

3236 EIFIONYDD AND PWLLHELI DIVISION
renamed **DWYFOR DIVISION**

3236 DWYFOR PSA
combined with 3060 *ARFON PSA and 3239 MEIRIONNYDD PSA to form* **3244 GWYNEDD PSA**

3237 ABERCONWY PSA
combined with 3052 *COLWYN PSA to form* **3062 CONWY PSA**

3238 YNYS MON/ANGLESEY LJA
see **NORTH WALES** ....p. 144

3239 MEIRIONNYD PSA
combined with 3060 *ARFON PSA and 3236 DWYFOR PSA to form* **3244 GWYNEDD PSA**

3244 GWYNEDD LJA
see **NORTH WALES** ....p. 144

3250 BRECKNOCK AND RADNORSHIRE LJA
see **MID AND WEST WALES** ....p. 142

3251 CARDIFF AND THE VALE OF GLAMORGAN LJA
see **SOUTH EAST WALES** ....p. 145

3252 CARMARTHENSHIRE LJA
see **MID AND WEST WALES** ....p. 142

3253 CEREDIGION AND PEMBROKESHIRE LJA
see **MID AND WEST WALES** ....p. 142

3262 CYNON VALLEY LJA
combined with 3264 *MERTHYR TYDFIL LJA and 3265 MISKIN LJA to form* **GLAMORGAN VALLEYS LJA**

3263 LOWER RHYMNEY VALLEY PSA
combined with 3267 *UPPER RHYMNEY VALLEY PSA and 3201 BEDWELLTY PSA (except Llanelly Hill) to form* **3209 NORTH WEST GWENT PSA**

3264 MERTHYR TYDFIL LJA
combined with 3262 *CYNON VALLEY LJA and 3265 MISKIN LJA to form* **GLAMORGAN VALLEYS LJA**

3265 MISKIN LJA
combined with 3262 *CYNON VALLEY LJA and 3264 MERTHYR TYDFIL LJA to form* **GLAMORGAN VALLEYS LJA**

3266 NEWCASTLE AND OGMORE LJA
see **SOUTH EAST WALES** ....p. 145

3267 UPPER RHYMNEY VALLEY PSA
combined with 3263 *LOWER RHYMNEY VALLEY PSA AND 3201 BEDWELLTY PSA (except Llanelly Hill) to form* **3209 NORTH WEST GWENT PSA**

3270 GLAMORGAN VALLEYS LJA
see **SOUTH EAST WALES** ....p. 145

3320 BRECON DIVISION
combined with 3324 DEFYNOCK DIVISION to form **3342 BRECON DIVISION**

3321 BUILTH DIVISION
combined with 3322 COLWYN DIVISION and 3335 PAINSCASTLE DIVISION to form **3345 BUILTH DIVISION**

3322 COLWYN DIVISION
combined with 3321 BUILTH DIVISION and 3335 PAINSCASTLE DIVISION to form **3345 BUILTH DIVISION**

3323 CRICKHOWELL DIVISION
combined with 3342 BRECON DIVISION (except for Ystradfellte) and 3338 TALGARTH DIVISION to form **3350 BRECON DIVISION**

3324 DEFYNOCK DIVISION
combined with 3320 BRECON DIVISION to form **3342 BRECON DIVISION**

3325 DEYTHEUR DIVISION
combined with 3328 LLANFYLLIN DIVISION and 3339 WELSHPOOL DIVISION to form **3341 WELSHPOOL DIVISION**

3326 KNIGHTON DIVISION
combined with 3343 EAST RADNOR DIVISION to form **3344 EAST RADNOR DIVISION**

3327 LLANDRINDOD WELLS DIVISION
combined with 3345 BUILTH DIVISION, 3344 EAST RADNOR DIVISION and 3337 RHAYADER DIVISION to form **3351 LLANDRINDOD WELLS DIVISION**

3328 LLANFYLLIN DIVISION
combined with 3325 DEYTHEUR DIVISION and 3339 WELSHPOOL DIVISION to form **3341 WELSHPOOL DIVISION**

3329 LLANIDLOES DIVISION
combined with 3347 NEWTOWN DIVISION to form **3352 NEWTOWN DIVISION**

3330 MACHYNLLETH DIVISION
combined with 3352 NEWTOWN DIVISION to form **3352 DE MALDWYN DIVISION** – see above

3331 MATHRAFAL DIVISION
combined with 3341 WELSHPOOL DIVISION to form **3346 WELSHPOOL DIVISION**

3332 MONTGOMERY DIVISION
combined with 3334 NEWTOWN DIVISION to form **3347 NEWTOWN DIVISION**

3333 NEW RADNOR DIVISION
combined with 3336 PRESTEIGNE DIVISION to form **3343 EAST RADNOR DIVISION**

3334 NEWTOWN DIVISION
combined with 3332 MONTGOMERY DIVISION to form **3347 NEWTOWN DIVISION**

3335 PAINSCASTLE DIVISION
combined with 3321 BUILTH DIVISION AND 3322 COLWYN DIVISION to form **3345 BUILTH DIVISION**

3336 PRESTEIGNE DIVISION
combined with 3333 NEW RADNOR DIVISION to form **3343 EAST RADNOR DIVISION**

3337 RHAYADER DIVISION
combined with 3345 BUILTH DIVISION, 3327 LLANDRINDOD WELLS DIVISION and 3344 EAST RADNOR DIVISION to form **3351 LLANDRINDOD WELLS DIVISION**

3338 TALGARTH DIVISION
combined with 3342 BRECON DIVISION (except for Ystradfellte) and 3323 CRICKHOWELL DIVISION TO FORM **3350 BRECON DIVISION**

3339 WELSHPOOL DIVISION
combined with 3325 DEYTHEUR DIVISION and 3328 LLANFYLLIN DIVISION to form **3341 WELSHPOOL DIVISION**

3340 YSRTADGYNLAIS DIVISION
combined with 3350 BRECON DIVISION to form **3350 DE BRYCHEINIOG DIVISION**

3341 WELSHPOOL DIVISION
combined with 3331 MATHRAFAL DIVISION to form **3346 WELSHPOOL DIVISION**

3342 BRECON DIVISION
(except for Ystradfellte) combined with 3323 CRICKHOWELL DIVISION and 3338 TALGARTH DIVISION to form **3350 BRECON DIVISION**

3343 EAST RADNOR DIVISION
combined with 3326 KNIGHTON DIVISION to form **3344 EAST RADNOR DIVISION**

3344 EAST RADNOR DIVISION
combined with 3345 BUILTH DIVISION, 3327 LLANDRINDOD WELLS DIVISION and 3337 RHAYADER DIVISION to form **3351 LLANDRINDOD WELLS DIVISION**

3345 BUILTH DIVISION
combined with 3327 LLANDRINDOD WELLS DIVISION, 3344 EAST RADNOR DIVISION and 3337 RHAYADER DIVISION to form **3351 LLANDRINDOD WELLS DIVISION**

3346 WELSHPOOL LJA
combined with 3352 DE MALDWYN LJA to form **3355 MONTGOMERYSHIRE LJA**

3347 NEWTOWN DIVISION
combined with 3329 LLANIDLOES DIVISION to form **3352 NEWTOWN DIVISION**

3348 CARDIFF LJA
combined with 3349 VALE OF GLAMORGAN LJA to form **CARDIFF AND THE VALE OF GLAMORGAN LJA**

3349 VALE OF GLAMORGAN LJA
combined with 3348 CARDIFF LJA to form **CARDIFF AND THE VALE OF GLAMORGAN LJA**

3350 BRECON DIVISION
combined with 3340 YSTRADGYNLAIS DIVISION to form **3350 DE BRYCHEINIOG DIVISION**

3350 DE BRYCHEINIOG LJA
combined with 3351 RADNORSHIRE AND NORTH BRECKNOCK to form **BRECKNOCK AND RADNORSHIRE LJA**

3351 LLANDRINDOD WELLS DIVISION
renamed **RADNORSHIRE AND NORTH BRECKNOCK DIVISION**

3351 RADNORSHIRE AND NORTH BRECKNOCK LJA
combined with 3350 DE BRYCHEINIOG to form **BRECKNOCK AND RADNORSHIRE LJA**

3352 NEWTOWN DIVISION
combined with 3330 MACHYNLLETH DIVISION to form **3352 DE MALDWYN DIVISION**

3352 DE MALDWYN LJA
combined with 3346 WELSHPOOL LJA to form **3355 MONTGOMERYSHIRE LJA**

3355 MONTGOMERYSHIRE LJA
see **MID AND WEST WALES** ....p. 142

3356 PEMBROKESHIRE LJA
combined with 3138 CEREDIGION to form **3253 CEREDIGION AND PEMBROKESHIRE LJA**

3357 PORT TALBOT DIVISION
combined with 3359 NEATH DIVISION to form **3359 NEATH PORT TALBOT DIVISION**

3358 LLIW VALLEY DIVISION
combined with 3360 SWANSEA DIVISION to form **3360 SWANSEA COUNTY DIVISION**

3359 NEATH DIVISION
combined with 3357 PORT TALBOT DIVISION to form **3359 NEATH PORT TALBOT DIVISION**

3359 NEATH PORT TALBOT LJA
see **MID AND WEST WALES** ....p. 142

3360 SWANSEA DIVISION
combined with 3358 LLIW VALLEY DIVISION to form **3360 SWANSEA COUNTY DIVISION**

NORTHERN IRELAND

9001 ANTRIM
Mrs L. Webster, Antrim Court Office, The Courthouse, 30 Castle Way, Antrim BT41 4AQ
Tel: 028 9446 2661
Fax: 028 9446 3301

Courts and times
Antrim
Adult: Fifth Monday in month, Tuesday 10:00
VC: Tuesday 09:30
YC: Second and fourth Monday in month 10:00
Dom: Third Monday in month 10:00
Dept: First Monday in month 10:00

9002 ARDS
Mr A. Heaney, Newtownards Court Office, The Courthouse, Regent Street, Newtownards BT23 4LP
Tel: 028 9181 4343
Fax: 028 9181 8024

Courts and times
Newtownards
Adult: Monday, Tuesday, Thursday 10:30
VC: Tuesday 11:00
YC: Second and fourth Tuesday in month, third Monday in month 10:30
FPC: First, second third and fourth Monday in month, Wednesday, first third and fourth Thursday in month 10:30
Dom: Fourth Thursday in month 10:30
Dept: Second Monday in month 10:30

9003 ARMAGH
Mrs M. Donaldson, Armagh Court Office, The Courthouse, The Mall, Armagh BT61 9DJ
Tel: 028 3752 2816
Fax: 028 3752 8194

Courts and times
Armagh
Adult: Second Monday in month, Tuesday 10:30
VC: Tuesday 10:00
YC: Second and fourth Friday in month 10:30
Dom: Fourth Friday in month 10:30
Dept: Third Friday in month 10:30

9004 BALLYMENA
Ms S. McCollum, Ballymena Court Office, The Courthouse, Albert Place, Ballymena, Co. Antrim BT43 5BS
Tel: 028 2564 9416
Fax: 028 2565 5371

Courts and times
Ballymena
Coleraine
Adult: Ballymena: Second Monday in month, fourth Tuesday in month, fifth Wednesday in month, Thursday 10:00

VC: Ballymena: Thursday 11:00
YC: Ballymena: First and third Tuesday in month 10:00
FPC: Ballymena: Friday 10:00; **Coleraine:** Second and fourth Monday in month, third Thursday in month 10:00
Dom: Ballymena: Second Tuesday in month 10:00
Dept: Ballymena: Fourth Tuesday in month 10:00 (alternate months)

9005 BALLYMONEY
combined with COLERAINE and MOYLE to form **The Petty Sessions District of NORTH ANTRIM**

9006 BANBRIDGE
Mrs G. Campbell, Banbridge Court Office, The Courthouse, 23 New Street, Newry BT35 6JD
Tel: 028 4062 362
Fax: 028 4062 3059

Courts and times
Newry
Adult: First Monday in month, first, third and fourth Thursday in month 10:30
YC: Third Monday in month 10:30
Dom: Third Monday in month 10:30
Dept: Second Thursday in month 10:30
FPC: First, third and fourth Thursday in month 12:00

9007/9008/9009 BELFAST AND NEWTOWNABBEY
Mrs P. McCourt, Laganside Courts, 45 Oxford Street, Belfast BT1 3LL
Tel: 028 9023 2721
Fax: 028 9031 5219

Courts and times
Laganside Courts, 45 Oxford Street, Belfast BT1 3LL
Old Town Hall Building, 80 Victoria Street, Belfast BT1 3FA
Adult: Laganside Courts: Weekdays 10:30
VC: Laganside Courts: Weekdays 09:45
Youth VC: Old Town Hall Building: Wednesday 11:00
YC: Old Town Hall Building: Monday, Wednesday, Friday 10:30
FPC: Old Town Hall Building: Monday, Tuesday, Thursday, Friday 09:45
Dom: Old Town Hall Building: First Tuesday in month, Wednesday 10:30
Dept: Laganside Courts: Tuesday 10:30

9010 CARRICKFERGUS AND NEWTOWNABBEY
renamed **NEWTOWNABBEY**

9012 CASTLEREAGH
Mr A. Heaney, Newtownards Court Office, The Courthouse, Regent Street, Newtownards BT23 4LP
Tel: 028 9181 4343
Fax: 028 9181 8024
Note: All business within this PS District has been incorporated into Ards PS District sittings.

9014 COLERAINE
combined with BALLYMONEY and MOYLE to form **The Petty Sessions District of NORTH ANTRIM**

9015 COOKSTOWN
combined with DUNGANNON to form **The Petty Sessions District of EAST TYRONE**

9016/9017 CRAIGAVON
Mr C. Cromie, Craigavon Court Office, The Courthouse, Central Way, Craigavon BT64 1AP
Tel: 028 3834 1324
Fax: 028 3834 1243

Courts and times
Craigavon Court Office, The Courthouse, Central Way, Craigavon BT64 1AP
The Courthouse, Railway Street, Lisburn
Adult: Craigavon: Fifth Monday in month, Wednesday, fifth Thursday in month, Friday 10:30
VC: Craigavon: Friday 09:45
YC: Craigavon: Second and fourth Tuesday in month 10:30
FPC: Craigavon: First, second , third and fourth Thursday in month 10:30; **Lisburn:** Second third and fourth Wednesday in month 10:30
Dom: Craigavon: First Monday in month, third Thursday in month 10:30
Dept: Craigavon: First Tuesday in month 10:30

9018 DOWN
Mr A. Heaney, Downpatrick Court Office, The Courthouse, English Street, Downpatrick BT30 6AB
Tel: 028 4461 4621
Fax: 028 4461 3969

Courts and times
Downpatrick Court Office, The Courthouse, English Street, Downpatrick BT30 6AB
Adult: Second and fourth Monday in month, Thursday, 10:00
VC: Thursday 09:30
YC: First and third Tuesday in month 10:00
Dom: Third Monday in month 10:00
Dept: First Monday in month 10:00

9019 DUNGANNON
combined with COOKSTOWN to form **The Petty Sessions District of EAST TYRONE**

EAST TYRONE
Miss R. Crockett, Dungannon Court Office, The Courthouse, 46 Killyman Road, Dungannon BT71 6DE
Tel: 028 8772 2992
Fax: 028 8772 8169

Courts and times
Dungannon Court Office, The Courthouse, 46 Killyman Road, Dungannon BT71 6DE
Adult: First, third and fourth Monday in month, third and fifth Tuesday in month, Wednesday, Friday 10:30
Dept: Second Monday in month 10:30
YC: First and third Tuesday in month 10:30
VC: Wednesday 12:00
Dom: Second Tuesday in month 10:30
FPC: Second and fifth Thursday in month, fourth Tuesday in month 10:30

9020 FERMANAGH
Mrs C. Deazley, Office Manager, Enniskillen Court Office, The Courthouse, East Bridge Street, Enniskillen BT74 7BP
Tel: 028 6632 2356
Fax: 028 6632 3636

Courts and times
Enniskillen Court Office, The Courthouse, East Bridge Street, Enniskillen BT74 7BP
Adult: First, third, fourth and fifth Monday in month, first and third Wednesday in month, first Tuesday in month 10:00
YC: Second Tuesday in month, fourth Wednesday in month 10:00
Dom: Third Tuesday in month 10:00
Dept: Second Monday in month, second Wednesday in month 10:00
VC: Monday 12:00

9024 LARNE
Ms S. McCollum, Ballymena Court Office, The Courthouse, Albert Place, Ballymena, Co. Antrim BT43 5BS
Tel: 028 2564 9416
Fax: 028 2565 5371

Courts and times
Ballymena
Adult: Second, third, fourth and fifth Friday in month 10:00
YC: Fourth Thursday in month 10:00
VC: Friday 10:30
Dom: Second Thursday in month 10:00
Dept: First Friday 10:00
Family: Third Thursday in month 10:00

9025 LIMAVADY
Clerk of Petty Sessions, Limavady Court Office, The Courthouse, Main Street, Limavady BT49 0EY
Tel: 028 7772 2688
Fax: 028 7776 8794

Courts and times
Limavady Court Office, The Courthouse, Main Street, Limavady BT49 0EY
Adult: First, second, fourth and fifth Wednesday in month 10:00
Dept: Third Wednesday in month 10:00

9026 LISBURN

Mrs S. Dougan, Lisburn Court Office, The Courthouse, Railway Street, Lisburn BT28 1XR
Tel: 028 9267 5336
Fax: 028 9260 4107

Courts and times
Lisburn Court Office, The Courthouse, Railway Street, Lisburn BT28 1XR
Adult: Monday, fifth Tuesday in month, fifth Wednesday in month, Thursday, second and fourth Friday in month 10:30
VC: Tuesday 10:45
YC: First and third Friday in month 10:30
Dom: First Tuesday in month 10:30
Dept: Third Tuesday in month 10:30

9028 LONDONDERRY

Mr L. Millar, Court Administrator, Londonderry Court Office, The Courthouse, Bishop Street, Londonderry BT48 6PQ
Tel: 028 7136 3448
Fax: 028 7137 2059

Courts and times
The Courthouse, Bishop Street, Londonderry BT48 6PQ
Adult: Monday, second and fifth Tuesday in month, Wednesday, first, second, fourth and fifth Thursday in month, Friday 10:00
YC: First, third and fourth Wednesday in month 10:00
VC: Thursday 12:00
FPC: Second and fourth Thursday in month, Friday 10:00
Dom: Fourth Monday in month 10:00
Dept: Third Thursday in month 10:00

9029 MAGHERAFELT

Clerk of Petty Sessions, Magherafelt Court Office, The Courthouse, Hospital Road, Magherafelt BT45 5DG
Tel: 028 7963 2121
Fax: 028 7963 4063

Courts and times
The Courthouse, Hospital Road, Magherafelt BT45 5DG
Adult: First, second, third and fourth Wednesday in month 10:00
YC: Third Monday in month 10:00
Dom: Third Monday in month 11:00
VC: Wednesday 12:00
Dept: First Monday in month 10:00

9030 MOYLE

combined with COLERAINE and BALLYMONEY to form **The Petty Sessions District of NORTH ANTRIM**

9032 NEWRY AND MOURNE

Mrs G. Campbell, Newry Court Office, The Courthouse, 23 New Street, Newry BT35 6JD
Tel: 028 3025 2040
Fax: 028 3026 9830

Courts and times
The Courthouse, 23 New Street, Newry BT35 6JD
Adult: Second, fourth and fifth Monday in month, Wednesday, third and fifth Thursday in month, second, fourth and fifth Friday in month 10:30
VC: Wednesday 10:00
YC: First and third Friday in month 10:30
FPC: First Monday in month, Tuesday 10:30
Dom: First Thursday in month 10:30
Dept: Third Monday in month 10:30

9033 NEWTOWNABBEY

CLOSED – Business transferred to BELFAST AND NEWTOWNABBEY

NORTH ANTRIM

Mr S. Tosh, Coleraine Court Office, The Courthouse, 46A Mountsandel Road, Coleraine, Co. Londonderry BT52 1NY
Tel: 028 7034 3437

Fax: 028 7032 0156

Courts and times

The Courthouse, 46A Mountsandel Road, Coleraine, Co. Londonderry BT52 1NY
Adult: Monday, fifth Tuesday in month, Wednesday, second, third, fourth and fifth Friday in month 10:00
YC: Second and fourth Tuesday in month 10:00
VC: Monday 09:45
Dom: First Thursday in month 10:00
Dept: First Friday in month 10:00

9034 NORTH DOWN

Mr A. Heaney, Newtownards Court Office, The Courthouse, Regent Street, NewtownardsBangor BT23 4LP
Tel: 028 9187 4343
Fax: 028 8181 8024

Courts and times

The Courthouse, Regent Street, Newtownards BT23 4LP
Adult: Wednesday, first, second and fifth Friday in month 10:30
YC: Second and fourth Tuesday in month, third Monday in month 10:30
VC: Tuesday 11:00
Dom: Fourth Friday in month 10:30
Dept: Third Friday in month 10:30

9035 OMAGH

Mrs J. McGonigle, Omagh Court Office, The Courthouse, High Street, Omagh BT78 1DU
Tel: 028 8224 2056
Fax: 028 8225 1198

Courts and times

The Courthouse, High Street, Omagh BT78 1DU
Adult: Tuesday, fourth Friday in month, fifth Wednesday in month, second and fifth Thursday in month 10:00
FPC: Third Monday in month, first, third and fourth Thursday in month 10:30
YC: Third Wednesday in month, first Friday in month 10:00
Dom: First Friday in month 10:00
VC: Tuesday 12:00
Dept: Second Friday in month 10:00

9036 STRABANE

Mrs J. McGonigle, Strabane Court Office, The Courthouse, Derry Road, Strabane BT82 8DT
Tel: 028 7138 2544
Fax: 028 7138 3209

Courts and times

The Courthouse, Derry Road, Strabane BT82 8DT
Adult: First, third, fourth and fifth Thursday in month, fifth Wednesday in month, first, second and fourth Friday in month 10:00
YC: Third Friday in month 10:00
Dom: Third Friday in month 11:00
VC: Thursday in month 11:30
Dept: Second Thursday in month 10:00

SCOTLAND

SHERIFFDOM OF GLASGOW AND STRATHKELVIN

Sheriff Principal: Craig A.L. Scott
Sheriffdom Business Manager: Steve Bain
Sheriffdom Legal Adviser: Patricia Wallace
Legal Advisers: Howard Rattray; Eliza Harkins
Fines Collection and Enforcement: tel: 0141 429 8888

9761 GLASGOW AND STRATHKELVIN SHERIFF, JUSTICE OF THE PEACE AND STIPENDIARY MAGISTRATE COURTS

Steve Bain, Sheriffdom Business Manager & Sheriff Clerk, Sheriff Court House, PO Box 23, 1 Carlton Place, Glasgow G5 9DA
Tel: 0141 429 8888
Fax: 0141 418 5244 (Admin Dept); 5248 (Civil Dept); 5270 (Solemn Criminal Dept); 5247 (Summary Criminal Dept); 5185 (JP/Stips); 5270 (Cashier Dept); 5398 (Fines Enforcement Office)
DX: 551020 (Sheriff Clerk); 551021 (Criminal Dept); 551022 (Sheriffs); 551023 (Small Claims and Commissary Dept); DX: 551024 (General Civil Dept)
Legal Post: LP-6 GLASGOW 2
Email: glasgow@scotcourts.gov.uk

Courts and times
Sheriff Court House, 1 Carlton Place, Glasgow
Trial: Weekdays 10:00
Criminal Custody (Sheriff): Weekdays 13:00
Criminal Custody (JP): Weekdays 10:00
Summary Cause: Payments: Alternate Wednesdays 10:00; **Heritable:** Tuesday 10:00
Small Claims, Payments and Miscellaneous: Friday 10:00
Appeal: Tuesday, Wednesday, Thursday 10:00
Adults with Incapacity: Alternate Wednesdays 10:00
Debtors (Scotland) Act: Monday 10:00
Miscellaneous Civil: Monday 11:30
Options Hearings: Family: Tuesday 09:30; **Commercial:** Wednesday 10:00; **Ordinary:** Friday 10:00

SHERIFFDOM OF GRAMPIAN, HIGHLAND AND ISLANDS

Sheriff Principal: Derek Pyle
Sheriffdom Business Manager: Audrey Bayliss, Scottish Court Service, 6 Ardross Terrace, Inverness
　　IV3 5NQ. Tel: 01463 251964
Sheriffdom Legal Adviser: Kay Polson, Aberdeen Justice of the Peace Court, Castle Street, Aberdeen
　　AB10 1WP. Tel: 01224 657200
Legal Advisers: Alison Stone, James McPherson and Sheila Shepherd, Aberdeen Sheriff Court; Fiona
　　Grant, Catriona MacDonald, Sandy Lorimer, Area Management Team Offices, 6 Ardross
　　Terrace, as above
Fines Collection and Enforcement: tel: 0845 602 5228

9251 ABERDEEN SHERIFF COURT AND JUSTICE OF THE PEACE COURT
F. Hendry, Sheriff Clerk, Sheriff Court House, Castle Street, Aberdeen AB10 1WP
Tel: 01224 657200
Fax: 01224 657234
DX: 61 ABERDEEN
Legal Post: LP-7 ABERDEEN 1
Email: aberdeen@scotcourts.gov.uk

Courts and times
Court House, Castle Street, Aberdeen
Criminal: Weekdays 10:00
Civil: Wednesday 09:45
Family and Child Welfare Hearings: Friday 09:45
Summary Cause: Thursday 10:00
Small Claims: Thursday 10:00
Commercial: Alternate Fridays 12:00
JP: Weekdays 10:00

9252 BANFF SHERIFF COURT AND JUSTICE OF THE PEACE COURT
Tracey Reid, Sheriff Clerk Depute, Sheriff Court House, Banff AB45 1AU
Tel: 01261 812140
Fax: 01261 818394
DX: 521325 BANFF
Legal Post: LP-5 BANFF
Email: banff@scotcourts.gov.uk

Courts and times
Sheriff Court House, Banff AB45 1AU
Criminal: Alternate Tuesdays 10:00
Ordinary: Tuesday once a month 10:00
Summary Cause: Tuesday once a month 11:00
Small Claims: Tuesday once a month 11:00
JP: Wednesday once a month 10:00

9343 DINGWALL SHERIFF COURT AND JUSTICE OF THE PEACE COURT
Ken Kerr, Sheriff Clerk Depute, Sheriff Court House, Dingwall IV15 9QX
Tel: 01349 863153
Fax: 01349 863153
DX: 520584 DINGWALL
Legal Post: LP-4 DINGWALL
Email: dingwall@scotcourts.gov.uk

Courts and times
Sheriff Court House, Dingwall
Criminal: Second Thursday in month and as required
Ordinary: Second Thursday in month 10:00
Summary Cause: Second Thursday in month 10:00
JP: Fourth Tuesday and Friday in month 10:00

9344 DORNOCH SHERIFF COURT AND JUSTICE OF THE PEACE COURT
Mrs Ruth Thomson, Sheriff Clerk Depute, Sheriff Court House, Dornoch IV25 3SD
Tel: 01862 810224
Fax: 01862 810224
Legal Post: LP-2 DORNOCH

Email: dornoch@scotcourts.gov.uk

Courts and times
Sheriff Court House, Dornoch
Criminal: Fourth Monday in month 10:00
Ordinary: Fourth Monday in month 10:00
Summary Cause: Fourth Monday in month 10:00
JP: Wednesday every eight weeks or as required

9341 ELGIN SHERIFF COURT AND JUSTICE OF THE PEACE COURT

Richard Cantwell, Sheriff Clerk, Sheriff Court House, Elgin IV30 1BU
Tel: 01343 542505
Fax: 01343 559517
DX: 520652 ELGIN
Legal Post: LP-8 ELGIN
Email: elgin@scotcourts.gov.uk

Courts and times
Sheriff Court House, Elgin
Criminal: Cited cases: Thursday 10:00, other days as required
Ordinary: Alternate Fridays 10:30
Summary Cause: Alternate Fridays 10:00
JP: Tuesday 10:00

9345 FORT WILLIAM SHERIFF COURT AND JUSTICE OF THE PEACE COURT

Verona MacDonald, Sheriff Clerk Depute, Sheriff Court House, High Street, Fort William PH33 6EE
Tel: 01397 702087
Fax: 01397 706214
DX: 531405 FORT WILLIAM
Legal Post: LP-2 FORT WILLIAM
Email: fortwilliam@scotcourts.gov.uk

Courts and times
Sheriff Court House, High Street, Fort William
Criminal: Monthly 10:00
Ordinary: Fourth Friday in month 10:00
Summary Cause: Fourth Friday in month 10:00
JP: Every four weeks 10:00

9346 INVERNESS SHERIFF COURT AND JUSTICE OF THE PEACE COURT

Mrs Frances MacPherson, Sheriff Clerk, Sheriff Court House, Inverness IV2 3EG
Tel: 01463 230782
Fax: 01463 710602
DX: IN25
Legal Post: LP-15
Email: inverness@scotcourts.gov.uk

Courts and times
Sheriff Court House, Inverness
Criminal: Weekdays 10:00 and Tuesday 10:30
Ordinary: Alternate Wednesdays 10:00
Summary Cause: Alternate Wednesdays 10:00
JP: Alternate Mondays, Wednesday, Friday 10:00

9805 KIRKWALL SHERIFF COURT

Gail Edwards, Sheriff Clerk Depute, Sheriff Court House, Kirkwall KW15 1PD
Tel: 01856 872110
Fax: 01856 874835
Legal Post: LP-7
Email: kirkwall@scotcourts.gov.uk
Note: No JP Court in Kirkwall

Courts and times
Sheriff Court House, Kirkwall
Criminal: Second Wednesday in month 10:00
Ordinary: Second Friday in month 10:00
Summary Cause: Second Friday in month 10:00
Small Claims: Second Friday in month 10:00

9812 LERWICK SHERIFF COURT
Sheriff Clerk Depute, Sheriff Court House, Lerwick ZE1 0HD
Tel: 01595 693914
Fax: 01595 693340
Email: lerwick@scotcourts.gov.uk
Note: No JP Court in Lerwick

Courts and times
Sheriff Court House, Lerwick
Criminal: Thursday 10:00
Trials: Wednesday 10:00
Ordinary: Second Tuesday 10:00
Summary Cause: Second Tuesday 10:00

9814 LOCHMADDY SHERIFF COURT
Margaret Campbell, Sheriff Clerk Depute, Sheriff Court House, Lochmaddy HS6 5AE
Tel: 01478 612191
Fax: 0844 561 3015
Email: lochmaddy@scotcourts.gov.uk

Courts and times
Sheriff Court House, Lochmaddy
Criminal: Fourth Tuesday in month and as required
Ordinary: Fourth Tuesday in month 10:30
Summary Cause: Fourth Tuesday in month 10:30

9253 PETERHEAD SHERIFF COURT AND JUSTICE OF THE PEACE COURT
Elaine McLeod, Sheriff Clerk, Sheriff Court House, Queen Street, Peterhead AB42 1TP
Tel: 01779 476676
Fax: 01779 472435
DX: 521376 PETERHEAD
Legal Post: LP-3 PETERHEAD
Email: peterhead@scotcourts.gov.uk

Courts and times
Sheriff Court House, Queen Street, Peterhead
Intermediate Diet: Second Wednesday in month 10:00
Criminal: Thursday 10:00
Trials: First and third Monday and Tuesday in month, third Friday in month 09:30
Custody: Weekdays 12:00
Ordinary: First and fourth Friday in month 09:30
Summary Cause: First and fourth Friday in month 11:30
JP: Fourth Monday and Friday in month 10:00

9347 PORTREE SHERIFF COURT AND JUSTICE OF THE PEACE COURT
Margaret Campbell, Sheriff Clerk Depute, Sheriff Court House, Portree IV51 9EH
Tel: 01478 612191
Fax: 01478 613203
Email: portree@scotcourts.gov.uk

Courts and times
Sheriff Court House, Portree
Criminal: Fourth Monday in month and as required
Ordinary: Fourth Monday in month 10:00
Summary Cause: Fourth Monday in month 10:00

9254 STONEHAVEN SHERIFF COURT AND JUSTICE OF THE PEACE COURT
Sheriff Clerk, Sheriff Court House, Stonehaven AB39 2JH
Tel: 01569 762758
Fax: 01569 762132
DX: 521023 STONEHAVEN
Legal Post: LP-3 STONEHAVEN
Email: stonehaven@scotcourts.gov.uk

Courts and times
Sheriff Court House, Stonehaven
Criminal: Alternate Wednesdays 10:00
Ordinary: Alternate Thursdays 10:00
Summary Cause: Alternate Thursdays 10:00 (same day as ordinary court)

Small Claims: Alternate Thursdays 10:00 (same day as ordinary court)
JP: Alternate Tuesdays 10:00

9384 STORNOWAY SHERIFF COURT AND JUSTICE OF THE PEACE COURT
Kenneth Finnie, Sheriff Clerk Depute, Sheriff Court House, 9 Lewis Street, Stornoway HS1 2JF
Tel: 01851 702231
Fax: 01851 704296
Email: stornoway@scotcourts.gov.uk
Courts and times
Sheriff Court House, 9 Lewis Street, Stornoway
Criminal: As required
Ordinary: Alternate Thursdays 10:00
Summary Cause: Alternate Thursdays 10:00
JP: Fourth Tuesday in month 10:00

9348 TAIN SHERIFF COURT AND JUSTICE OF THE PEACE COURT
Donna Jack, Sheriff Clerk Depute, Sheriff Court House, Tain IV19 1AB
Tel: 01862 892518
Fax: 01862 892518
Email: tain@scotcourts.gov.uk
Courts and times
Sheriff Court House, Tain
Criminal: Trials: Thursday/Friday once a month; **Cited:** Monday once a month 10:00
Ordinary: Fourth Thursday in month 10:00
Summary Cause: Fourth Thursday in month 11:00
JP: Fourth Thursday in month 10:00

9891 WICK SHERIFF COURT AND JUSTICE OF THE PEACE COURT
Janet McEwan MBE, Sheriff Clerk Depute, Sheriff Court House, Wick KW1 4AJ
Tel: 01955 602846
Fax: 01955 602846
Legal Post: LP-4
Email: wick@scotcourts.gov.uk
Courts and times
Sheriff Court House, Wick
Criminal: Cited Cases: Alternate Fridays 10:00; **Others:** As required
Ordinary: Alternate Mondays 10:00
Summary Cause: Alternate Mondays 10:00
JP: Fourth Thursday in month 10:00

SHERIFFDOM OF LOTHIAN AND BORDERS

Sheriff Principal: Mhairi M. Stephen
Sheriffdom Business Manager: David Shand, Edinburgh Sheriff Court, 27 Chamber Street, Edinburgh EH1 1LB. Tel: 0131 225 2525
Sheriffdom Legal Adviser: David Kemp, Edinburgh Justice of the Peace Court, 27 Chamber Street, Edinburgh EH1 1LB. Tel: 0131 225 2525
Legal Advisers: Deirdre Morrison, Margaret Dundas, Alison Brown, Julia Dunbar, Anne Mainland, Angela Ward, Michael Wright
Fines Collection and Enforcement: tel: 0131 247 2566

9729 DUNS SHERIFF COURT
Mark Kubeczka, Sheriff Clerk, Sheriff & JP Court House, 8 Newtown Street, Duns TD11 3DT
Tel: 01835 863231
Fax: 01835 864110
DX: 581222 JEDBURGH
Legal Post: LP-3 JEDBURGH
Email: jedburgh@scotcourts.gov.uk
Note: This court is only open on court sitting days. Staff are located in Jedburgh and administration of the business is carried out in Jedburgh.

Courts and times
Sheriff & JP Court House, 8 Newtown Street, Duns
Criminal: Alternate Wednesdays 10:00
Civil: Alternate Wednesdays 10:00
Summary Cause: Alternate Wednesdays 10:00

9350 DUNS JUSTICE OF THE PEACE COURT
Sheriff & JP Court House, 8 Newtown Street, Duns TD11 3DT
Tel: 01835 863231
Fax: 01835 864110
Legal Post: LP-3 JEDBURGH
Email: jedburgh@scotcourts.gov.uk
Note: This court is only open on court sitting days. Staff are located in Jedburgh and administration of the business is carried out in Jedburgh.

Courts and times
Sheriff & JP Court House, 8 Newtown Street, Duns TD11 3DT
JP: Alternate Tuesdays 10:00 and as required

9741 EDINBURGH SHERIFF COURT
David Shand, Sheriff Clerk, Sheriff Court House, 27 Chambers Street, Edinburgh EH1 1LB
Tel: 0131 225 2525
Fax: 0131 225 4422
DX: 550308 ED 37 (Admin/Crime/Cash); 550312 ED 37 (Civil); 550313 ED37 (Commissary)
Legal Post: LP-2 EDINBURGH 10
Email: edinburgh@scotcourts.gov.uk
Courts and times
Sheriff Court House, 27 Chambers Street, Edinburgh
Criminal: Weekdays 10:00
Ordinary: Weekdays 10:00
Options: Weekdays 10:00
Family: Weekdays 12:00
Summary Cause: Wednesday and Friday 09:45 or as required
Small Claims – Preliminary Hearings: Wednesday and Friday 10:30

9478 EDINBURGH JUSTICE OF THE PEACE COURT
David Kemp, Sheriffdom Legal Advisor, Sheriff Court House, 27 Chambers Street, Edinburgh EH1 1LB
Tel: 0131 225 2525
Fax: 0131 225 4422
DX: 550308 ED 37
Legal Post: LP-2 EDINBURGH 10
Email: edinburgh@scotcourts.gov.uk

Courts and times
Sheriff Court House, 27 Chambers Street, Edinburgh
JP: Weekdays 10:00

9771 HADDINGTON SHERIFF COURT
John O'Donnell, Sheriff Clerk, Sheriff Court House, Court Street, Haddington EH41 3HN
Tel: 01620 822325 822936
Fax: 01620 826350
DX: 540732 HADDINGTON
Email: haddington@scotcourts.gov.uk

Courts and times
Sheriff Court House, Court Street, Haddington
Criminal: Wednesday, Thursday, Friday
Ordinary: Alternate Mondays 11:30
Summary Cause: Alternate Mondays 11:30

9270 HADDINGTON JUSTICE OF THE PEACE COURT
John O'Donnell, Sheriff Clerk, Sheriff & JP Court House, Court Street, Haddington EH41 3HN
Tel: 01620 822325; 822936
Fax: 01620 825350
DX: 540732 HADDINGTON
Email: haddington@scotcourts.gov.uk

Courts and times
Sheriff & JP Court House, Court Street, Haddington
JP: Tuesday 10:00

9791 JEDBURGH SHERIFF COURT
Mark Kubeczka, Sheriff Clerk, Sheriff Court House, Castlegate, Jedburgh TD8 6AR
Tel: 01835 863231
Fax: 01835 864110
DX: 581222 JEDBURGH
Legal Post: LP-3 JEDBURGH
Email: jedburgh@scotcourts.gov.uk

Courts and times
Sheriff Court House, Castlegate, Jedburgh
Criminal: Thursday and Friday 10:00
Civil: Tuesday 10:00
Summary Cause: Tuesday 10:00

9351 JEDBURGH JUSTICE OF THE PEACE COURT
Sheriff & JP Court House, Castlegate, Jedburgh TD8 6AR
Tel: 01835 863231
Fax: 01835 864110
DX: 581222 JEDBURGH
Legal Post: LP-3 JEDBURGH
Email: jedburgh@scotcourts.gov.uk

Courts and times
Sheriff & JP Court House, Castlegate, Jedburgh
JP: Alternate Tuesdays 10:00. Additional sittings as required

---

9815 LIVINGSTON SHERIFF COURT
D. Fyfe, Sheriff Clerk, The Civic Centre, Howden South Road, Livingston EH54 6FF
Tel: 01506 402400
Fax: 01506 415262
DX: 552062 LIVINGSTON 7
Legal Post: LP-2 LIVINGSTON 2
Email: livingston@scotcourts.gov.uk

Courts and times
The Civic Centre, Howden South Road, Livingston
Ordinary: Wednesday

9380 LIVINGSTON JUSTICE OF THE PEACE COURT
Sheriff and JP Court, The Civic Centre, Howden South Road, Livingston EH54 6FF
Tel: 01506 402400
Fax: 01506 415262

DX: 552062 LIVINGSTON 7
Legal Post: LP-2 LIVINGSTON 2
Email: livingston@scotcourts.gov.uk
Courts and times
The Civic Centre, Howden South Road, Livingston
JP: Tuesday and Thursday

9852 PEEBLES SHERIFF COURT

Mrs M. McCabe, Sheriff Clerk, c/o Sheriff Court Selkirk, Ettrick Terrace, Selkirk TD1 1TB
Tel: 01750 721269
Fax: 01750 722884
DX: 581011 SELKIRK
Legal Post: LP-2 SELKIRK
Email: peebles@scotcourts.gov.uk
Note: Peebles Sheriff Court is only open on court sitting days. Staff are located in Selkirk and administration of the business is carried out in Selkirk Sheriff Court.
Courts and times
Sheriff Court Selkirk, Ettrick Terrace, Selkirk
Criminal: First Wednesday in month 10:00
Ordinary: Third Wednesday in month 10:00
Summary Cause: Third Wednesday in month 10:00
Small Claims: Third Wednesday in month 10:00

9352 PEEBLES JUSTICE OF THE PEACE COURT

c/o Sheriff Court Selkirk, Etbrick Terrace, Selkirk TD1 1TB
Tel: 01750 721269
Fax: 01750 722884
DX: 581011 SELKIRK
Email: peebles@scotcourts.gov.uk
Note: Peebles JP Court is only open on court sitting days. Staff are located in Selkirk and administration of the business is carried out in Selkirk Sheriff Court.
Courts and times
Sheriff Court Selkirk, Etbrick Terrace, Selkirk
JP: Thursday once a month 10:00

9871 SELKIRK SHERIFF COURT

M. McCabe, Sheriff Clerk, Sheriff Court House, Etbrick Terrace, Selkirk TD7 4LE
Tel: 01750 721269
Fax: 01750 722884
DX: 581011 SELKIRK
Legal Post: LP-2 SELKIRK
Email: selkirk@scotcourts.gov.uk
Courts and times
Sheriff Clerk, Sheriff Court House, Etbrick Terrace, Selkirk
Criminal: Monday 10:00, alternate Tuesdays 10:00
Ordinary: Alternate Thursdays 10:00 during session
Summary Cause: Alternate Thursdays 10:00 during session
Small Claims: Alternate Thursdays 10:00 during session

9353 SELKIRK JUSTICE OF THE PEACE COURT

Sheriff & JP Court House, Etbrick Terrace, Selkirk TD7 4LE
Tel: 01750 721269
Fax: 01750 722884
DX: 581011 SELKIRK
Legal Post: LP-2 SELKIRK
Email: selkirk@scotcourts.gov.uk
Courts and times
Sheriff & JP Court House, Etbrick Terrace, Selkirk
JP: Alternate Thursdays 10:00 and as required

SHERIFFDOM OF NORTH STRATHCLYDE

Sheriff Principal: Bruce A. Kerr QC
Sheriffdom Business Manager: Lisa Davis, Paisley Sheriff Court, St James' Street, Paisley PA3 2HW.
 Tel: 0141 887 5291
Sheriffdom Legal Adviser: Anne Hilland, Paisley Justice of the Peace Court, St James' Street, Paisley
 PA3 2HW. Tel: 0141 887 5291
Legal Advisers for Dumbarton, Greenock and Paisley: Eileen Burns, Angela Devine, Kathleen
 Graham, Vivian Lindsay, Peter Livingstone, Catriona Sagar
Legal Advisers for Irvine and Kilmarnock: Angus Livingstone, Kevin Walsh
Legal Adviser for Dunoon, Oban, Campbeltown and Lochgilphead: Frances Roberts
Fines Collection and Enforcement: tel: 01475 787073

9716 CAMPBELTOWN SHERIFF COURT AND JUSTICE OF THE PEACE COURT
Graham Whitelaw, Sheriff Clerk Depute, Sheriff Court House, Castlehill, Campbeltown PA28 6AN
Tel: 01586 552503
Fax: 01586 554967
Legal Post: LP-3 CAMPBELTOWN
Email: campbeltown@scotcourts.gov.uk

Courts and times
Sheriff Court House, Castlehill, Campbeltown
Criminal: As required
Ordinary: Fourth Friday in month 10:00
Summary Cause: Fourth Friday in month 10:00

9376 DUMBARTON JUSTICE OF THE PEACE COURT
JP Administration, Senior Legal Advisor, Dumbarton JP Court, Church Street, Dumbarton G82 1QR
Tel: 01389 763266
Fax: 01389 764085
DX: 500597 DUMBARTON
Email: dumbarton@scotcourts.gov.uk

Courts and times
Dumbarton JP Court, Church Street, Dumbarton
JP: Tuesday, Wednesday, Thursday 10:00

9723 DUMBARTON SHERIFF COURT
Sheriff Clerk, Sheriff Court House, Church Street, Dumbarton G82 1QR
Tel: 01389 763266
Fax: 01389 764085
DX: 500597 DUMBARTON
Email: dumbarton@scotcourts.gov.uk

Courts and times
Sheriff Court House, Church Street, Dumbarton
Criminal: Weekdays
Ordinary: Thursday 10:00
Summary Cause: Alternate Wednesdays 10:00

9728 DUNOON SHERIFF COURT AND JUSTICE OF THE PEACE COURT
Kim Wilson, Sheriff Clerk Depute, Sheriff Court House, George Street, Dunoon PA23 8BQ
Tel: 0300 790 0049
Fax: 01369 702191
DX: 591655 DUNOON
Legal Post: LP-2 DUNOON
Email: dunoon@scotcourts.gov.uk

Courts and times
Sheriff Court House, George Street, Dunoon
Criminal: As required
Ordinary: Alternate Tuesdays 10:00
Summary Cause: Alternate Tuesdays 11:00

9762 GREENOCK SHERIFF COURT AND JUSTICE OF THE PEACE COURT
Allister Wilson, Sheriff Clerk, Sheriff Court House, 1 Nelson Street, Greenock PA15 1TR
Tel: 01475 787073

Fax: 01475 729746
DX: GR16 GREENOCK
Legal Post: LP-5 GREENOCK 1
Email: greenock@scotcourts.gov.uk
Courts and times
Sheriff Court House, 1 Nelson Street, Greenock
Criminal: As required
Ordinary: Monday 10:00
Summary Cause: Monday 11:00

9354 IRVINE JUSTICE OF THE PEACE COURT

St Marnock Street, Kilmarnock KA1 1ED
Tel: 01563 550024
Fax: 01563 543568
DX: KK20 KILMARNOCK
Legal Post: LP-5 KILMARNOCK
Email: irvine@scotcourts.gov.uk
Courts and times
St Marnock Street, Kilmarnock
JP: Wednesday and Thursday 10:00

9801 KILMARNOCK SHERIFF COURT AND JUSTICE OF THE PEACE COURT

Chris McGrane, Sheriff Clerk, Sheriff Court House, St Marnock Street, Kilmarnock KA1 1ED
Tel: 01563 550024
Fax: 01563 543568
DX: KK20 KILMARNOCK
Legal Post: LP-5 KILMARNOCK
Email: kilmarnock@scotcourts.gov.uk
Courts and times
Sheriff Court House, St Marnock Street, Kilmarnock
Criminal: Weekdays
Ordinary: Wednesday 10:00
Summary Cause: Alternate Fridays 10:00
Small Claims: Alternate Fridays 10:00
JP: Monday 12:00, Tuesday and Friday 10:00

LOCHGILPHEAD JUSTICE OF THE PEACE COURT

Police Buildings, Lochnell Street, Lochgilphead PA31 8JJ
Email: dunoon@scotcourts.gov.uk
Note: Court staff only attend when the court is sitting. Staff can be contacted at Dunoon Sheriff Court.

9841 OBAN SHERIFF COURT AND JUSTICE OF THE PEACE COURT

Graham Whitelaw, Sheriff Clerk Depute, Sheriff Court House, Albany Street, Oban PA34 4AL
Tel: 01631 562414
Fax: 01631 562037
DX: OB8 OBAN
Legal Post: LP-4 OBAN
Email: oban@scotcourts.gov.uk
Courts and times
Sheriff Court House, Albany Street, Oban
Criminal: As required
Ordinary: Fourth Thursday in month 10:00
Summary Cause: Fourth Thursday in month 10:00

9851 PAISLEY SHERIFF COURT AND JUSTICE OF THE PEACE COURT

Fiona Fraser, Sheriff Clerk, Sheriff Court House, St James' Street, Paisley PA3 2HW
Tel: 0141 887 5291
Fax: 0141 887 6702
DX: PA48 PAISLEY
Legal Post: LP-12 Paisley
Email: paisley@scotcourts.gov.uk

Courts and times
Sheriff Court House, St James' Street, Paisley
Criminal: Weekdays
Ordinary: Monday 10:00
Summary Cause: Friday 09:30
JP: Weekdays 10:00

9861 ROTHESAY SHERIFF COURT
Allister Wilson, Sheriff Clerk, (Greenock), Eaglesham House, Mount Pleasant Road, Rothesay, Isle of Bute PA20 9HQ
Tel: 01700 502982; 01475 787073
Fax: 01700 504112
DX: GR16 GREENOCK
Legal Post: LP-5 GREENOCK 1
Email: rothesay@scotcourts.gov.uk
All administration for Rothesay Sheriff Court is conducted by Greenock Sheriff Court.

Courts and times
Eaglesham House, Mount Pleasant Road, Rothesay, Isle of Bute
Criminal: Monday (and at Greenock Sheriff Court other days)
Ordinary: Alternate Mondays 10:00
Summary Cause: Alternate Mondays 10:00

SHERIFFDOM OF SOUTH STRATHCLYDE, DUMFRIES AND GALLOWAY

Sheriff Principal: Brian A. Lockhart

Sheriffdom Business Manager: Sheila Hindes, Airdrie Sheriff Court, Graham Street, Airdrie ML6 6EE. Tel: 01236 751121

Sheriffdom Legal Adviser: Phyllis Hands, Airdrie Sheriff Court, Graham Street, Airdrie ML6 6EE. Tel: 01236 751121

Legal Advisers: Fiona Ross, Dumfries Sheriff Court; Alan Rosamund, Ayr Sheriff Court; Valerie Dorans, Airdrie Sheriff Court; John Donnelly, Ronald Bain, Angus Livingston, Hamilton JP Court

Fines Collection and Enforcement: contact individual courts

9702 AIRDRIE SHERIFF COURT

Miss A. Currie, Sheriff Clerk, Sheriff Court House, Graham Street, Airdrie ML6 6EE
Tel: 01236 751121
Fax: 01236 747497
DX: 570416 AIRDRIE
Legal Post: LP-7 AIRDRIE
Email: airdrie@scotcourts.gov.uk

Courts and times
Sheriff Court House, Graham Street, Airdrie
Criminal: Weekdays
Civil: Thursday 10:00
Summary Cause: Alternate Tuesdays 10:00

9704 AYR SHERIFF COURT

Alan Johnston, Sheriff Clerk, Sheriff Court House, Wellington Square, Ayr KA7 1EE
Tel: 01292 268474/292200
Fax: 01292 292249
DX: AY16 AYR
Legal Post: LP-6 AYR
Email: ayr@scotcourts.gov.uk

Courts and times
Sheriff Court House, Wellington Square, Ayr
Criminal: Weekdays
Ordinary: Thursday 10:00
Summary Cause: Alternate Fridays 10:00
Small Claims: Alternate Fridays 10:00

9560 AYR JUSTICE OF THE PEACE COURT

Alan Johnston, Sheriff Clerk, Sheriff Court House, Wellington Square, Ayr KA7 1EE
Tel: 01292 268474/292200
Fax: 01292 292249
DX: AY16 AYR
Legal Post: LP-6 AYR
Email: ayr@scotcourts.gov.uk

Courts and times
Sheriff Court House, Wellington Square, Ayr
Criminal: Friday 10:00
Trial and Intermediate Diets: Three Tuesdays in four, Thursday 10:00
Custody: Monday 14:30, Wednesday 11:00

9355 COATBRIDGE JUSTICE OF THE PEACE COURT

Miss A. Currie, Sheriff Clerk, Sheriff Court House, Graham Street, Airdrie ML6 6EE
Tel: 01236 751121
Fax: 01236 747497
DX: 570416 AIRDRIE
Legal Post: LP-7 AIRDRIE
Email: airdrie@scotcourts.gov.uk

Courts and times
435 Main Street, Coatbridge
JP: Monday, Tuesday, Thursday

9531 CUMBERNAULD JUSTICE OF THE PEACE COURT
Miss A. Currie, Sheriff Clerk, Sheriff Court House, Graham Street, Airdrie ML6 6EE
Tel: 01236 751121
Fax: 01236 747497
DX: 570416 AIRDRIE
Legal post: LP-7 Airdrie
Email: airdrie@scotcourts.gov.uk
Courts and times
Bron Way, Cumbernauld
JP: Friday

9724 DUMFRIES SHERIFF COURT AND JUSTICE OF THE PEACE COURT
Miss E. S. O. Young, Sheriff Clerk, Sheriff Court House, Dumfries DG1 2AN
Tel: 01387 262334
Fax: 01387 262357
DX: 580617 DUMFRIES
Legal Post: LP-5 DUMFRIES
Email: dumfries@scotcourts.gov.uk
Courts and times
Sheriff Court House, Dumfries
Criminal: Weekdays 10:00
Ordinary: First, second and third Thursday in month 10:00
Summary Cause: Fourth Thursday in month 10:00
Small Claims: Fourth Thursday in month 10:00
Dumfries JP: Tuesday, fourth Wednesday in month 10:00
Annan JP: Alternate Thursdays 10:00

9772 HAMILTON SHERIFF COURT
Maureen McLean, Sheriff Clerk, Sheriff Court House, 4 Beckford Street, Hamilton ML3 0BT
Tel: 01698 282957
Fax: 01698 201365 (Criminal); 201366 (Fines)
Civil Department, Birnie House, Caird Park, Hamilton Business Park, Caird Street, Hamilton ML3 0AL
Tel: 01698 201375
Fax: 01698 284870
DX: HA16 HAMILTON
Legal Post: LP-4 HAMILTON 2
Email: hamilton@scotcourts.gov.uk
Courts and times
Sheriff Court House, 4 Beckford Street, Hamilton
Criminal: Weekdays
Options Hearing: Tuesday 14:00
Summary Cause Heritable: Monday 11:00
Summary Cause: Thursday 10:00
Small Claims: Thursday 10:00
Ordinary: Wednesday 10:00

9566 HAMILTON JUSTICE OF THE PEACE COURT
Maureen McLean, Sheriff Clerk, Sheriff Clerk's Office, Sheriff Court House, 4 Beckford Street, Hamilton ML3 0BT
Tel: 01698 282957
Fax: 01698 201365
DX: HA16 HAMILTON
Legal Post: LP-4 HAMILTON
Email: hamilton@scotcourts.gov.uk
Courts and times
Sheriff Court House, 4 Beckford Street, Hamilton
Trials: Monday 10:00, alternate Wednesdays and Fridays
Cited: Alternate Wednesdays and Fridays 10:00

9532 MOTHERWELL JUSTICE OF THE PEACE COURT
Maureen McLean, Sheriff Clerk, Sheriff Court House, 4 Beckford Street, Hamilton ML3 0BT
Tel: 01698 282957
Fax: 01698 201365
DX: HA16 HAMILTON
Legal Post: LP-4 HAMILTON 2

Email: hamilton@scotcourts.gov.uk

Courts and times
Sheriff Court House, 4 Beckford Street, Hamilton
Civic Centre, Windmill Street, Motherwell ML1 1AB. Tel: 0131 248 1810. Fax: 01698 267495. Email: motherwell@scotcourts.gov.uk
Trials: Hamilton: Monday, Thursday, alternate Fridays 10:00
Cited: Civic Centre, Motherwell: times on application

9804 KIRKCUDBRIGHT SHERIFF COURT AND JUSTICE OF THE PEACE COURT
Sheriff Clerk Depute, Sheriff Court House, Kirkcudbright DG6 4JW
Tel: 01557 330574
Fax: 01557 331764
DX: 580812 KIRKCUDBRIGHT
Legal Post: LP-2 KIRKCUDBRIGHT
Email: kirkcudbright@scotcourts.gov.uk

Courts and times
Sheriff Court House, Kirkcudbright
Criminal: Thursday
Ordinary: Thursday
Summary Cause: Second and fourth Thursday in month 10:00
Small Claims: Second and fourth Thursday in month 10:00
JP: One Wednesday in four

9811 LANARK SHERIFF COURT AND JUSTICE OF THE PEACE COURT
John G. Foy, Sheriff Clerk, Sheriff Court House, 24 Hope Street, Lanark ML11 7NE
Tel: 01555 661531
Fax: 01555 664319
DX: 570832 LANARK
Legal Post: LP-2 LANARK
Email: lanark@scotcourts.gov.uk

Courts and times
Sheriff Court House, 24 Hope Street, Lanark
Custody: Monday 14:00, Tuesday, Wednesday, Thursday, Friday 12:30
Criminal: Tuesday, Wednesday, Thursday 10:00
Ordinary: Alternate Tuesdays 11:00
Summary Cause: Alternate Tuesdays 10:00
JP: Three Wednesdays in four

9875 STRANRAER SHERIFF COURT AND JUSTICE OF THE PEACE COURT
B.J. Lindsay, Sheriff Clerk, Sheriff Court House, Stranraer DG9 7AA
Tel: 01776 702138; 706135
Fax: 01776 706792
DX: 581261 STRANRAER
Legal Post: LP-2 STRANRAER
Email: stranraer@scotcourts.gov.uk

Courts and times
Sheriff Court House, Stranraer
Criminal: Monday, Tuesday, Wednesday 10:00
Ordinary: Second and fourth Friday in month 10:00
Small Claims: Second and fourth Friday in month 10:00
Summary Cause: Second and fourth Friday in month 10:00
JP: Alternate Thursdays 10:00

SHERIFFDOM OF TAYSIDE, CENTRAL AND FIFE

Sheriff Principal: R.A. Dunlop QC
Sheriffdom Business Manager: Pam McFarlane, Stirling Sheriff Court, Viewfield Place, Stirling FK8 1NH. Tel: 01786 462191
Sheriffdom Legal Adviser: Alison Comiskey, Dundee Justice of the Peace Court, 6 West Bell Street, Dundee DD1 9AD. Tel: 01382 229961
Legal Advisers: Hilary Stephen, Kirkcaldy Sheriff Court; Jean Davis, Dunfermline Sheriff Court; Joyce Horsman and Iain Lockhart, Perth Sheriff Court; Tracey Scott, Stirling Sheriff Court; Amanda Inglis, Falkirk Sheriff Court; Stephen Wilson, Dundee Justice of the Peace Court
Fines Collection and Enforcement: tel: 01382 318251

9703 ALLOA SHERIFF COURT AND JUSTICE OF THE PEACE COURT
David Graham, Sheriff Clerk, Sheriff Court House, 47 Drysdale Street, Alloa FK10 1JA
Tel: 01259 722734
Fax: 01259 219470
DX: 560433 ALLOA
Legal Post: LP-3 ALLOA
Email: alloa@scotcourts.gov.uk

Courts and times
Sheriff Court House, 47 Drysdale Street, Alloa
Criminal: As required
JP: Alternate Tuesdays 10:00
Ordinary: Alternate Fridays 10:00
Summary Cause: Alternate Fridays 10:00
Small Claims: Alternate Fridays 10:00

9705 ARBROATH SHERIFF COURT AND JUSTICE OF THE PEACE COURT
Sheriff Clerk, Sheriff Court House, 88–92 High Street, Arbroath DD11 1HL
Tel: 01241 876600
Fax: 01241 874413
DX: 530442 ARBROATH
Legal Post: LP-3 ARBROATH
Email: arbroath@scotcourts.gov.uk

Courts and times
Sheriff Court House, 88–92 High Street, Arbroath
Criminal: Tuesday, Wednesday, Thursday 10:00
Ordinary: Monday 10:00
Summary Cause: Monday 10:00
Small Claims: Monday 10:00
JP: Friday 10:00

9717 CUPAR SHERIFF COURT AND JUSTICE OF THE PEACE COURT
Nicola Fraser, Sheriff Clerk, Sheriff Court House, Cupar KY15 4LX
Tel: 01334 652121
Fax: 01334 656807
DX: 560545 CUPAR
Legal Post: LP-11 CUPAR
Email: cupar@scotcourts.gov.uk

Courts and times
Sheriff Court House, Cupar
Criminal: Thursday
Ordinary: Alternate Wednesdays 10:00
Summary Cause: Alternate Wednesdays 14:00
Small Claims: Alternate Wednesdays 14:00
JP: Alternate Fridays 10:00

9726 DUNDEE SHERIFF COURT AND JUSTICE OF THE PEACE COURT
L. McIntosh, Sheriff Clerk, Sheriff Court House, Dundee DD1 9AD
Tel: 01382 229961
Fax: 01382 318222
DX: DD33 DUNDEE
Legal Post: LP-21 Dundee

Email: dundee@scotcourts.gov.uk

Courts and times
Sheriff Court House, Dundee
Criminal: Weekdays 09:30
Ordinary: Tuesday 10:00
Family: Thursday 10:00
Summary Cause: Monday 10:00
Small Claims: Monday 10:00
JP: Weekdays 10:00

9727 DUNFERMLINE SHERIFF COURT AND JUSTICE OF THE PEACE COURT
Johanne White, Sheriff Clerk, Sheriff Court House, 1–6 Carnegie Drive, Dunfermline KY12 7HJ
Tel: 01383 724666
Fax: 01383 621205
DX: DF17 DUNFERMLINE
Legal Post: LP-5 DUNFERMLINE
Email: dunfermline@scotcourts.gov.uk

Courts and times
Sheriff Court House, 1–6 Carnegie Drive, Dunfermline
Criminal: Weekdays 10:00
Ordinary: Monday 10:00
Summary Cause: Friday every four weeks 09:45
Small Claims: Friday every four weeks 10:00
JP: Tuesday, alternate Fridays 10:00

9751 FALKIRK SHERIFF COURT AND JUSTICE OF THE PEACE COURT
Dennis McCall, Sheriff Clerk, Sheriff Court House, Camelon, Falkirk FK1 4AR
Tel: 01324 620822
Fax: 01324 678238
DX: 552070 FALKIRK
Legal Post: LP 2 FALKIRK
Email: falkirk@scotcourts.gov.uk

Courts and times
Sheriff Court House, Camelon, Falkirk FK1 4AR
Criminal: Weekdays
Ordinary: Wednesday 10:00
Summary Cause: Wednesday 09:30 and 12:00
Small Claims: Wednesday 09:30
JP: Monday and Thursday 10:00

9752 FORFAR SHERIFF COURT AND JUSTICE OF THE PEACE COURT
Christine M. Petch, Sheriff Clerk, Sheriff Court House, Market Street, Forfar DD8 3LA
Tel: 01307 462186
Fax: 01307 462268
DX: 530674 FORFAR
Email: forfar@scotcourts.gov.uk

Courts and times
Sheriff Court House, Market Street, Forfar
Criminal: Thursday 10:00 and as required
Ordinary: Wednesday 10:00
Summary Cause: Wednesday 09:45
Small Claims: Wednesday 09:45
JP: Alternate Wednesdays 10:00

9803 KIRKCALDY SHERIFF COURT AND JUSTICE OF THE PEACE COURT
Gail Smith, Sheriff Clerk, Sheriff Court House, Whytescauseway, Kirkcaldy KY1 1XQ
Tel: 01592 260171
Fax: 01592 642361
DX: KY17 KIRKCALDY
Legal Post: LP-7 KIRKCALDY
Email: kirkcaldy@scotcourts.gov.uk

Courts and times
Sheriff Court House, Whytescauseway, Kirkcaldy
Criminal: Weekdays 10:00

Ordinary: Alternate Fridays 09:30
Options Hearings: Alternate Fridays 09:30
Child Welfare Hearings: Wednesday 09:30
Summary Cause: Friday 11:30
Summary Cause Heritable: Alternate Fridays 14:00
Small Claims: Friday 11:30
JP: Monday and Thursday 10:00

9853 PERTH SHERIFF COURT AND JUSTICE OF THE PEACE COURT
Mr A. Nicol, Sheriff Clerk, Sheriff Court House, Perth PH2 8NL
Tel: 01738 620546
Fax: 01738 623601
DX: PE20 PERTH
Legal Post: LP-8 PERTH
Email: perth@scotcourts.gov.uk

Courts and times
Sheriff Court House, Perth PH2 8NL
Criminal: As required
Ordinary: Alternate Wednesdays 10:00
Summary Cause: Alternate Wednesdays 10:00
Small Claims: Alternate Wednesdays 10:00
JP: Tuesday and Thursday 10:00

9872 STIRLING SHERIFF COURT AND JUSTICE OF THE PEACE COURT
Anne Reid, Sheriff Clerk, Sheriff Court House, Stirling FK8 1NH
Tel: 01786 462191
Fax: 01786 470456
DX: ST15 STIRLING
Legal Post: LP-6 STIRLING
Email: stirling@scotcourts.gov.uk

Courts and times
Sheriff Court House, Stirling
Criminal: Weekdays
Ordinary: Alternate Tuesdays 10:00
Summary Cause: Alternate Tuesdays 10:00
Small Claims: Alternate Tuesdays 10:00
JP: Wednesday and Friday 10:00

NUMERICAL INDEX TO COURT CODES OF SHERIFF COURTS

Court No		Page
9251	Aberdeen	205
9252	Banff	205
9253	Peterhead	207
9354	Stonehaven	207
9341	Elgin	206
9343	Dingwall	205
9344	Dornoch	205
9345	Fort William	206
9346	Inverness	206
9347	Portree	207
9348	Tain	208
9380	Livingston	210
9384	Stornoway	208
9702	Airdrie	215
9703	Alloa	218
9704	Ayr	215
9705	Arbroath	218
9716	Campbeltown	212
9717	Cupar	218
9723	Dumbarton	212
9724	Dumfries	216
9726	Dundee	218
9727	Dunfermline	219
9728	Dunoon	212
9729	Duns	209
9741	Edinburgh	209
9751	Falkirk	219
9752	Forfar	219
9761	Glasgow and Strathkelvin	204
9762	Greenock	212
9771	Haddington	210
9772	Hamilton	216
9791	Jedburgh	210
9801	Kilmarnock	213
9803	Kirkcaldy	219
9804	Kirkcudbright	217
9805	Kirkwall	206
9811	Lanark	217
9812	Lerwick	207
9814	Lochmaddy	207
9841	Oban	213
9851	Paisley	213
9852	Peebles	211
9853	Perth	220
9861	Rothesay	214
9871	Selkirk	211
9872	Stirling	220
9875	Stranraer	217
9891	Wick	208

NUMERICAL INDEX TO COURT CODES OF JUSTICES OF THE PEACE COURTS

Index of the Justice of the Peace Courts created by the Criminal Proceedings etc. (Reform) (Scotland) Act 2007.

HISTORICAL INDEX TO COURT CODES OF DISTRICT COURTS (NOW DISESTABLISHED)

in use after 1 September 1998

Court No	
9400	Aberdeen (City of) DC (DISESTABLISHED)
9405	Aberdeenshire DC at Banff
9407	Aberdeenshire DC at Inverurie (DISESTABLISHED)
9408	Aberdeenshire DC at Peterhead (DISESTABLISHED)
9409	Aberdeenshire DC at Stonehaven (DISESTABLISHED)
9415	Angus DC at Arbroath (DISESTABLISHED)
9417	Angus DC at Forfar (DISESTABLISHED)
9426	Argyll & Bute DC at Campbeltown (DISESTABLISHED)
9427	Argyll & Bute DC at Dunoon (DISESTABLISHED)
9428	Argyll & Bute DC at Helensburgh (DISESTABLISHED)
9429	Argyll & Bute DC at Lochgilphead (DISESTABLISHED)
9430	Argyll & Bute DC at Oban (DISESTABLISHED)
9440	Clackmannanshire DC at Alloa (DISESTABLISHED)
9445	Dumfries and Galloway DC at Annan (DISESTABLISHED)
9446	Dumfries and Galloway DC at Dumfries (DISESTABLISHED)
9447	Dumfries and Galloway DC at Kirkcudbright (DISESTABLISHED)
9449	Dumfries and Galloway DC at Sanquhar (CLOSED)
9450	Dumfries and Galloway DC at Stranraer (DISESTABLISHED)
9456	Dundee (City of) DC (DISESTABLISHED)
9460	East Ayrshire DC at Cumnock (DISESTABLISHED)
9461	East Ayrshire DC at Kilmarnock (DISESTABLISHED)
9465	East Dunbartonshire DC at Kirkintilloch (DISESTABLISHED)
9466	East Dunbartonshire DC at Milngavie (DISESTABLISHED)
9474	East Renfrewshire DC at Giffnock (DISESTABLISHED)
9478	Edinburgh (City of) DC (DISESTABLISHED)
9482	Falkirk DC (DISESTABLISHED)
9485	Fife DC at Cupar (DISESTABLISHED)
9486	Fife DC at Dunfermline (DISESTABLISHED)
9487	Fife DC at Kirkcaldy (DISESTABLISHED)
9495	Glasgow (City of) DC (DISESTABLISHED)
9500	Highland DC at Dingwall (DISESTABLISHED)
9501	Highland DC at Dornoch (DISESTABLISHED)
9502	Highland DC at Fort William (DISESTABLISHED)
9503	Highland DC at Inverness (DISESTABLISHED)
9504	Highland DC at Kingussie (DISESTABLISHED)
9505	Highland DC at Nairn (DISESTABLISHED)
9506	Highland DC at Portree (DISESTABLISHED)
9508	Highland DC at Wick (DISESTABLISHED)
9509	Highland DC at Tain (DISESTABLISHED)
9514	Inverclyde DC at Greenock (DISESTABLISHED)
9518	Midlothian DC at Loanhead (DISESTABLISHED)
9522	Moray DC at Elgin (DISESTABLISHED)
9526	North Ayrshire DC at Irvine (DISESTABLISHED)
9530	North Lanarkshire DC at Coatbridge (DISESTABLISHED)
9531	North Lanarkshire DC at Cumbernauld (DISESTABLISHED)
9532	North Lanarkshire DC at Motherwell (DISESTABLISHED)
9538	Perth & Kinross DC at Perth (DISESTABLISHED)
9542	Renfrewshire DC at Paisley (DISESTABLISHED)
9560	South Ayrshire DC at Ayr (DISESTABLISHED)
9561	South Ayrshire DC at Girvan (DISESTABLISHED)
9565	South Lanarkshire DC at East Kilbride (DISESTABLISHED)
9566	South Lanarkshire DC at Hamilton (DISESTABLISHED)

9567	South Lanarkshire DC at Lanark (DISESTABLISHED)
9568	South Lanarkshire DC at Rutherglen (DISESTABLISHED)
9572	Stirling DC (DISESTABLISHED)
9575	West Dunbartonshire DC at Clydebank (DISESTABLISHED)
9576	West Dunbartonshire DC at Dumbarton (DISESTABLISHED)
9584	Western Isles DC at Stornoway (DISESTABLISHED)

HISTORICAL INDEX TO COURT CODES OF DISTRICT COURTS (NOW DISESTABLISHED)

in use prior to 1 September 1998

Court No	
9901	Angus DC at Arbroath (DISESTABLISHED)
	Angus DC at Forfar (DISESTABLISHED)
9902	Dumfries and Galloway DC at Annan (DISESTABLISHED)
9903	Argyll and Bute DC at Campbeltown (DISESTABLISHED)
	Argyll and Bute DC at Dunoon (DISESTABLISHED)
	Argyll and Bute DC at Helensburgh (DISESTABLISHED)
	Argyll and Bute DC at Lochgilphead (DISESTABLISHED)
	Argyll and Bute DC at Oban (DISESTABLISHED)
9904	Highland DC at Kingussie (DISESTABLISHED)
9905	Aberdeenshire DC at Banff (DISESTABLISHED)
	Aberdeenshire DC at Peterhead (DISESTABLISHED)
9906	East Dunbartonshire DC at Milngavie (DISESTABLISHED)
9907	Scottish Borders DC at Duns (DISESTABLISHED)
9908	Highland DC at Wick (DISESTABLISHED)
9909	Clackmannanshire DC at Alloa (DISESTABLISHED)
9910	West Dunbartonshire DC at Clydebank (DISESTABLISHED)
9911	North Lanarkshire DC at Cumbernauld (DISESTABLISHED)
9912	East Ayrshire DC at Cumnock (DISESTABLISHED)
9913	North Ayrshire DC at Irvine (DISESTABLISHED)
9914	West Dunbartonshire DC at Dumbarton (DISESTABLISHED)
9915	Dundee, (City of) DC (DISESTABLISHED)
9916	Fife DC at Dunfermline (DISESTABLISHED)
9917	South Lanarkshire DC at East Kilbride (DISESTABLISHED)
9918	East Lothian DC at Haddington (DISESTABLISHED)
9919	East Renfrewshire DC at Giffnock (DISESTABLISHED)
9920	Edinburgh, (City of) DC (DISESTABLISHED)
9921	Scottish Borders DC at Selkirk (Ettrick & Lauderdale Division) (DISESTABLISHED)
9922	Falkirk DC (DISESTABLISHED)
9923	Glasgow, (City of) DC (DISESTABLISHED)
9924	Aberdeenshire DC at Inverurie (DISESTABLISHED)
9925	South Lanarkshire DC at Hamilton (DISESTABLISHED)
9926	Inverclyde DC at Greenock (DISESTABLISHED)
9927	Highland DC at Inverness (DISESTABLISHED)
9928	East Ayrshire DC at Kilmarnock (DISESTABLISHED)
9929	Aberdeenshire DC at Stonehaven (DISESTABLISHED)
9930	Fife DC at Kirkcaldy (DISESTABLISHED)
9931	South Ayrshire DC at Ayr (DISESTABLISHED)
	South Ayrshire DC at Girvan (DISESTABLISHED)
9932	South Lanarkshire DC at Lanark (DISESTABLISHED)
9933	Highland DC at Fort William (DISESTABLISHED)
9935	North Lanarkshire DC at Coatbridge (DISESTABLISHED)
9936	Moray DC at Elgin (DISESTABLISHED)
9937	North Lanarkshire DC at Motherwell (DISESTABLISHED)
9938	Highland DC at Nairn (DISESTABLISHED)
9939	Dumfries and Galloway DC at Dumfries (DISESTABLISHED)
	Dumfries and Galloway DC at Sanquhar (CLOSED) (DISESTABLISHED)
9940	Fife DC at Cupar (DISESTABLISHED)
9941	Perth and Kinross DC at Perth (DISESTABLISHED)
9942	Renfrewshire DC at Paisley (DISESTABLISHED)
9943	Highland DC at Dingwall (DISESTABLISHED)
9944	Scottish Borders DC at Jedburgh (Roxburgh Division) (DISESTABLISHED)
9945	Highland DC at Portree (DISESTABLISHED)

9946	Dumfries and Galloway DC at Kirkcudbright (DISESTABLISHED)
9947	Stirling DC (DISESTABLISHED)
9948	East Dunbartonshire DC at Kirkintilloch (DISESTABLISHED)
9949	Highland DC at Dornoch (DISESTABLISHED)
9950	Scottish Borders DC at Peebles (Tweeddale Division) (DISESTABLISHED)
9951	West Lothian DC at Livingston (DISESTABLISHED)
9952	Western Isles DC at Stornoway (DISESTABLISHED)
9953	Dumfries and Galloway DC at Stranraer (DISESTABLISHED)

INDEX TO ALL COURTS OF SUMMARY JURISDICTION

Chesham	1115	148
Cheshunt	1877	167
Chester	1173	150
Chester, Ellesmere Port and Neston	1188	150
Chester-le-Street	1576	158
Chesterfield	1418	155
Chichester	2928	188
Chichester and District	2936	188
Chiltern	1128	148
Chippenham	3007	189
Chipping Norton	2673	179
Chorley	1998	171
Christchurch	1503	157
Church	1999	171
Cirencester	1673	161
Cirencester, Fairford and Tetbury	1689	162
City of Hereford	1851	165
City of London	2570	178
	6570	191
City of Salford	1747	163
City of Westminster	2660	179
City of Worcester	1865	166
	1874	166
Claro	2527	176
Cleddau	3139	194
Cleethorpes	1930	169
Clerkenwell	2642	178
Coatbridge	9355	215
Cockermouth	1365	153
Colchester	1613	160
Coleford	1674	161
Coleraine	9014	200
Colwyn (Clwyd)	3052	192
Colwyn (Powys)	3322	197
Community Justice Centre, North Liverpool	3340	198
Congleton	1174	150
Conwy	3062	192
Conwy and Llandudno	3224	195
Cookstown	9015	200
Coquetdale (renamed Alnwick)	2347	175
Corby	2321	174
Coventry	2910	187
Craigavon	9016	222
Crawley	2929	188
Crewe and Nantwich	1175	150
Crickhowell	3323	197
Cricklade	3008	189
Cromer	1393	154
Crowborough	1598	159
Croydon MC	2576	178
	6576	191
Cullompton	1478	156
Cumbernauld JP	9531	216
Cupar	9717	218
Cwmbran	3202	194
Cynon Valley	3262	196

D

Dacorum	1878	167
Darlington	1577	158

Durham (North)	1583	159
Durham (South)	1584	159
Dursley	1675	161
Dwyfor	3236	196
Dyffryn Clwyd	3053	192

E

Ealing MC	2734	181
Easington	1580	158
Easingwold	2544	177
East Berkshire	1072	147
East Cambridgeshire	1166	150
East Coquetdale Ward	2339	175
East Cornwall	1289	152
East Derbyshire	1429	155
East Dereham	1388	154
East Dorset	1522	158
East Elloe	2057	173
East Gwent	3208	195
East Hertfordshire	1888	167
East Kent	1957	170
East Lancashire	1725	162
East Lincolnshire	2073	173
East London	2574	178
	6574	191
East Middle	1262	150
East Oxfordshire	2717	181
East Penwith	1263	151
East Powder	1264	151
East Radnor	3343	198
	3344	198
East Retford	2553	177
East South	1265	151
East Tyrone	-	223
East Ward	1366	153
East Yorkshire	1928	168
Eastbourne	1599	159
Eastbourne and Hailsham	1605	159
Eastleigh	1764	164
Eccles	1737	163
Eccleshall	2783	183
Eden	1324	152
Edinburgh	9741	209
Edinburgh (City of) JP	9478	209
Eifionydd	3225	195
Eifionydd and Pwllheli	3236	196
Elgin	9341	206
Ellesmere Port and Neston	1176	150
Elloes, Bourne and Stamford	2076	173
Ely	1138	149
Enfield	2757	182
Epping and Ongar	1616	160
Epsom	2837	185
Epworth and Goole	1928	168
Esher and Walton	2838	185
Essex, Mid-North	1612	160
Essex, Mid-South	1610	159
Essex, North-East	1613	160
Essex, North-West	1619	160
Essex, South-East	1629	161

Goole and Howdenshire	1928	168
Gosport	1766	164
Grantham and Sleaford	2077	174
Gravesham	1958	170
Great Yarmouth	1391	154
	1443	155
Greater Manchester Public Law Family Proceedings Courts and Manchester City Private Law Family Proceedings Courts		
Greenock	9762	212
Greenwich	2575	178
	6575	191
Greenwich YC	6656	192
Grimsby and Cleethorpes	1940	169
Grimsby (Borough)	1929	168
Grimsby (County)	1930	169
Guildford	2841	185
Gwent	3211	195
Gwent (North West)	3209	195
Gwent (South East)	3210	195
Gwynedd	3244	196
Gwyrfai	3227	195

H

Haddington	9771	210
Haddington JP	9270	210
Hailsham	1600	159
Halesowen	2912	187
Halifax	2982	188
Hallikeld	2529	176
Halstead	1618	160
Halstead and Hedingham	1628	161
Halton	1177	150
Hamilton	9772	216
Hammersmith	2570	178
	6570	191
Hampstead	2740	181
Hang, East	2530	176
Hang, West	2531	176
Haringey	2742	181
Harlow	1619	160
Harrogate and Skipton	2358	176
Harrow	2760	182
Hartismere	2819	184
Hartlepool	1247	150
Harwich	1620	160
Hastings	1601	159
Hastings and Rother	1606	159
Hatfield	1879	167
Havant	1767	164
Haverfordwest	3117	193
Haverhill	2825	184
Haverhill and Sudbury	2864	186
Havering	1837	165
Hawarden	3055	192
Hawkshead	1367	153
Helston and Kerrier	1267	151
Hendon	2571	178
	6571	191
Henley	2675	179
Hereford (City of)	1851	165

King's Lynn	1392	154
Kingston upon Hull	1933	169
Kingston-upon-Thames	2812	184
Kington	1855	165
Kirkcaldy	9803	219
Kirkcudbright	9804	217
Kirklees	2987	189
Kirkwall	9805	206
Knighton	3326	197
Knowsley	2266	174

L

Lackford (renamed Mildenhall)	2821	184
Lampeter	3118	193
Lanark	9811	217
Lanbaurgh East	1248	150
Lancaster	2002	171
Larne	9024	201
Lavender Hill	2577	178
	6577	191
Lawford's Gate	1014	146
Ledbury	1856	165
Leeds	2988	189
Leeds District	2992	189
Leek	2784	183
Leicester (City)	2039	172
Leicester (County)	2040	172
Leicester	2089	172
Leigh	1743	163
Leighton Buzzard	1054	147
Leominster and Wigmore	1857	165
Lerwick	9812	207
Lesnewth	1269	151
Lewes	1603	159
Lewes and Crowbrough	1607	159
Lewisham YC	6656	192
Lichfield	2785	183
Lichfield and Tamworth	2860	186
Limavady	9025	201
Lincoln (City)	2061	173
Lincoln (County)	2072	173
Lincoln District	2079	174
Lincoln (Kesteven)	2062	173
Lincolnshire (North)	1903	168
Lindsey (Lincoln and Wragby)	2063	173
Linslade	1118	148
Linton	1141	149
Lisburn	9026	202
Liskerrett	1270	151
Liverpool	2267	174
Liverpool and Knowsley	1730	191
Livingston	9380	210
Llandeilo	3119	193
Llandovery	3120	193
Llandrindod Wells (renamed Radnorshire and North Brecknock)	3327	197
	3351	198
Llandyssul	3121	193
Llanelli	3122	193
Llanfyllin	3328	197
Llanidloes	3329	197

Mid Northants	2324	174
Mid-North Essex	1612	160
Mid-South Essex	1610	159
Mid Staffordshire	2795	183
Mid Staffordshire and Rugeley	2799	186
Mid Sussex	2932	188
Mid Warwickshire	2903	187
Mid Worcestershire	1872	166
Mildenhall	2821	184
Milford Haven	3123	193
Milton Keynes	1124	168
Miskin	3265	196
Mold	3056	192
Monmouth	3204	195
Montgomery	3332	197
Montgomeryshire	3355	198
Moreton and Wallingford	2676	180
Morley	2989	189
Morpeth Ward	2342	175
Motherwell JP	9532	216
Moyle	9030	202

N

Nant Conwy	3228	195
Narberth	3124	193
Neath	3359	198
Neath Port Talbot	3359	198
New Forest	1779	164
New Radnor	3333	197
New Spelthorne (renamed Feltham)	2769	182
New Windsor	1070	147
Newark	2556	178
Newark and Southwell	2567	178
Newbury	1069	147
Newcastle and Ogmore	3266	196
Newcastle Emlyn	3125	193
Newcastle-under-Lyme	2786	183
Newcastle-under-Lyme and Pirehill North	2797	183
Newcastle-upon-Tyne	2351	185
Newent	1680	161
Newmarket	1142	149
Newmarket (Cambs)	1164	150
Newmarket (Suffolk)	2823	184
Newnham	1681	161
Newport	3205	195
Newport Pagnell	1120	148
Newry and Mourne	9032	202
	3334	197
Newtown	3347	198
	3352	198
Newtownabbey	9033	202
Norfolk	1972	171
Norman Cross	1143	149
North and East Surrey	2845	185
North and East Hertfordshire	1889	168
North Anglesey	3229	195
North Antrim	-	202
North Avon	1021	146
North Bedfordshire (renamed Bedford and Mid Bedfordshire)	124	146
North Cotswold	1694	162

Nottingham (County)	2558	178
Nuneaton	2896	186

O

Oban	9841	213
Odiham	1770	164
Odsey	1882	167
Okehampton	1483	156
Oldham	1734	163
Old Street	2648	179
Omagh	9035	203
Ormskirk	2003	171
Orwell	2824	184
Oswestry	3277	191
Oundle and Thrapston	2326	175
Oxford	2678	180
	2777	182
Oxfordshire	2777	182

P

Painscastle	3335	197
Paisley	9851	213
Peebles	9852	211
Peebles JP	9352	211
Pembroke	3126	193
Pembrokeshire	3356	198
Pencader	3127	193
Pendle	2004	171
Penllyn	3230	196
Pennine	(no ct no)	
Penrith and Alston	1378	153
	1384	154
Penryn	1271	151
Penwith	1272	151
Pershore	1859	166
Perth	9853	220
Peterborough	1162	149
Peterhead	9253	207
Petersfield	1771	164
Petworth	2933	188
Pirehill North	2787	183
Plymouth	1484	156
	1290	152
Plympton	1485	156
Pontefract	2994	189
Pontypool	3206	195
Poole	1505	157
Port Talbot	3357	198
Portree	9347	207
Portsmouth	1772	164
Powder Tywardreath	1273	151
Principal Registry of the Family Division		106
Presteigne	3336	197
Preston	2005	171
Pudsey and Otley	2990	189
Pwllheli	3231	196
Pydar	1274	151

R

Radnor, East see East Radnor Radnorshire and North Brecknock	3351	198

Sevenoaks	1963	170
Severnminster (renamed Kidderminster)	1842	165
Shaftesbury	1506	157
	1513	158
Sheffield	2773	182
Shepton Mallet	2707	180
Sherborne	1507	158
Shipston-on-Stour	2898	187
Shrewsbury	3279	191
Shrewsbury and North Shropshire	3279	191
Sittingbourne	1964	170
Skegness	2082	174
Skipton	2538	177
Skyrack and Wetherby	2991	189
Sleaford	2066	173
	2080	174
Slough	1072	147
Sodbury	1016	146
Soke of Peterborough	1158	149
Solihull	2916	187
Somerset	1022	146
Somerton	2708	180
South and Middle Holderness	1902	168
South Anglesey	3232	196
South Ayrshire DC at Ayr	9560	215
South Cambridgeshire	1163	150
South Cheshire	1187	150
South Derbyshire	1425	155
South Devon	1302	152
South Durham	1584	159
South East Cornwall	1280	152
South East Essex	1629	161
South East Gwent	3210	195
South East Hampshire	1782	165
South East London	2575	178
	6575	191
South East Northumberland	2352	175
South East Staffordshire	2799	186
South East Suffolk	2866	186
South East Surrey	2847	185
South East Surrey	2856	186
South East Wiltshire	3027	190
South Essex	1971	171
South Gloucestershire	1693	162
South Hams	1496	157
South Hampshire	1783	165
South Herefordshire	1869	166
South Holderness	1937	169
South Hunsley and Beacon and Howdenshire	1901	167
South Hunsley Beacon	1901	167
	1938	169
South Lakeland	1398	154
South Lakes	1381	154
South Lanarkshire DC at Hamilton	9566	216
South Lincolnshire	2105	174
South London	2576	178
	6576	191
South Meirionnydd	3235	196
South Mimms	1884	167

Sussex (Central)	2950	188
Sussex (Eastern)	2948	188
Sussex (Northern)	2947	188
Sussex (Western)	2949	188
Sutton MC	2756	181
	2733	181
Sutton Coldfield	2909	187
Swaffham	1395	154
Swansea	3360	199
Swindon	3015	190

T

Tain	9348	208
Talgarth	3338	197
Talybont	3233	196
Tameside	1748	163
Tamworth	2793	183
Taunton Deane	2709	180
Taunton Deane and West Somerset	2709	180
Tavistock	1487	156
Teesdale and Wear Valley	1582	159
Teesside	1249	150
Teignbridge	1488	156
Telford & South Shropshire	3282	191
Tenbury	1863	166
Tenby	3130	194
Tendring	1625	160
Tetbury	1685	162
Tewksbury	1686	162
Thame and Henley	2719	181
	2778	182
Thames	2574	178
	6574	191
Thanet	1968	170
Thetford	1396	154
Thornbury	1017	146
Thurrock	1626	160
Tisbury and Mere	3016	190
Tiverton	1489	156
Todmorden	2983	189
Tonbridge and Malling	1965	170
Torbay	1490	157
Toseland	1147	149
Totnes	1491	157
Tottenham MC	2572	178
	6572	191
Totton and New Forest	1776	164
Towcester	2327	175
Tower Bridge	2576	178
	6576	191
Trafford	1742	163
Tregaron	3131	194
Trowbridge	3017	190
Truro and South Powder	1282	152
Truro and West Powder	1277	151
Tunbridge Wells and Cranbrook	1966	170
Tynedale	2346	175

U

Upper Rhymney Valley	3267	196

West Suffolk	2867	186
West Ward	1374	153
West Wiltshire	3024	190
Westbury	3019	190
Westminster	2570	178
	6570	191
Weston-super-Mare	1019	146
Weymouth and Portland	1510	158
Whitby Strand	2540	177
Whitehaven	1375	153
Whitland	3132	194
Whitminster	1687	162
Whittlesey	1148	149
Whorwellsdown	3020	190
Wick	9891	208
Wigan	1745	163
	1746	163
Wigan and Leigh LJA	1749	163
Wigton	1376	153
Willesden	2762	182
Wilton Beacon	1939	169
Wiltshire	3015	190
Wimbledon	2577	178
	6577	191
Wimborne	1511	158
Wincanton	2712	180
Winchcombe	1688	162
Winchester	1777	164
Windsor	1074	147
Windsor County	1073	147
Winslow	1122	148
Wirral	2271	174
Wisbech	1160	149
Wisbech (Borough)	1149	149
Wisbech (Isle)	1150	149
Witham	1627	160
Witney	2703	180
	2779	182
Woking	2844	185
Wolds	2078	174
Wolverhampton	2919	187
Wonford	1492	157
Woodbridge	2829	184
Woodspring (renamed North Somerset)	1023	146
Woodstock	2701	180
Woolwich	2643	178
Worcester (City of)	1865	166
	1874	166
Worcester (County)	1866	166
Worcester (County)(Motorway)	1867	166
Workington	1377	153
Worksop	2560	178
Worksop and Retford	2087	178
Worthing	2935	188
Worthing and District	2937	188
Wrekin (The)	3280	191
Wrexham Maelor	3058	192
Wycombe	1127	148
Wycombe and Beaconsfield	1130	148

Part IV

Coroners and Coroner's Officers

CORONERS AND CORONER'S OFFICERS

CHIEF CORONER OF ENGLAND AND WALES
His Honour Judge Peter Thornton QC

THE ROYAL HOUSEHOLD
Senior Coroner: M.J.C. Burgess
49 Ormond Avenue, Hampton, Middlesex TW12 2RY

AVON

AVON
Coroner: Ms M.E. Voisin
Coroner's Court, The Courthouse, Old Weston Road, Flax Bourton, Bristol BS48 1UL
Tel: 01275 461920
Fax: 01275 462749
Email: coroners.officers@bristol.gov.uk

BEDFORDSHIRE

BEDFORDSHIRE & LUTON
Coroner: Mr Tom R. Osborne
Tel: 0300 300 6559
The Court House, Woburn Street, Ampthill MK45 2HX
Tel: 0300 300 6557/6558
Fax: 0300 300 8267

BERKSHIRE

BERKSHIRE
Coroner: Peter J. Bedford
Yeomanry House, 131 Castle Hill, Reading RG1 7TA
Tel: 0118 937 3528
Fax: 0118 937 5448
Email: peter.bedford@reading.gov.uk
Coroner's Officers:
Paul Beecroft; Karen Benson; Tracy Lockett
Tel: 0118 322 8789
Annabelle Curtis; Paul Cadman
Tel: 01344 823528
Anna Soylemezli; Janine Prunty
Tel: 01753 633732

BUCKINGHAMSHIRE

BUCKINGHAMSHIRE
Coroner: R.A. Hulett
29 Windsor End, Beaconsfield HP9 2JJ
Tel: 01494 475505
Fax: 01494 673760
DX: 34502 BEACONSFIELD
Email: coroners@buckscc.gov.uk
Coroner's Officers:
As above

MILTON KEYNES
Coroner: Thomas Osborne
Postal address: Coroner's Office, Milton Keynes Council, 1 Saxon Gate East, Central Milton Keynes MK9 3EJ
Court address: Milton Keynes Coroner's Court, Crownhill Crematorium Site, Dansteed Way, Milton Keynes MK8 0AH
Tel: 01908 254327
Fax: 01908 253636
Email: coroners.office@milton-keynes.gov.uk
Coroner's Officer:
As above

CAMBRIDGESHIRE

NORTH & EAST CAMBRIDGESHIRE
Coroner: William R. Morris
Coroner's Office, Lawrence Court, Princes Street, Huntingdon PE29 3PA
Tel: 0345 045 1364
Fax: 01480 372777
Email: hmcoroners.cambridge@cambridgeshire.gov.uk

SOUTH & WEST CAMBRIDGESHIRE
Coroner: David S. Morris
Coroner's Office, Lawrence Court, Princes Street, Huntingdon PE29 3PA
Tel: 0345 045 1364
Fax: 01480 372777
Email: coroners@cambridgeshire.gov.uk

PETERBOROUGH
Coroner: David Heming
The Registrar Office, 33 Thorpe Road, Peterborough PE3 6AB
Tel: 01733 452275 (office); 01733 452275 (coroner); Mob: 07920 160718
Fax: 0870 238 4085
Email: hmcoroner@peterborough.gov.uk
Coroner's Officers:
Gemma James
Tel: 01733 452372
Email: gemma.james@peterborough.gov.uk
Alan Peart
Tel: 01733 452373
Email: alan.peart@peterborough.gov.uk

CHESHIRE

CHESHIRE
Coroner: N.L. Rheinberg
The West Annexe, Town Hall, Sankey Street, Warrington WA1 1UH
Tel: 01925 444216
Fax: 01925 444219
Email: nrheinberg@warrington.gov.uk

CORNWALL

CORNWALL
Coroner: Dr E.E. Carlyon
The New Lodge, Penmount Crematorium, Newquay Road, Truro, TR4 9AA
Tel: 01872 261612
Email: cornwallcoroner@cornwall.gov.uk
Coroner's Officers:
Truro Police Station, The New Lodge, Penmount Crematorium, Newquay Road, Truro, TR4 9AA

Tel: (enquiries) 01872 326075; (to report a death) 01872 326207

ISLES OF SCILLY
Coroner: I.M. Arrow
Cary Chambers, 1 Palk Street, Torquay TQ2 5EL
Tel: 01803 380705
Fax: 01803 380704
Email: hmcoroner@torbay.gov.uk

CUMBRIA

NORTH & WEST CUMBRIA
Coroner: David Ll. Roberts
Fairfield, Station Road, Cockermouth CA13 9PT
Tel: 01900 706902
Fax: 01900 706915
Email: hmcoroner.northwest@cumbria.gov.uk

SOUTH & EAST CUMBRIA
Coroner: Ian Smith
Central Police Station, Market Street, Barrow-in-Furness LA14 2LE
Tel: 01229 848966
Fax: 01229 848953

DERBYSHIRE

DERBY & SOUTH DERBYSHIRE
Senior Coroner: Dr Robert Hunter
St Katherine's House, St Mary's Wharf, Mansfield Road, Derby DE1 3TQ
Tel: 01332 343225
Fax: 01332 294942
Email: derby.coroner@derbyshire.gov.uk

SCARSDALE & HIGH PEAK
Senior Coroner: Dr Robert Hunter
Coroner's Court, 5–6 Royal Court, Basil Close, Chesterfield S41 7SL
Tel: 01246 201391
Fax: 01246 273058

DEVON

EXETER & GREATER DEVON
Coroner: Dr Elizabeth Ann Earland
Room 226, Devon County Hall, Topsham Road, Exeter EX2 4QD
Tel: 01392 383636
Fax: 01392 383635
Email: coroner@exgd-coroner.co.uk

PLYMOUTH & SOUTH WEST DEVON
Coroner: I.M. Arrow
3 The Crescent, Plymouth PL1 3AB
Tel: 01752 204636
Fax: 01752 313297
Email: hmcoroner@plymouth.gov.uk

TORBAY & SOUTH DEVON
Coroner: I.M. Arrow
Cary Chambers, 1 Palk Street, Torquay TQ2 5EL
Tel: 01803 380705
Fax: 01803 380704
Email: hmcoroner@torbay.gov.uk

DORSET

DORSET
Coroner: S.S. Payne
The Coroner's Court, Stafford Road, Bournemouth BH1 1PA
Tel: 01202 310049
Fax: 01202 780423
DX: 156942 BOURNEMOUTH 3
Email: coroner@bournemouth.gov.uk
Coroner's Officers:
Tel: 01202 789057/879/353/154
Fax: 01202 780423

COUNTY DURHAM

COUNTY DURHAM AND DARLINGTON
Senior Coroner: Andrew Tweddle LL.B.
Assistant Coroners: J.R. Leslie Hamilton LI.M. F.R.C.S; Crispin Oliver M.A.; Oliver R. Longstaff B.A.
HM Coroner's Office, Fourth Floor, Civic Centre, North Terrace, Crook DL15 9ES
Postal address: HM Coroner's Office, PO Box 282, Bishop Auckland DL14 4FY
Tel: 03000 265556
Fax: 0191 3280057
Email: hmcoroner@durham.gov.uk
Coroner's Officers:
Durham Constabulary, Spennymoor Police Station, Wesleyan Road, Spennymoor DL16 6FB
Tel: 0345 606 0365

HARTLEPOOL
Coroner: C.W.M. Donnelly
c/o Donnelly McArdle Adamson, Solicitors, 155 York Road, Hartlepool TS26 9EQ
Tel: 01429 861563
Fax: 01429 260199

EAST YORKSHIRE

EAST RIDING & KINGSTON-UPON-HULL
Coroner: Prof. Paul V. Marks
Coroner's Office & Court, The Guildhall, Alfred Gelder Street, Kingston-upon-Hull HU1 2AA
Tel: 01482 613009
Fax: 01482 613020
Email: Julie.K.Wright@hullcc.gov.uk

ESSEX

ESSEX, THURROCK AND SOUTHEND
Coroner: Mrs Caroline Beasley-Murray
Area Coroner: Mrs Eleanor McGann
HM Coroner's Office, A Block, Victoria Road South, Chelmsford CM1 1QH
Tel: 0333 013 5000
Fax: 01245 437947/8
Email: coroner@essex.gov.uk

GLOUCESTERSHIRE

GLOUCESTERSHIRE
Coroner: Ms Katy Skerrett
Gloucestershire Coroner's Court, Corinium Avenue, Barnwood, Gloucester GL4 3DJ
Tel: 01452 305661

Fax: 01452 412618
Email: coroner@gloucestershire.gov.uk

GREATER MANCHESTER

MANCHESTER
Senior Coroner: N.S. Meadows
PO Box 532, Manchester Town Hall, Albert Square M60 2LA
Tel: 0161 219 2222
Fax: 0161 274 7329
Email: coroners@manchester.gov.uk

MANCHESTER NORTH
Coroner: Simon Nelson
Rochdale Coroners Office, 4th Floor, Telegraph House, Baillie Street, Rochdale OL16 1QY
Tel: 01706 924815
Email: coroners@rochdale.gov.uk

MANCHESTER SOUTH
Senior Coroner: J.S. Pollard
Area Coroner: Miss Joanne Kearsley
The Coroner's Court 1 Mount Tabor Street, Stockport SK1 3AG
Tel: 0161 474 3993
Fax: 0161 474 3994
Email: john.pollard@stockport.gov.uk

MANCHESTER WEST
Coroner: Mrs Jennifer Leeming
Paderborn House, Civic Centre, Howell Croft North, Bolton BL1 1JW
Tel: 01204 338799
Fax: 01204 338798
Email: coroners@bolton.gov.uk

HAMPSHIRE

SOUTHAMPTON AND WESTERN HAMPSHIRE
Coroner: G.A. Short
Castle Hill, The Castle, Winchester, SO23 HUL
Tel: 01962 667884
Fax: 01962 667893
Email: hampshirecoroners@hants.gov.uk

NORTH EAST
Coroner: A.M. Bradley
Goldings, London Road, Basingstoke RG21 4AN
Tel: 01256 478119
Fax: 01256 814292
Coroner's Officer: David Richards
As above

PORTSMOUTH & SOUTH EAST HAMPSHIRE
Coroner: David Clark Horsley
The Guildhall, Guildhall Square, Portsmouth PO1 2AB
Tel: 023 9268 8326
Fax: 023 9268 8331
Email: coroners.office@portsmouthcc.gov.uk

HEREFORDSHIRE

HEREFORDSHIRE
Senior Coroner: H.G.M. Bricknell
The Town Hall, St Owen Street, Hereford HR1 2PJ

Tel: 01432 261813
Fax: 01432 261720
Email: coroners@herefordshire.gov.uk

HERTFORDSHIRE

HERTFORDSHIRE
Coroner: E.G. Thomas
The Old Courthouse, St Albans Road East, Hatfield AL10 0ES
Tel: 01707 292707
Fax: 01707 897399
DX: 100702 HATFIELD
Email: coroner.service@hertfordshire.gov.uk
Coroner's Officers:
As above

ISLE OF WIGHT

ISLE OF WIGHT
Coroner: Mrs C. Sumeray
3–9 Quay Street, Newport, Isle of Wight PO30 5BB
Tel: 01983 520697
Fax: 01983 527678
Email: coroners@iow.gov.uk

KENT

CENTRAL & SOUTH EAST KENT
Coroner: Rachel Redman
Elphicks Farmhouse, Hunton, Maidstone ME15 0SB
Tel: 01622 820412
Fax: 01622 820800
Email: rredman@kentcoroner.co.uk
Coroner's Officers:
Ashford Police Station, Tufton Street, Ashford TN23 1BT
Tel: (Ashford) 01233 896242; (Folkestone/Hythe) 896171; (Dover; Faversham) 896172
Fax: 01233 896249

MID KENT & MEDWAY
Coroner: Patricia Harding
The Archbishop's Palace, Mill Street, Maidstone ME15 6YE
Tel: 03000 410502 (new & current cases); 03000 410503 (all other enquiries)
Fax: 01622 663690
Email: mkmcoroner@kent.gov.uk
Coroner's Officers:
The Archbishop's Palace, Mill Street, Maidstone ME15 6YE
Tel: 03000 410502 (new & current cases); 03000 410503 (all other enquiries)
Fax: 01622 663690

NORTH EAST KENT
Coroner: Alan Blunsdon
St Peters House, Dane Valley Road, Broadstairs, Kent CT10 3JJ
Tel: 01843 863260
Fax: 01843 603927
Coroner's Officers:
Margate Police Station, Fort Hill, Margate
Tel: 01843 222170/1/3/5
Fax: 01843 222172

NORTH WEST KENT
Coroner: Roger Hatch
The White House, Melliker Lane, Hook Green, Meopham DA13 0JB
Tel: 01474 815747
Fax: 01474 815356
Email: nwkentcoroner@aol.com
Coroner's Officers:
Tunbridge Wells Police Station, Crescent Road, Tunbridge Wells TN1 2LU
Tel: 01892 502171/137
Fax: 01892 502172
North Kent Police Station, Thames Way, Northfleet DA11 8BD
Tel: 01474 366481/2
Fax: 01474 366489

LANCASHIRE

BLACKBURN, HYNDBURN AND RIBBLE VALLEY
Coroner: M.J.H. Singleton
Blackburn Central Library, Town Hall Street, Blackburn BB2 1AG
Tel: 01254 588680; mob: 07968 326068
Fax: 01254 588681
Email: michael.singleton@blackburn.gov.uk
Coroner's Officers: John Clucas; Debbie Stewart; Darren Wingrove
The Royal Blackburn Hospital, Haslingden Road, Blackburn BB2 3HH
Tel: 01254 734116; mob: 07983 016369; 07940 93955

BLACKPOOL/FYLDE
Coroner: Alan Anthony Wilson
Municipal Buildings, Blackpool Council, Corporation Street, Blackpool FY1 1GB
Tel: 01253 477128
Fax: 01253 477129
Email: kerry.hall@blackpool.gov.uk
Coroner's Officers:
Lancashire Constabulary, Montague Street, Blackpool
Tel: 01253 604207
Fax: 01253 604200

EAST LANCASHIRE
Coroner: Richard G. Taylor
6a Hargreaves Street, Burnley BB11 1ES (coroner)
Lyndhurst House, Todmorden Road, Burnley, Lancs BB10 4AB (coroner's office)
Tel: 01282 838356
Fax: 01282 425041
Email: rtaylor@southernslaw.info; eastlancscoroners@lancashire.gov.uk
DX: 23860 BURNLEY
Coroner's Officers:
Tel: 01282 804508/539
Email: Jayne.Morant@lancashire.pnn.police.uk
Martin.Hall2@lancashire.pnn.police.uk

PRESTON & WEST LANCASHIRE
Coroner: Dr James Adeley
2 Faraday Court, Faraday Drive, Fulwood, Preston PR2 9NB
Tel: 01772 703700
Fax: 01772 704422
Coroner's Officers:
Royal Preston Hospital, Sharoe Green Lane North, Fulwood, Preston
Tel: 01772 524740
Fax: 01772 524361
Chorley Police Station, St Thomas's Road, Chorley
Tel: 01257 246207
Fax: 01257 246348
Royal Lancaster Infirmary, Ashton Road, Lancaster LA1 4RP

Tel: 01524 516353
Fax: 01524 516059

LEICESTERSHIRE

LEICESTER CITY & SOUTH LEICESTERSHIRE
Coroner: C.E. Mason
The Town Hall, Leicester LE1 9BG
Email: leicester.coroner@leicester.gov.uk
Coroner's Officers:
Tel: 0116 454 1030

RUTLAND & NORTH LEICESTERSHIRE
Senior Coroner: T.H. Kirkman
Coroner's Office, Southfield Road, Loughborough LE11 2TR
Tel: 0116 305 7732
Fax: 01509 550473
Email: hmcoroner@leics.gov.uk

LINCOLNSHIRE

CENTRAL LINCOLNSHIRE
Coroner: S.P.G. Fisher
Lindum House, 10 Queen Street, Spilsbury PE23 5JE
Tel: 01522 552500
Fax: 01522 516055
Email: lincscoroner@lincolnshire.gov.uk
Coroner's Officers:
Area Police HQ, West Parade, Lincoln LN1 1YP
Tel: 01522 885217
Fax: 01522 885344
County Police Station, The Wong, Horncastle LN9 6EB
Tel: 01205 312330
Fax: 01205 312310

NORTH LINCOLNSHIRE & GRIMSBY
Coroner: Paul Kelly
HM Coroner's Office, The Town Hall, Knoll Street, Cleethorpes DN35 8LN
Tel: 01472 324005
Fax: 01472 324007
Email: coroners@nelincs.gov.uk

SOUTH LINCOLNSHIRE
Coroner: A.R.W. Forrest
Unit 1, Gilbert Drive, Endeavour Park, Boston PE21 7QT
Tel: 01522 552064
Coroner's Officer: J. Bradwell; K. Chamberlain
County Police Station, Lincoln Lane, Boston PE21 8QS
Tel: 01205 312217/311
Fax: 01205 312353
Email: james.bradwell@lincs.pnn.police.uk
kevin.chamberlain@lincs.pnn.police.uk

LONDON

CITY OF LONDON
Coroner: Paul Matthews
City of London Coroner's Court, Walbrook Wharf, 78–83 Upper Thames Street, London EC4R 3TD
Tel: 020 7332 1598
Fax: 020 7332 1800
Email: barry.tuckfield@cityoflondon.gov.uk

EASTERN DISTRICT OF GREATER LONDON
Coroner: Nadia Persaud
Coroner's Court, Queens Road, Walthamstow E17 8QP
Tel: 020 8496 5000
Fax: (Barking, Dagenham, Havering, Romford) 020 8496 3378; (Newham, Redbridge, Walthamstow) 020 8496 3379
Email: sue.hardie@walthamforest.gov.uk

INNER NORTH LONDON
Senior Coroner: Ms Mary E. Hassell
St Pancras Coroner's Court, Camley Street, London NIC 4PP
Tel: 020 7974 4545
Fax: 020 7383 2485
Poplar Coroner's Court, 127 Poplar High Street, London E14 0AE
Tel: 020 7538 1201
Fax: 020 7538 0565

INNER SOUTH LONDON
Coroner: Dr Andrew Harris
St Blaise Building, Bromley Civic Centre, Stockwell Close, Bromley BR1 3UH
Tel: 020 7525 4200
Email: andrew.harris@southwark.gov.uk

INNER WEST LONDON
Coroner: Fiona J. Wilcox
Westminster Coroner's Court, 65 Horseferry Road, London SW1P 2ED
Tel: 020 7802 4750
Fax: 020 7828 2837
Wandsworth and Merton Office, 5th Floor, Westminster City Hall, 64 Victoria Street, London SW1E 6QP
Tel: 020 7641 5305

NORTH LONDON
Senior Coroner: Andrew Walker
29 Wood Street, Barnet, London EN5 4BE
Tel: 020 8447 7680
Fax: 020 8447 7689/7690
Coroner's Clerk: Jacqueline Reid
Tel: 020 8447 7693; mob: 07772 137993
Email: jacqueline.reed@hmc-northlondon.co.uk

SOUTHERN DISTRICT OF GREATER LONDON
Coroner: Dr Roy Palmer
Croydon Coroner's Court, Barclay Road, Croydon CR9 3NE
Tel: 020 8681 3275
Email: info@southlondoncoroner.org
Website: www.southlondoncoroner.org
Coroner's Officers:
St Blaise Building, Bromley Civic Centre, Stockwell Close, Bromley BR1 3UH
Tel: 020 8313 1883

WEST LONDON
Coroner: Mr Chinyere Inyame
25 Bagleys Lane, Fulham, London SW6 2QA
Tel: 020 8753 6800/02
Fax: 020 8753 6803
Email: hmcoroner@lbhf.gov.uk

MERSEYSIDE

LIVERPOOL
Coroner: A.J.A. Rebello OBE
Gerard Majella Courthouse, Boundary Street, Liverpool L5 2QD
Tel: 0151 225 5770/5057/5058
Fax: 0151 703 6838

Email: coroner@liverpool.gov.uk

SEFTON, KNOWSLEY & ST HELENS
Coroner: Christopher Kent Sumner
Southport Town Hall, Lord Street, Southport PR8 1DA
Tel: 0151 934 2746/9
Fax: 01704 534321
Email: coroner@sefton.gov.uk
Coroner's Officers:
Sefton North, Sefton South
Southport Police Station, Law Courts, Southport
Tel: 0151 777 3480
Fax: 01704 512784
Email: coroner@sefton.gov.uk
Knowsley & St Helens
Coroner's Office, Whiston Hospital, Whiston, Merseyside
Tel: 0151 430 1238
Fax: 0151 426 6694
Email: coroner@sefton.gov.uk

WIRRAL
Coroner: A Rebello
Wirral Coroner's Office, St George's Hall (William Brown Street Entrance), St George's Place,
Liverpool L1 1JJ
Tel: 0151 691 8648
Email: hmcoroner@wirral.gov.uk

NORFOLK

NORFOLK
Coroner: Mrs Jacqueline Lake
Office: 69–75 Thorpe Road, Norwich NR1 1UA
Court: Eastgate House, 122A Thorpe Road, Norwich NR1 1RT
Tel: 01603 663302
Fax: 01603 665511
Email: norfolk@coroner.norfolk.gov.uk
Coroner's Officers:
King's Lynn Police Station, St James Street, King's Lynn, Norfolk PE30 5DE
Tel: 01553 665088
Fax: 01553 665017

NORTH YORKSHIRE

EASTERN DISTRICT
Coroner: M.D. Oakley
Rose Cottage, Oswaldkirk, York YO62 5XT
Tel: 01439 788339; mob: 07860 789957
Email: moakleyrosecott@aol.com
Coroner's Officers:
Police Station, Northway, Scarborough YO12 7AD
Tel: 01723 509332
Fax: 01723 509030
Police Station, 72 High Street, Northallerton DL7 8BR
Tel: 01609 789458
Fax: 01609 789413

WESTERN DISTRICT
Coroner: R. Turnbull
21 Grammar School Lane, Northallerton DL6 1DF
Tel: 01609 533805; 533843 (Secretary)
Fax: 01609 780793
Email: coronersadmin@northyorks.gov.uk

Coroner's Officers:
Police Station, North Yorkshire Police, Beckwith Head Road, Beckwith, Harrogate HG1 1FR
Tel: 01423 539332
Fax: 01423 539302
Police Station, 72 High Street, Northallerton DL7 8ES
Tel: 01609 789458
Fax: 01609 789413
Police Station, Otley Street, Skipton BD23 1EZ
Tel: 01423 539731
Fax: 01423 539701
Police Station, Portholme Road, Selby YO8 4QQ
Tel: 01904 669654
Fax: 01904 669651

TEESSIDE
Acting Senior Coroner: Miss C. Bailey
The Coroners Service, Middlesbrough Town Hall, Albert Road Middlesbrough TS1 2QJ
Tel: 01642 729350
Fax: 01642 729948
Email: teessidecoroner@middlesbrough.gcsx.gov.uk

YORK
Senior Coroner: W.D.F. Coverdale
Sentinel House, Peasholme Green, York YO1 7PP
Tel: 01904 716000
Fax: 01904 716100
DX: 61510 YORK
Email: donald.coverdale@warekay.co.uk
Coroner's Officers:
North Yorkshire Police Divisional HQ, Fulford Road, York YO1 4BY
Tel: 01904 669332
Fax: 01904 479965

NORTHAMPTONSHIRE

NORTHAMPTONSHIRE
Coroner: Mrs A. Pember
110 Whitworth Road, Northampton NN1 4HJ
Tel: 01604 624732
Fax: 01604 623681
Email: coroners@northantscoroner.com
Coroner's Officers:
Campbell Square Police Station, Northampton NN1 3EL
Tel: 03000 111 222
Fax: 01604 888801
Kettering Police Station, London Road, Kettering NN15 7PQ
Tel: 03000 111 222
Fax: 01604 888729

NORTHUMBERLAND

NORTH NORTHUMBERLAND
Senior Coroner: Tony Brown
Assistant Coroners: Paul Dunn; Carly Elizabeth Henley; Andrew Philip Hetherington; David Mitford
17 Church Street, Berwick-upon-Tweed TD15 1EE
Tel: 01289 304318
Fax: 01289 303591
Email: jane.tait@northumberland.gov.uk
Coroner's Officer:
Northumbria Police, Berwick Police Station, 40 Church Street, Berwick-upon-Tweed TD15 1DZ
Tel: 01661 861243
Fax: 01661 861253

SOUTH NORTHUMBERLAND
Coroner: E. Armstrong
Old Library, The Business Centre, 54 Savillle Street, North Shields NE30 1NT
Tel: 0191 643 6929/6930
Email: ann.battensby@northumberland.gov.uk

NOTTINGHAMSHIRE

NOTTINGHAMSHIRE
Coroner: Miss M. Casey
HM Coroner's Office, The Council House, Old Market Square, Nottingham NG1 2DT
Tel: 0115 841 5553
Fax: 0115 876 5689
Email: coroners@nottinghamcity.gov.uk

OXFORDSHIRE

OXFORDSHIRE
Coroner: D.M. Salter
Court: Coroner's Court, County Hall, New Road, Oxford OX1 1ND
Office: Oxfordshire Coroner's Office, Oxford Register Office, 2nd Floor, 1 Tidmarsh Lane, Oxford OX1 1NS
Tel: 01865 815020
Fax: 01865 783391
Email: coroners.oxfordshire@oxfordshire.gov.uk

SHROPSHIRE

MID & NORTH-WEST SHROPSHIRE
Coroner: J.P. Ellery
HM Coroner's Service, Third Floor, Guildhall, Frankwell Quay, Shrewsbury SY3 8HQ
Tel: 01743 281297/8
Fax: 01743 281290
Email: john.ellery@shropshire.gov.uk
Coroner's Officer:
West Mercia Police, Police HQ, Clive Road, Monkmoor, Shrewsbury SY2 5RW
Tel: 01743 237445
Fax: 01743 264879

SOUTH SHROPSHIRE
Coroner: J.P. Ellery
HM Coroner's Service, Third Floor, Guildhall, Frankwell Quay, Shrewsbury SY3 8HQ
Tel: 01743 281297/8
Fax: 01743 2812890
Email: john.ellery@shropshire.gov.uk
Coroner's Officers:
Ludlow Police Station, Lower Galdeford, Ludlow, Shropshire SY8 1SA
Tel: 0300 333 3000 ext. 4608
Fax: 01584 879302

TELFORD & WREKIN BOROUGH COUNCIL
Coroner: J.P. Ellery
HM Coroner's Service, Third Floor, Guildhall, Frankwell Quay, Shrewsbury SY3 8HQ
Tel: 01743 281297/8
Fax: 01743 2812890
Email: john.ellery@shropshire.gov.uk
Coroner's Officers:
West Mercia Police, Wellington Police Station, Victoria Road, Wellington, Telford TF1 1LQ
Tel: 01743 791937/792863
Fax: 01743 792248

SOMERSET

EASTERN SOMERSET
Coroner: T. Williams
22 Bath Street, Frome BA11 1DL
Tel: 0117 973 4259
Fax: 0117 973 6430
Email: info@hmcoroner.co.uk

WESTERN SOMERSET
Coroner: Michael Richard Rose
Blackbrook Gate, Blackbrook Park Avenue, Taunton TA1 2PG
Tel: 0845 209 1796
Fax: 0845 209 2572
DX: 97175 TAUNTON (Blackbrook)
Email: coroner@clarkewillmott.com
Coroner's Officers:
The Police Station, Shuttern, Taunton TA1 3QA
Tel: 01823 363271
Fax: 01823 363103

SOUTH YORKSHIRE

EAST DISTRICT
Coroner: Ms Nicola J. Mundy
Coroner's Court & Office, Doncaster Crown Court, College Road, Doncaster DN1 3HS
Tel: 01302 320844
Fax: 01302 364833
Email: hmc.doncaster@doncaster.gov.uk
Coroner's Officers:
As above.
Tel: 01302 556382/349598
Fax: 01302 364833

WEST DISTRICT
Coroner: C.P. Dorries OBE
Medico-Legal Centre, Watery Street, Sheffield S3 7ET
Tel: 0114 273 8721
Fax: 0114 272 6247/278 4909
Email: medico-legalcentre@sheffield.gov.uk
Coroner's Officers:
As above. And also:
Barnsley Police Station, Churchfield, Barnsley
Tel: 0122 673 6031
Fax: 0122 673 6295

STAFFORDSHIRE

STAFFORDSHIRE SOUTH
Coroner: A.A. Haigh
Coroner's Office, 1 Staffordshire Place, Stafford ST16 2LP
Tel: 01785 276127
Fax: 01785 276128
DX: 712320 STAFFORD 5
Email: sscor@staffordshire.gov.uk
Coroner's Officers:
Justice Department, Block 9, Weston Road Police Complex, Stafford ST18 0YY
Tel: (Stafford) 01785 235537; (Burton-on-Trent) 01785 235510; mob: 07870 684969; (Cannock) 01785 235524

STOKE-ON-TRENT & NORTH STAFFORDSHIRE
Coroner: I.S. Smith
Coroner's Court & Chambers, 547 Hartshill Road, Hartshill, Stoke-on-Trent ST4 6HF
Tel: 01782 234777
Fax: 01782 232074
Email: coroners@stoke.gov.uk

SUFFOLK

SUFFOLK
Coroner: Dr Peter Dean
Coroners Service Referral Unit, 3rd Floor, Landmark House, 4 Egerton Road, Ipswich IP1 5PF
Tel: 01473 613888 ext. 3159
Fax: 01473 383207
Email: coroners.service@suffolk.gcsx.gov.uk
Coroner's Officers:
As above, and also:
Suffolk Police, Old Nelson Street, Lowestoft
Tel: 01986 835167
Fax: 01986 835174
Coroners Service, Raingate Street, Bury IP33 2AP
Tel: 01284 774167
Fax: 01284 774204

SURREY

SURREY
Coroner: R. Travers
HM Coroner's Court, Station Approach, Woking GU22 7AP
Tel: 01483 776138
Fax: 01483 765460
Coroner's Officers:
Tel: 01483 637300
Fax: 01483 634814

SUSSEX (EAST)

CITY OF BRIGHTON & HOVE
Coroner: Veronica Hamilton-Deeley
The Coroner's Office, Woodvale, Lewes Road, Brighton BN2 3QB
Tel: 01273 292046
Fax: 01273 292047
Coroner's Officers:
Brighton Police Station, John Street, Brighton BN2 2LA
Tel: 01273 665525
Fax: 01273 404042

EAST SUSSEX
Coroner: A.R. Craze
28/29 Grand Parade, St Leonard's-on-Sea TN37 6DR
Tel: 01424 200144
Fax: 01424 200145
Email: eastsussex.coroner@eastsussex.gov.uk
Coroner's Officers:
Hammonds Drive Patrol Centre, Hammonds Drive, Eastbourne BN23 1PW
Tel: 01273 475432
Fax: 01273 404300
The Police Station, Bohemia Road, Hastings TN34 1BT
Tel: 01273 404371
Fax: 01273 404394

SUSSEX (WEST)

WEST SUSSEX
Coroner: Penelope A. Schofield
County Record Office, Orchard Street, Chichester PO19 1DD
Tel: 0330 222 7100
Fax: 01243 753644
Email: hm.coroner@westsussex.gov.uk
Coroner's Officers:
Centenary House, Durrington Lane, Worthing
Tel: 01243 404012/3
Fax: 01243 404020
Police Station, Hurst Road, Horsham
Tel: 01243 404163
Fax: 01243 404186

TYNE AND WEAR

GATESHEAD & SOUTH TYNESIDE
Coroner: T. Carney
35 Station Road, Hebburn NE31 1LA
Tel: 0191 483 8771
Fax: 0191 428 6699
Email: t.carney@terence-carney.co.uk
Coroner's Officers (Gateshead):
35 Station Road, as above
Tel: 0191 483 8192
Fax: 0191 483 9069
Coroner's Officers (South Tyneside):
35 Station Road, as above
Tel: 0191 483 8189
Fax: 0191 483 9761

NEWCASTLE-UPON-TYNE
Coroner: Karen Lorraine Dilks
Coroner's Department, Civic Centre, Barras Bridge, Newcastle-upon-Tyne NE1 8PS
Tel: 0191 277 7280
Fax: 0191 261 2952
Email: karen.dilks@newcastle.gov.uk

NORTH TYNESIDE
Coroner: E. Armstrong
Howard House, North Tyneside Business Centre, 54A Favill Street, North Shields NE30 1NT
Tel: 0191 643 6929
Fax: 0191 643 6932
Email: ann.battensby@northumberland.gov.uk
Coroner's Officers:
Joanne O'Boyle; Yvonne Venus
Tel: 0191 295 7154
Fax: 0191 295 7158
Email: joanne.oboyle.4381@northumbria.pnn.police.uk;
yvonne.venus.9302@northumbria.pnn.police.uk

CITY OF SUNDERLAND
Coroner: D. Winter
Civic Centre, Burdon Road, Sunderland SR2 7DN
Tel: 0191 561 7843
Fax: 0191 553 7803
Email: derek.winter@sunderland.gov.uk

WARWICKSHIRE

WARWICKSHIRE
Coroner: S. McGovern
HM Coroner Office, Warwickshire Justice Centre, Newbold Terrace, Leamington Spa CV32 4EL
Tel: 01926 684065
Fax: 01926 682513
Email: coronerofficer@warwickshire.pnn.police.uk
Coroner's Officers:
Warwickshire Justice Centre, as above
Tel: 01926 684228/4065/4111/4101
Fax: 01926 682513

WEST MIDLANDS

BIRMINGHAM/SOLIHULL
Coroner: Mrs Louise Hunt
Coroner's Court, 50 Newton Street, Birmingham B4 6NE
Tel: 0121 303 3228
Fax: 0121 233 4841
Email: coroner@birmingham.gov.uk

COVENTRY
Coroner: Sean P. McGovern
Civic Centre, 1 Little Park Street, Coventry CV1 5RS
Tel: 024 7683 4140
Fax: 024 7683 4922
Email: coroner@coventry.gov.uk

BLACK COUNTRY
Coroner: Robin J. Balmain
Smethwick Council House, High Street, Smethwick B66 3NT
Tel: 0845 352 7483
Fax: 0121 569 5384
Email: sandwell_coroners@sandwell.gov.uk
Coroner's Officers:
As above.

WEST YORKSHIRE

EASTERN DISTRICT
Coroner: D. Hinchliff
Coroner's Office, 71 Northgate, Wakefield WF1 3BS
Tel: 01924 302180
Fax: 01924 302184
Email: hmcoroner@wakefield.gov.uk
Coroner's Officers:
Symons House, Belgrave Street, Leeds LS2 8DD
Tel: 0113 397 0600/0602/0607
Fax: 0113 245 4892
Email: leedscoroner@wakefield.gov.uk
71 Northgate, Wakefield WF1 3BS
Tel: 01924 293270; 292683; 292684; 293265
Fax: 01924 302184

WESTERN DISTRICT
Coroner: Prof. Paul V. Marks
Coroner's Office, The City Courts, Bradford BD1 1LA
Tel: 01274 391362
Fax: 01274 721794
Email: hmc@bradford.gov.uk
Coroner's Officers:

Lawcroft House, Lilycroft Road, Bradford BD9 5AF
Tel: 01274 475299
West Yorkshire Police, Dewsbury Division, Aldams Road, Dewsbury
Tel: 01924 431070
West Yorkshire Police, Huddersfield Division, Civic Centre, Huddersfield
Tel: 01484 436700
HM Coroner's Office, 8 Carlton Street, Halifax HX1 2AL
Tel: 01422 354606
Fax: 01422 380153

WILTSHIRE

WILTSHIRE & SWINDON
Coroner: David W.G. Ridley
Wiltshire & Swindon Coroner's Court, 26 Endless Street, Salisbury SP1 1DP
Tel: 01722 438900
Fax: 01722 332223
Email: wscoronersoffice@wiltshire.gov.uk
Coroner's Officers:
As above; and:
Divisional Police HQ, Police Station, Gablecross, Shrivenham Road, South Marston, Swindon SN3 4RB
Tel: 01793 507841
Fax: 01793 507840

WORCESTERSHIRE

WORCESTERSHIRE
Coroner: G.U. Williams
The Court House, Bewdley Road, Stourport-on-Severn DY13 8XE
Tel: 01299 824029
Fax: 01299 879238
Email: coroner@worcestershire.gov.uk
Coroner's Officers:
Police Station, Castle Street, Worcester WR1 3AD
Tel: 01905 331026
Fax: 01905 331025
Police Station, Grove Street, Redditch B98 8DD
Tel: 01527 586186
Fax: 01527 586116

WALES

BRIDGEND & GLAMORGAN VALLEYS [PEN-Y-BONT & CHYMOEDD MORGANWG]
Coroner: Andrew Barkley
The Coroner's Office, Rock Grounds, Aberdare CF44 7AE
Tel: 01685 885202
Fax: 01685 885250
Email: coroner.admin@rctcbc.gov.uk
Coroner's Officer: Patrick Williams
Police Station, Swan Street, Merthyr Tydfil
Tel: 01685 724228
Coroner's Officer: Andrew Levett
Police Station, 1–3 Heol y Gyfraith, Talbot Green, Rhondda Cynon Taff
Tel: 01443 743698
Coroner's Officer: Mark Adams
Police Station, Bridgend
Tel: 01656 762968

CARDIFF & THE VALE OF GLAMORGAN [CAERDYDD & BRO MORGANNWG]
Acting Coroner: Andrew Barkley
Coroner's Court and Offices, Central Police Station, Cathays Park, Cardiff CF10 3NN
Tel: 029 2022 2111 ext. 30697/8/9
Fax: 029 2023 3886

CARDIGANSHIRE [SIR ABERTEIFI]
Coroner: P.L. Brunton
6 Upper Portland Street, Aberystwyth, Ceredigion SY23 2DU
Tel: 01970 612567; 617931
Fax: 01970 615572
Email: peter.brunton@bruntonandco.co.uk
Coroner's Officer:
Aberystwyth Police Station, Boulevard St Brieuc, Aberystwyth SY23 1PH
Tel: 01970 612791
Fax: 01970 625174

CARMARTHENSHIRE [SIR GAERFYRDDIN]
Coroner: Mark Layton
The Town Hall, Hamilton Terrace, Milford Haven SA73 3JW
Tel: 01646 698129
Fax: 01646 690607
Email: hmcpembs1@btconnect.com

GWENT
Coroner: D.T. Bowen
Victoria Chambers, 11 Clytha Park Road, Newport NP20 4PB
Tel: 01633 264194
Fax: 01633 841146
Email: davidtbowen@colbornex.org.uk

NEATH & PORT TALBOT [CASTELL-NEDD & PHORT TALBOT]
Acting Senior Coroner: Colin Phillips
Assistant Coroner: Paul Bennett; Aled Gruffydd
The Coroner's Office, The Civic Centre, Oystermouth Road, Swansea SA1 3SN
Tel: 01792 636237
Fax: 01792 636603
Email: coroner@swansea.gov.uk
Coroner's Officer:
Swansea Central Police Station, Grove Place, Swansea
Tel: 01792 540698/540633/562784/450690

NORTH WALES (EAST AND CENTRAL) [GOGLEDD CYMRU (DWYRIAN A CANOL)]
Coroner: John Gittins
County Hall, Wynnstay Road, Ruthin LL15 1YN
Tel: 01824 708047
Fax: 01824 708048
DX: 21839 RUTHIN
Email: coroner@denbighshire.gov.uk
Coroner's Officers:
North Wales Police, Central Division Headquarters, Ffordd William Morgan, St Asaph Business Park, St Asaph, Denbighshire LL17 0HQ
Tel: 01745 588607
Eastern Control Room, Police Station, Bodhyfryd, Wrexham LL12 7BW
Tel: 01978 348555

NORTH WEST WALES [GOGLEDD GORLLEWIN CYMRU]
Coroner: D. Pritchard Jones
37 Castle Square, Caernarfon, Gwynedd LL55 2NN
Tel: 01286 672804
Fax: 01286 675217
Email: coroner@pritchardjones.co.uk

PEMBROKESHIRE [SIR BENFRO]
Coroner: Mark Layton
The Town Hall, Hamilton Terrace, Milford Haven SA73 3JW
Tel: 01646 698129

Fax: 01646 690607
Email: hmcpembs1@btconnect.com
Coroner's Officer: Jeremy Davies
The Police Station, Charles Street, Milford Haven SA73 2HP
Tel: 01646 690799
Fax: 01646 698873

POWYS [POWYS]
Acting Coroner: Andrew Barkley
Coroner's Office, 1st Floor Rock Ground, Aberdare, Rhondda-Cynnon-taf CF44 7AE
Tel: 01685 885202
Fax: 01685 885250
Coroner's Officer:
Martin Follows
Tel: 07432 726783
Email: martin.follows@dyfed-powys.pnn.police.uk

CITY AND COUNTY OF SWANSEA [ABERTAWE]
Acting Senior Coroner: Colin Phillips
Assistant Coroner: Paul Bennett; Aled Gruffydd
The Coroner's Office, The Civic Centre, Oystermouth Road, Swansea SA1 3SN
Tel: 01792 636237
Fax: 01792 636603
Email: coroner@swansea.gov.uk
Coroner's Officer:
Swansea Central Police Station, Grove Place, Swansea
Tel: 01792 540698/540633/562784/450690

ALPHABETICAL INDEX TO CORONERS' DISTRICTS

Part V

PROBATE REGISTRARS AND PROBATE COURTS

Probate Registrars and Probate Courts

All registries are open Monday to Friday. Most are open from 09:30–16:00 (London 10:00–16:00).

BIRMINGHAM (DISTRICT REGISTRY)
The Priory Courts, 33 Bull Street, Birmingham B4 6DU
Tel: 0121 681 3400/1
Email: birminghamdprenquiries@hmcts.gsi.gov.uk;
birminghamdprsolicitorsenquiries@hmcts.gsi.gov.uk

BODMIN (SUB-REGISTRY)
Magistrates' Courts, Launceston Road, Bodmin, Cornwall PL31 2AL
Postal address: The Civil Justice Centre, 2 Redcliff Street, Bristol BS1 6GR
Tel: 01208 261581
Email: bristoldprenquiries@hmcts.gsi.gov.uk; bristoldprolicitorsenquiries@hmcts.gsi.gov.uk

BRIGHTON (DISTRICT REGISTRY)
William Street, Brighton, East Sussex BN2 0RF
Tel: 01273 573510
Fax: 01273 625845
Email: brightondprsolicitorsenquiries@hmcts.gsi.gov.uk; brightondprenquiries@hmcts.gsi.gov.uk

BRISTOL (DISTRICT REGISTRY)
2 Redcliff Street, Bristol BS1 6GR
Tel: 0117 366 4960/1
Email: bristoldprenquiries@hmcts.gsi.gov.uk; bristoldprsolicitorsenquiries@hmcts.gsi.gov.uk

CAERNARFON (SUB-REGISTRY)
The Criminal Justice Centre, Llanberis Road, Caernarfon, Gwynedd LL55 2DF
Postal address: Cardiff Probate Registry of Wales, 3rd Floor, Cardiff Magistrates' Court, Fitzalan Place, Cardiff, South Wales CF24 0RZ
Tel: 01286 669755
Email: caernarfonpsr@hmcts.gsi.gov.uk

CARDIFF PROBATE REGISTRY OF WALES
3rd Floor, Cardiff Magistrates' Court, Fitzalan Place, Cardiff, South Wales CF24 0RZ
Tel: 029 2047 4373
Fax: 029 2045 6411
Email: cardiffdprenquiries@hmcts.gsi.gov.uk; cardiffdprsolicitorsenquiries@hmcts.gsi.gov.uk

CARLISLE (SUB-REGISTRY)
Courts of Justice, Earl Street, Carlisle, Cumbria CA1 1DJ
Postal address: Newcastle DPR, No 1 Waterloo Square, Newcastle-upon-Tyne NE1 4DR
Tel: 0191 211 2170
Email: newcastledprsolicitorsenquiries@hmcts.gsi.gov.uk; newcastledprenquiries@hmcts.gsi.gov.uk
Office open by appointment only

CARMARTHEN (SUB-REGISTRY)
Carmarthen Hearing Centre, Hill House, Picton Terrace, Carmarthen SA31 3BT
Tel: 01267 226781
Email: carmarthenpsr@hmcts.gsi.gov.uk; carmarthenpsr@hmcts.gsi.gov.uk

CHESTER (SUB-REGISTRY)
Chester Civil Justice Centre, Trident House, Little St John Street, Chester CH1 1SN
Postal address: Liverpool District Probate Registry, Queen Elizabeth II Law Courts, Derby Square, Liverpool L2 1XA
Tel: 0151 236 8264
Email: liverpooldprenquiries@hmcts.gsi.gov.uk; liverpooldprsolicitorsenquiries@hmcts.gsi.gov.uk
Office open by appointment only

EXETER (SUB-REGISTRY)
1st Floor, Exeter Crown and County Courts, Southernhay Gardens, Exeter EX1 1UH
Postal address: Bristol District Probate Registry, The Civil Justice Centre, 2 Redcliff Street, Bristol BS1 6GR
Tel: 0117 366 4960
Email: bristolpsrsolicitorsenquiries@hmcts.gsi.gov.uk; exeterpsrenquiries@hmcts.gsi.gov.uk

GLOUCESTER (SUB-REGISTRY)
2nd Floor, Combined Court Building, Kimbrose Way, Gloucester GL1 2DG
Postal address: Oxford District Probate Registry, Combined Court Building, St Aldates, Oxford OX1 1LY
Tel: 01452 834966 or 01865 793050
Email: gloucesterpsrenquiries@hmcts.gsi.gov.uk

IPSWICH (DISTRICT REGISTRY)
Ground Floor, 8 Arcade Street, Ipswich IP1 1EJ
Tel: 01473 284260
Fax: 01473 231951
Email: ipswichdprsolicitorsenquiries@hmcts.gsi.gov.uk; ipswichdprenquiries@hmcts.gsi.gov.uk

LANCASTER (SUB-REGISTRY)
Room 111, Mitre House, Church Street, Lancaster LA1 1HE
Postal address: Queen Elizabeth II Law Courts, Derby Square, Liverpool L2 1XA
Tel: 0151 236 8264
Email: liverpooldprenquiries@hmcts.gsi.gov.uk; liverpooldprsolicitorsenquiries@hmcts.gsi.gov.uk
Open by appointment only

LEEDS (DISTRICT REGISTRY)
York House, 31 York Place, Leeds LS1 2BA
Tel: 0113 389 6133
Fax: 0113 389 6123
Email: leedsdprsolicitorsenquiries@hmcts.gsi.gov.uk; leedsdprenquiries@hmcts.gsi.gov.uk

LEICESTER (SUB-REGISTRY)
Crown Court Building, 90 Wellington Street, Leicester LE1 6HG
Tel: 0116 285 3380 or 01865 793050
Email: leicesterpsrenquiries@hmcts.gsi.gov.uk

LINCOLN (SUB-REGISTRY)
360 High Street, Lincoln LN5 7PS
Postal address: Leeds District Probate Registry, York House, 31 York Place, Leeds LS1 2BA
Tel: 01522 523648
Email: lincolnpsrenquiries@hmcts.gsi.gov.uk; lincolnpsrsolicitorsenquiries@hmcts.gsi.gov.uk

LIVERPOOL (DISTRICT REGISTRY)
Queen Elizabeth II Law Courts, Derby Square, Liverpool L2 1XA
Tel: 0151 236 8264
Fax: 0151 227 4634
Email: liverpool.dpr@hmcts.gsi.gov.uk; liverpooldprsolicitorsenquiries@hmcts.gsi.gov.uk

LONDON PROBATE DEPARTMENT
London Probate Department, 7th Floor, 42–49 High Holborn, First Avenue House, Holborn, London WC1V 6NP
Tel: 020 7421 8500/9
Email: londonpersonalapplicationenquiries@hmcts.gsi.gov.uk

MAIDSTONE (SUB-REGISTRY)
The Law Courts, Barker Road, Maidstone ME16 8EQ
Postal address: Brighton District Probate Registry, Wiliam Street, Brighton, East Sussex BN2 0RF
Tel: 01273 573510
Email: brightondprenquiries@hmcts.gsi.gov.uk; brightondprsolicitorsenquiries@hmcts.gsi.gov.uk
Office open by appointment only

MANCHESTER (DISTRICT REGISTRY)
Manchester Civil Justice Centre, Ground Floor, 1 Bridge Street West, PO Box 4240, Manchester M60 9DJ
Tel: 0161 240 5701/2
Email: manchesterdprsolicitorsenquiries@hmcts.gsi.gov.uk; manchesterdprenquiries@hmcts.gsi.gov.uk

MIDDLESBROUGH (SUB-REGISTRY)
Teesside Combined Court Centre, Russell Street, Middlesbrough TS1 2AE
Postal address: Central Lofts, No.1 Waterloo Square, Newcastle-upon-Tyne NE1 4DR
Tel: 0191 211 2170
Email: newcastledprenquiries@hmcts.gsi.gov.uk; newcastledprsolicitorsenquiries@hmcts.gsi.gov.uk

NEWCASTLE-UPON-TYNE (DISTRICT REGISTRY)
1 Waterloo Square, Newcastle-upon-Tyne NE1 4DR
Tel: 0191 211 2170
Fax: 0191 211 2184
Email: newcastledprenquiries@hmcts.gsi.gov.uk; newcastledprsolicitorsenquiries@hmcts.gsi.gov.uk

NORWICH (SUB-REGISTRY)
Combined Court Building, The Law Courts, Bishopgate, Norwich NR3 1UR
Postal address: Ipswich District Probate Registry, Ground Floor, 8 Arcade Street, Ipswich IP1 1EJ
Tel: 01603 728267
Email: norwichpsrsolicitorsenquiries@hmcts.gsi.gov.uk; norwichpsrenquiries@hmcts.gsi.gov.uk

NOTTINGHAM (SUB-REGISTRY)
60 Canal Street, Nottingham NG1 7EJ
Postal address: Birmingham District Probate Registry, The Priory Courts, 33 Bull Street, Birmingham B4 6DU
Tel: 0121 681 3400
Email: birminghamdprenquiries@hmcts.gsi.gov.uk;
birminghamdprsolicitorsenquiries@hmcts.gsi.gov.uk
Open by appointment only

OXFORD (DISTRICT REGISTRY)
Combined Court Building, St Aldates, Oxford OX1 1LY
Tel: 01865 793050/5
Email: oxforddprsolicitorsenquiries@hmcts.gsi.gov.uk; oxforddprenquiries@hmcts.gsi.gov.uk

PETERBOROUGH (SUB-REGISTRY)
1st Floor, Crown Building, Rivergate, Peterborough PE1 1EJ
Postal address: Ipswich District Probate Registry, Ground Floor, 8 Arcade Street, Ipswich IP1 1EJ
Tel: 01473 284260
Email: ipswichdprsolicitorsenquiries@hmcts.gsi.gov.uk; ipswichdprenquiries@hmcts.gsi.gov.uk
Open by appointment only

SHEFFIELD (SUB-REGISTRY)
The Law Courts, 50 West Bar, Sheffield, South Yorkshire S3 8PH
Postal address: PO Box 832, The Law Courts, 50 West Bar, Sheffield S3 8YR
Tel: 0114 281 2596
Email: sheffieldpsrenquiries@hmcts.gsi.gov.uk; sheffieldpsrsolicitorsenquiries@hmcts.gsi.gov.uk

STOKE-ON-TRENT (SUB-REGISTRY)
Combined Court Centre, Bethesda Street, Hanley, Stoke-on-Trent ST1 3BP
Postal address: Birmingham District Probate Registry, The Priory Courts, 33 Bull Street, Birmingham B4 6DU
Tel: 0121 681 3400
Email: birminghamdprenquiries@hmcts.gsi.gov.uk; stokeontrentpsrenquiries@hmcts.gsi.gov.uk

WINCHESTER (DISTRICT REGISTRY)
4th Floor, Cromwell House, Andover Road, Winchester SO23 7EW
Tel: 01962 897029
Email: winchesterdprsolicitorsenquiries@hmcts.gsi.gov.uk; winchesterdprenquiries@hmcts.gsi.gov.uk

YORK (SUB-REGISTRY)
Piccadilly House, 55 Piccadilly, York YO1 9WL
Postal address: York House, 2nd Floor, 31 York Place, Leeds LS1 2BA
Tel: 0113 389 6133
Email: leedsdprenquiries@hmcts.gsi.gov.uk; leedsdprenquiries@hmcts.gsi.gov.uk
Open by appointment only

Part VI

THE CROWN PROSECUTION SERVICE (CPS)

CROWN PROSECUTION SERVICE (CPS)

Director of Public Prosecutions: Alison Saunders CB

Chief Executive: Peter Lewis CB
Address: Rose Court, 2 Southwark Bridge, London SE1 9HS
Tel: 020 3357 0899
Email: enquiries@cps.gsi.gov.uk
Website: www.cps.gov.uk
Twitter: @cpsuk

Part VII

CROWN OFFICE AND PROCURATOR FISCAL SERVICE (SCOTLAND) (COPFS)

CROWN OFFICE AND PROCURATOR FISCAL SERVICE (SCOTLAND) (COPFS)

The Crown Office and Procurator Fiscal Service (COPFS) is Scotland's sole prosecution service. It is also responsible for the investigation of deaths that require further explanation, and for investigating allegations of criminal conduct against police officers.

COPFS is brigaded into four federations: National, North, West and East. The National Federation comprises Corporate Services and Serious Casework.

CROWN OFFICE

25 Chambers Street, Edinburgh EH1 1LA
Tel: 0844 561 2000
Website: www.copfs.gov.uk
Crown Agent/Chief Executive: Catherine Dyer
Director of Serious Casework: John Logue
COPFS National Enquiry Point: Tel: 0845 561 3000

Procurator Fiscal Service

EAST FEDERATION

29 Chambers Street, Edinburgh EH1 1LD
Tel (all offices): 0844 561 3000 (from a landline); 01389 739557 (from a mobile)
Website: www.copfs.gov.uk

Procurator Fiscal for the East of Scotland: John Dunn

Head of Business Management for the East of Scotland: Nancy Darroch

Procurator Fiscal for High Court for the East of Scotland: Nicola Patrick

Procurator Fiscal for Sheriff and Jury for the East of Scotland: Laura McPherson

Procurator Fiscal for Summary for the East of Scotland: Andrew Richardson

Procurator Fiscal for Initial Case Processing for the East of Scotland: Ruth McQuaid

---

ALLOA
Sheriff Court, Alloa FK10 1HR
Sheriff and JP Court
Alloa

DUNFERMLINE
Sheriff Court, Carnegie Drive, Dunfermline KY12 7HW
Sheriff and JP Court
Dunfermline

EDINBURGH
29 Chambers Street, Edinburgh EH1 1LB
Sheriff and JP Court
Edinburgh

FALKIRK
Mansionhouse Road, Camelon, Falkirk FK1 4LW
Sheriff and JP Court
Falkirk

HADDINGTON
10–12 Court Street, Haddington EH41 3JA
Sheriff and JP Court
Haddington

JEDBURGH
Sheriff Court, Jedburgh TD8 6AR
Sheriff and JP Court
Jedburgh

KIRKCALDY
Wing D, Carlyle House, Carlyle Road, Kirkcaldy KY1 1DB
Sheriff and JP Court
Kirkcaldy

LIVINGSTON
West Lothian Civic Centre, Howden South Road, Livingston EH54 6FF
Sheriff and JP Court
Livingston

SELKIRK
Sheriff Court, Selkirk TD7 4LE
Sheriff and JP Court
Selkirk

STIRLING
Carseview House, Castle Business Park, Stirling FK9 4SW
Sheriff and JP Court
Stirling

NORTH FEDERATION

c/o Caledonian House, Greenmarket, Dundee DD1 4QA
Tel (all offices): 0844 561 3000 (from a landline); 01389 739557 (from a mobile)
Website: www.copfs.gov.uk

Procurator Fiscal for the North of Scotland: Liam Murphy

Head of Business Management for the North of Scotland: Rosemary Fallon

Procurator Fiscal for High Court for the North of Scotland: Andrew Shanks

Procurator Fiscal for Sheriff and Jury for the North of Scotland: Andrew McIntyre

Procurator Fiscal for Summary for the North of Scotland: Andrew Laing

Procurator Fiscal for Initial Case Processing for the North of Scotland: Andrew Laing

ABERDEEN
Atholl House, 84–88 Guild Street, Aberdeen AB11 6QA
Sheriff and JP Court
Aberdeen

BANFF
Sheriff Court, Banff AB45 1AU
Sheriff and JP Court
Banff

DINGWALL
County Buildings, Ferry Road, Dingwall IV15 9QX
Sheriff and JP Court
Dingwall

DUNDEE
Caledonian House, Greenmarket, Dundee DD1 4QA
Sheriff and JP Court
Dundee

ELGIN
48 South Street, Elgin IV30 1JX
Sheriff and JP Court
Elgin

FORFAR
Sheriff Court, Forfar DD8 3LA
Sheriff and JP Court
Forfar

FORT WILLIAM
2nd Floor, Tweeddale, High Street, Fort William PH33 6EU
Sheriff and JP Court
Fort William

INVERNESS
Great Glen House, Leachkin Road, Inverness IV3 8NW
Sheriff and JP Court
Inverness

KIRKWALL
Sheriff Court, Kirkwall KW15 1PD
Sheriff Court
Kirkwall

LERWICK
Sheriff Court, Lerwick ZE1 0HD
Sheriff Court
Lerwick

LOCHMADDY
Sheriff Court, Lochmaddy HS6 5AE
Sheriff Court
Lochmaddy

PERTH
82 Tay Street, Perth PH2 8NN
Sheriff and JP Court
Perth

PETERHEAD
70 St Peter Street, Peterhead AB42 1QB
Sheriff and JP Court
Peterhead

PORTREE
Sheriff Court, Portree IV51 9EH
Sheriff and JP Court
Portree

STORNOWAY
Sheriff Court Buildings, Lewis Street, Stornoway HS1 2JF
Sheriff and JP Court
Stornoway

TAIN
11 Stafford Street, Tain IV19 1BP
Sheriff and JP Court
Tain

WICK
Sheriff Court, Wick KW1 4AJ
Sheriff and JP Court
Wick

WEST FEDERATION
10 Ballater Street, Glasgow G5 9PS
Tel (all offices): 0844 561 3000 (from a landline); 01389 739557 (from a mobile)
Website: www.copfs.gov.uk

Procurator Fiscal for the West of Scotland: David Harvie

Head of Business Management for the West of Scotland: Paul Lowe

Procurator Fiscal for High Court for the West of Scotland: Anthony McGeehan

Procurator Fiscal for Sheriff and Jury for the West of Scotland: Anthony McGeehan

Procurator Fiscal for Initial Case Processing and Summary for the West of Scotland: Geri Watt

AIRDRIE
87A Graham Street, Airdrie ML6 6DE
Sheriff and JP Court
Sheriff Court: Airdire
JP Court: Coatbridge

AYR
37 Carrick Street, Ayr KA7 1NS
Sheriff and JP Court
Ayr

CAMPBELTOWN
Sheriff Court, Campbeltown PA28 6AN
Sheriff and JP Court
Campbeltown

DUMBARTON
St Mary's Way, Dumbarton G82 1NL
Sheriff and JP Court
Dumbarton

DUMFRIES
44 Buccleuch Street, Dumfries DG1 2AP
Sheriff and JP Court
Dumfries

DUNOON
Sheriff Court, Dunoon PS23 8BQ
Sheriff and JP Court
Dunoon

GLASGOW
10 Ballater Street, Glasgow G5 9PS
Sheriff and JP Court
Sheriff Court: Glasgow & Strathkelvin
JP Court: Glasgow

GREENOCK
Victory Court, Cartsburn Maritime, Arthur Street, Greenock PA15 4RT
Sheriff and JP Court
Greenock

HAMILTON
Cameronian House, 3/5 Almada Street, Hamilton ML3 0HG
Sheriff and JP Court
Sheriff Court: Hamilton
JP Court: Hamilton / Motherwell

KILMARNOCK
St Marnock Street, Kilmarnock KA1 1DZ

Sheriff and JP Court
Kilmarnock

LANARK
Sheriff Court, 24 Hope Street, Lanark ML11 7NE

Sheriff and JP Court
Lanark

OBAN
Third Floor, Boswell House, Argyll Square, Oban PA34 4BD

Sheriff and JP Court
Oban

PAISLEY
1 Love Street, Paisley PA3 2DA

Sheriff and JP Court
Paisley

STRANRAER
Sheriff Court, Stranraer DG9 7AA

Sheriff and JP Court
Stranraer

Part VIII

NATIONAL OFFENDER MANAGEMENT SERVICE AND PENAL ESTABLISHMENTS

National Offender Management Service

ENGLAND AND WALES

HEADQUARTERS

Clive House, 70 Petty France, London SW1H 9EX
Email: public.enquiries@noms.gsi.gov.uk
Website: www.justice.gov.uk/about/noms/index
Chief Executive Officer: Michael Spurr. Tel: 0300 047 5163.
Director of Finance & Analysis: Andrew Emmett. Tel: 0300 047 6730
Director of HR: Carol Carpenter. Tel: 0300 047 5161
Director of NOMS ICT & Change (Interim): Ben Booth. Tel: 0300 047 5167
Director of Commissioning & Commercial (Interim): Ian Blakeman. Tel: 0300 047 5318
Director of Public Sector Prisons: Phil Copple. Tel: 0300 047 5152
Director of Probation: Colin Allars. Tel: 0300 047 5157
Director of National Operational Services: Digby Griffith. Tel: 0300 047 5868
Director of NOMS in Wales: Sarah Payne. Tel: 02920 785 007

REGIONS

For prison details, categories, etc, see the table beginning on p 290.

EAST MIDLANDS

Public Sector Prisons (NOMS), Empriss House, Unit C Meridian Business Park, Leicester, LE19 1WP
Tel: 0116 281 4018
Fax: 0116 281 4060
Deputy Director of Custody: Neil Richards (Acting)
Secretary: Antoinette Steele. Tel: 0116 281 4021
Operations Manager: Barbara White. Tel: 0116 281 4033

Prisons

Foston Hall	Nottingham
Gartree	Onley
Glen Parva	Ranby
Leicester	Stocken
Lincoln	Sudbury
Morton Hall	Whatton
North Sea Camp	

EAST OF ENGLAND

Stirling House, Bury Road, Stradishall, Suffolk CB8 9YL
Tel: 01440 7432775
Deputy Director of Custody: Adrian Smith

Prisons

Bedford	Littlehey
Bure	The Mount
Chelmsford	Norwich
Highpoint	Warren Hill
Hollesley Bay	Wayland

GREATER LONDON

Red Zone, Point 6.01, Sixth Floor, Clive House, 70 Petty France, London SW1H 9EX
Tel: 0300 047 5868
Deputy Director of Custody: Nick Pascoe
Secretary: Jackie Wright. Tel: 0300 047 5887
Operations Manager: Nikki Marfleet. Tel: 0300 047 5874

Prisons

Brixton	Isis
Coldingley	Pentonville
Downview	Send
Feltham	Wandsworth
Highdown	Wormwood Scrubs
Holloway	

KENT & SUSSEX

80 Sir Evelyn Road, Rochester, Kent ME1 3NF
Fax: 01634 673029
Deputy Director Custody: Michelle Jarman-Howe. Tel: 01634 673011
Secretary: Pauline Kidney. Tel: 01634 673010
Operations Manager: Jonathan Christopher. Tel: 01634 673022

Prisons

Blantyre House	Lewes
Cookham Wood	Maidstone
Dover	Rochester
East Sutton Park	Sheppey Cluster
Ford	

NORTH EAST

Forest House, Aykley Heads Business Park, Aykley Heads, Durham DH1 5TS
Tel: 0191 376 6803
Fax: 0191 376 6801
Deputy Director of Custody: Alan Tallentire. Tel: 0191 376 6803
Secretary: Gillian Beeston. Tel: 0191 376 6803
Operations Manager: Neil Evans. Tel: 0191 3766816

Prisons

Deerbolt	Kirklevington Grange
Durham	Low Newton
Holme House	

NORTH WEST

Wymott Conference Centre, Ulnes Walton Lane, Leyland PR26 8LT
Postal address: PO Box 368, Leyland PR25 9EJ
Tel: 01772 442442
Fax: 01772 442083
Deputy Director of Custody: Alan Scott. Tel: 01772 442442
Secretary: Kathryn Bullock. Tel: 01772 442 442
Operations Managers: Eileen Fenerty-Lyons. Tel: 01772 442444

Prisons

Buckley Hall	Liverpool
Garth	Preston
Haverigg	Risley
Hindley	Styal
Kennet	Thorn Cross
Kirkham	Wymott
Lancaster Farms	

SOUTH CENTRAL

South Central Office HMP Winchester, Romsey Road, Winchester SO22 5DF
Deputy Director of Custody: Claudia Sturt. Tel: 0754 573 2731
Business Manager: Rachel Hardy. Tel: 01962 723090
Operations Manager: Neil Howard. Tel: 07973 457492
Area Estates Manager: Phil Harle. Tel: 01296 442706

Prisons

Aylesbury	Grendon/Spring Hill
Bullingdon	Haslar

Huntercombe
Isle of Wight

Winchester

SOUTH WEST
1 Tortworth Road, Leyhill, Wotton-under-Edge, Gloucestershire GL12 8BQ
Deputy Director of Custody: Ferdie Parker. Tel: 01454 264271
Secretary: Vacant. Tel: 01454 264271
Operations Manager: Lucy Young. Tel: 01454 264272

Prisons

Bristol
Channings Wood
Dartmoor
Eastwood Park
Erlestoke

Exeter
Guys Marsh
Leyhill
Portland
The Verne

WEST MIDLANDS
West Midlands DDC Team, Regional Office, c/o HMP Stafford, 54 Gaol Road, Stafford ST16 3AW
Tel: 01785 773077
Deputy Director of Custody: Luke Serjeant
Secretary: Sarah Keay. Tel: 01785 773077.
Office Co-ordinator: Michelle Thomas Tel: 01785 773278
Operations Manager: Debbie Lewis. Tel: 01785 773148

Prisons

Brinsford
Drake Hall
Featherstone
Hewell

Stafford
Stoke Heath
Swinfen Hall
Werrington

YORKSHIRE & HUMBERSIDE
DDC Office, HMP Askham Grange, Main Street, Askham Richard, York YO23 3FT
Tel: 01904 772000
Fax: 01904 772145
Deputy Director of Custody: Paul Baker. Tel: 01904 772056
Secretary: Clare Burton. Tel: 01904 772056
Operations Manager: Andy Crofts

Prisons

Askham Grange
Hull
Humber
Leeds
Lindholme

Moorland & Hatfield
New Hall
Wealstun
Wetherby

WALES
NOMS in Wales, 3rd Floor, Churchill House, Churchill Way, Cardiff CF10 2HH
Lead Governor, Public Sector Prisons: Richard Booty. Tel: 029 2067 8385
Secretary: TBC. Tel: 029 2067 8385

Prisons

Cardiff
Swansea

Usk/Prescoed
Parc

HIGH SECURITY
Clive House, 70 Petty France, London SW1H 9EX
Deputy Director of Custody: Richard Vince. Tel: 0300 047 6104
Secretary: Danielle Haylor. Tel: 0300 047 6104

Prisons

Belmarsh
Frankland
Full Sutton

Long Lartin
Manchester
Wakefield

Whitemoor   Woodhill

DIRECTORATE OF COMMISSIONING & COMMERCIAL
Room 1.15, First Floor, Clive House, 70 Petty France, London SW1H 9EX
Tel: 0300 047 5157
Fax: 0300 047 6819
Deputy Director of Contracted Custodial Services: Brian Pollett. Tel: 0300 047 5889
Operations Manager: Pauline Skinner. Tel: 0300 047 5889
Contracted Prisons

Altcourse
Ashfield
Birmingham
Bronzefield
Doncaster
Dovegate
Forest Bank

Lowdham Grange
Northumberland
Oakwood
Peterborough
Rye Hill
Thameside

DIRECTORATE PROBATION
Room 7.08, Seventh Floor, Clive House, 70 Petty France, London SW1H 9EX
Tel: 0300 047 5157
Fax: 0300 047 6819

NATIONAL PROBATION SERVICE

NPS North West
Deputy Director Roz Hamilton
5th Floor, Oakland House
Talbot Road
Manchester
M16 0PQ
NPS North East
Deputy Director Lynda Marginson
45 Division Street
Sheffield
S1 4GE
 NPS South East
Deputy Director Sonia Crozier
151 Buckingham Palace Road
London
SW1W 9SZ
 NPS London

Deputy Director Sara Robinson
Address as per above
 NPS Midlands
Deputy Director Sarah Chand
5 St Philips Place
Birmingham
B3 2PW
 NPS Director Business Development
Jim Barton
Address as above
 NPS South West
Deputy Director Angela Cossins
Queensway House
The Hedges
St Georges
Weston Super Mare
BS22 7BB

YOUTH JUSTICE BOARD FOR ENGLAND AND WALES
1 Drummond Gate, London SW1V 2QZ.
Tel: 020 3372 8000. Fax: 020 3372 8002.
Website: www.yjb.gov.uk

PENAL ESTABLISHMENTS ENGLAND AND WALES (WITH CATEGORIES)

*	contracted prison
ABCD	prisoner categories (see Prison Service Order 0900 Categorisation)
CL	Closed
F	Females
HC	holding centre
IRC	immigration removal centre
J	Juveniles
L	Local
M	Males
O	Open
RC	remand centre
RES	resettlement
S-O	semi-open
YOI	young offenders' institution

Further information can be found on the prison service website www.justice.gov.uk/about/hmps

HMP ALTCOURSE*
Higher Lane, Fazakerley, Liverpool L9 7LH
Tel: 0151 522 2000. Fax: 0151 522 2121
(M, L)

HMP ASHFIELD*
Shortwood Road, Pucklechurch, Bristol BS16 9QJ
Tel: 0117 303 8000. Fax: 0117 303 8001
(M, C)

HMP/YOI ASKHAM GRANGE
Askham Richard, York YO23 3FT
Tel: 01904 772000. Fax: 01904 772001
(F, O)

HMYOI AYLESBURY
Bierton Road, Aylesbury, Buckinghamshire HP20 1EH
Tel: 01296 444000. Fax: 01296 444001
(YOI(M), A, CL, RES)

HMP BEDFORD
St Loyes Street, Bedford MK40 1HG
Tel: 01234 373000. Fax: 01234 273568
(M, L, YOI(CL))

HMP BELMARSH
Western Way, Thamesmead, London SE28 0EB
Tel: 020 8331 4400. Fax: 020 8331 4401
(M, A, CL)

HMP BIRMINGHAM*
Winson Green Road, Birmingham B18 4AS
Tel: 0121 598 8000. Fax: 0121 345 2501
(M, L)

HMP BLANTYRE HOUSE
Goudhurst, Cranbrook, Kent TN17 2NH
Tel: 01580 213200. Fax: 01580 213201
(M, C, S-O)

HMP/YOI BRINSFORD
New Road, Featherstone, Wolverhampton WV10 7PY
Tel: 01902 533450. Fax: 01902 533451
(YOI, CL, RC)

HMP BRISTOL
19 Cambridge Road, Bristol BS7 8PS
Tel: 0117 372 3100. Fax: 0117 372 3113
(M, L)

HMP BRIXTON
PO Box 269, Jebb Avenue, Brixton, London SW2 5XF
Tel: 020 8588 6000. Fax: 020 8588 6191
(M, B, L)

HMP BRONZEFIELD*
Woodthorpe Road, Ashford, Middlesex TW15 3JZ
Tel: 01784 425690. Fax: 01784 425691
(F)

HMP BUCKLEY HALL
Buckley Hall Road, Rochdale, Lancashire OL12 9DP
Tel: 01706 514300. Fax: 01706 514399
(M, C)

HMP BULLINGDON
PO Box 50, Bicester, Oxfordshire OX25 1PZ
Tel: 01869 353100. Fax: 01869 353101
(M, C, CL, L)

HMP BURE
Jaguar Drive, Badersfield, Norwich NR10 5GB
Tel: 01603 326000. Fax: 01603 326001
(M, C)

HMP/RC CARDIFF
Knox Road, Cardiff CF24 0UG
Tel: 029 2092 3100. Fax: 029 2092 3318
(M, L, RC)

HMP CHANNINGS WOOD
Denbury, Newton Abbot, Devon TQ12 6DW
Tel: 01803 814600. Fax: 01803 814601
(M, C, CL)

HMP/YOI CHELMSFORD
200 Springfield Road, Chelmsford CM2 6LQ
Tel: 01245 552000. Fax: 01245 552001
(M, L, RC)

HMP COLDINGLEY
Shaftesbury Road, Bisley, Woking, Surrey GU24 9EX
Tel: 01483 344300. Fax: 01483 344427
(M, C, CL)

HMYOI COOKHAM WOOD
Sir Evelyn Road, Rochester, Kent ME1 3LU
Tel: 01634 202500. Fax: 01634 202501
(J, CL)

HMP DARTMOOR
Princetown, Yelverton, Devon PL20 6RR
Tel: 01822 322000. Fax: 01822 322001
(M, C, CL)

HMYOI DEERBOLT
Bowes Road, Barnard Castle, Co. Durham DL12 9BG
Tel: 01833 633200. Fax: 01833 633201
(YOI, CL)

HMP/YOI DONCASTER*
Off North Bridge Road, Marshgate, Doncaster DN5 8UX
Tel: 01302 760870. Fax: 01302 760851
(M, L)

HMP DOVEGATE*
Uttoxeter, Staffordshire ST14 8XR
Tel: 01283 829400. Fax: 01283 820066
(M, B, CL)

IRC DOVER
The Citadel, Western Heights, Dover, Kent CT17 9DR
Tel: 01304 246400. Fax: 01304 246401
(CL, IR, C)

HMP DOWNVIEW
Sutton Lane, Sutton, Surrey SM2 5PD
Tel: 020 8196 6300. Fax: 020 8196 6301
(F, C, CL)

HMP/YOI DRAKE HALL
Eccleshall, Staffordshire ST21 6LQ
Tel: 01785 774100. Fax: 01785 774010
(F, S-O, YOI)

HMP DURHAM
Old Elvet, Durham DH1 3HU
Tel: 0191 332 3400. Fax: 0191 332 3401
(M, CL, L, YOI)

HMP/YOI EAST SUTTON PARK
Sutton Valence, Maidstone, Kent ME17 3DF
Tel: 01622 785000. Fax: 01622 785001
(F, O)

HMP ELMLEY (SHEPPEY CLUSTER)
Church Road, Eastchurch, Sheerness, Kent ME12 4DZ
Tel: 01795 802000. Fax: 01795 802001
(M, B, CL, L, YOI)

HMP ERLESTOKE
Devizes, Wiltshire SN10 5TU
Tel: 01380 814250. Fax: 01380 814273
(M, C, CL)

HMP/YOI EXETER
New North Road, Exeter, Devon EX4 4EX
Tel: 01392 415650. Fax: 01392 415691
(M, L, RC)

HMP FEATHERSTONE
New Road, Featherstone, Wolverhampton WV10 7PU
Tel: 01902 703000. Fax: 01902 703001
(M, C, CL)

HMP/YOI FELTHAM
Bedfont Road, Feltham, Middlesex TW13 4ND
Tel: 020 8844 5000. Fax: 020 8844 5001
(M, CL, RC)

HMP FORD
Arundel, West Sussex BN18 0BX
Tel: 01903 663000. Fax: 01903 663001
(M, D, O)

HMP/YOI FOREST BANK*
Agecroft Road, Pendlebury, Salford M27 8FB
Tel: 0161 925 7000. Fax: 0161 925 7001
(M, L, YOI)

HMP/YOI FOSTON HALL
Foston, Derbyshire DE65 5DN
Tel: 01283 584300. Fax: 01283 584301
(F, CL)

HMP FRANKLAND
Brasside, Durham DH1 5YD
Tel: 0191 376 5000. Fax: 0191 376 5001
(M, A, CL)

HMP FULL SUTTON
Full Sutton, York YO41 1PS
Tel: 01759 475100. Fax: 01759 371206
(M, A, CL)

HMP GARTH
Ulnes Walton Lane, Leyland, Lancashire PR26 8NE
Tel: 01772 443300. Fax: 01772 443301
(M, B, CL)

HMP GARTREE
Gallow Field Road, Market Harborough, Leicestershire LE16 7RP
Tel: 01858 426600. Fax: 01858 426601
(M, B, CL)

HMYOI & RC GLEN PARVA
Tigers Road, Wigston, Leicestershire LE18 4TN
Tel: 0116 228 4100. Fax: 0116 228 4000
(CL, RC, YOI)

HMP GRENDON
Grendon Underwood, Aylesbury, Buckinghamshire HP18 0TL
Tel: 01296 445000. Fax: 01296 445001
(M, B, CL)

HMP/YOI GUYS MARSH
Shaftesbury, Dorset SP7 0AH
Tel: 01747 856400. Fax: 01747 856401
(M, C, CL)

IRC HASLAR
2 Dolphin Way, Gosport, Hampshire PO12 2AW
Tel: 023 9260 4000. Fax: 023 9260 4001
(HC)

HMP HAVERIGG
North Lane, Millom, Cumbria LA18 4NA
Tel: 01229 713000. Fax: 01229 713001
(M, C, CL)

HMP HEWELL
Hewell Lane, Redditch, Worcestershire B97 6QS
Tel: 01527 785000. Fax: 01527 785001
(M, B, C, D)

HMP HIGH DOWN
Sutton Lane, Sutton, Surrey SM2 5PJ
Tel: 020 7147 6300. Fax: 020 7147 6301
(M, L)

HMP HIGHPOINT
Stradishall, Newmarket, Suffolk CB8 9YG
Tel: 01440 743100. Fax: 01440 743092
(M, C, CL)

HMYOI HINDLEY
Gibson Street, Bickershaw, Wigan, Lancashire WN2 5TH
Tel: 01942 663100. Fax: 01942 663101
(RC, CL, YOI)

HMP HOLLESLEY BAY
Woodbridge, Suffolk IP12 3JW
Tel: 01394 412400. Fax: 01394 410115
(M, D, O, YOI)

HMP/YOI HOLLOWAY
Parkhurst Road, Holloway, London N7 0NU
Tel: 020 7979 4400. Fax: 020 7979 4401
(F, L)

HMP HOLME HOUSE
Holme House Road, Stockton-on-Tees, Cleveland TS18 2QU
Tel: 01642 744000. Fax: 01642 744001
(M, CL, L, YOI, C)

HMP HULL
Hedon Road, Hull HU9 5LS
Tel: 01482 282200. Fax: 01482 282400
(M, L, YOI(CL))

HMP HUMBER
4 Sands Lane, Everthorpe, Brough, East Yorkshire HU15 2JZ
Wolds: Tel: 01430 428000. Fax: 01430 428001
Everthorpe: Tel: 01430 426500. Fax: 01430 426501

HMP HUNTERCOMBE
Huntercombe Place, Nuffield, Henley-on-Thames, Oxfordshire RG9 5SB
Tel: 01491 643100. Fax: 01491 643101
(CL)

HMP ISIS
Western Way, Thamesmead, London SE28 0NZ
Tel: 020 3356 4000. Fax: 020 3356 4001
(C, YOI)

HMP ISLE OF WIGHT
Clissold Road, Newport, Isle of Wight PO30 5RS
Tel: 01983 556300. Fax: 01983 556362
(M, B, C)

HMP KENNET
Parkbourn, Maghull, Liverpool L31 1HX
Tel: 0151 213 3000. Fax: 0151 213 3103
(M, C)

HMP KIRKHAM
Freckleton Road, Kirkham, Preston, Lancashire PR4 2RN
Tel: 01772 675400. Fax: 01772 675401
(M, D, O)

HMP KIRKLEVINGTON GRANGE
Yarm, Cleveland TS15 9PA
Tel: 01642 792600. Fax: 01642 792601
(M, C, D, RES)

HMP/YOI LANCASTER FARMS
Stone Row Head, off Quernmore Road, Lancaster LA1 3QZ
Tel: 01524 563450. Fax: 01542 563451
(J, YOI, RC, CL)

HMP LEEDS
Gloucester Terrace, Armley, Leeds LS12 2TJ
Tel: 0113 203 2600. Fax: 0113 203 2601
(M, L)

HMP LEICESTER
116 Welford Road, Leicester LE2 7AJ
Tel: 0116 228 3000. Fax: 0116 228 3001
(M, L)

HMP/YOI LEWES
1 Brighton Road, Lewes, East Sussex BN7 1EA
Tel: 01273 785100. Fax: 01273 785101
(M, L, YOI(CL))

HMP LEYHILL
Wotton-under-Edge, Gloucestershire GL12 8BT
Tel: 01454 264000. Fax: 01454 264001
(M, D, O)

HMP LINCOLN
Greetwell Road, Lincoln LN2 4BD
Tel: 01522 663000. Fax: 01522 663001
(M, L)

HMP IRC LINDHOLME
Bawtry Road, Hatfield Woodhouse, Doncaster, South Yorkshire DN7 6EE
Tel: 01302 524700. Fax: 01302 524750
(M, C, CL, O, IRC)

HMP LITTLEHEY
Perry, Huntingdon, Cambridgeshire PE28 OSR
Tel: 01480 335000. Fax: 01480 335070
(M, C, CL)

HMP LIVERPOOL
68 Hornby Road, Liverpool L9 3DF
Tel: 0151 530 4000. Fax: 0151 530 4001
(M, C, CL)

HMP LONG LARTIN
South Littleton, Evesham, Worcestershire WR11 8TZ
Tel: 01386 295100. Fax: 01386 295101
(M, A, CL)

HMYOI LOW NEWTON
Brasside, Durham DH1 5YA
Tel: 0191 376 4000. Fax: 0191 376 4001
(F, L, CL, YOI)

HMP LOWDHAM GRANGE*
Old Epperstone Road, Lowdham, Nottingham NG14 7DA
Tel: 0115 966 9200. Fax: 0115 966 9220
(M, B, CL)

HMP MAIDSTONE
36 County Road, Maidstone, Kent ME14 1UZ
Tel: 01622 775300. Fax: 01622 775301
(M, C, CL) (HMP Maidstone is a Foreign National Establishment)

HMP MANCHESTER
Southall Street, Manchester M60 9AH
Tel: 0161 817 5600. Fax: 0161 817 5601
(M, A, CL)

HMPYOI MOORLAND & HATFIELD
Bawtry Road, Hatfield Woodhouse, Doncaster, South Yorkshire DN7 6BW
Tel: 01302 523000. Fax: 01302 523001
(M, C, CL, YOI)
Thorne Road, Hatfield, Doncaster DN7 6EL
Tel: 01405 746500. Fax: 01405 746501.
(M, D, O, YOI)

HMP MORTON HALL
Swinderby, Lincoln LN6 9PT
Tel: 01522 666700. Fax: 01522 666750
(IRC)

HMP THE MOUNT
Molyneaux Avenue, Bovingdon, Hemel Hempstead, Hertfordshire HP3 0NZ
Tel: 01442 836300. Fax: 01442 836301
(M, C, CL)

HMP/YOI NEW HALL
Dial Wood, Flockton, Wakefield, West Yorkshire WF4 4XX
Tel: 01924 803000. Fax: 01924 803001
(F, CL, YOI(CL))

HMP NORTH SEA CAMP
Freiston, Boston, Lincolnshire PE22 0QX
Tel: 01205 769300. Fax: 01205 769301
(M, D, O)

HMP/YOI NORTHUMBERLAND*
Morpeth, Northumberland NE65 9XG
Tel: 01670 383100. Fax: 01670 383101
(CL, C, M)

HMP/YOI NORWICH
Knox Road, Norwich NR1 4LU
Tel: 01603 708600. Fax: 01603 708601
(M, L, YOI(CL))

HMP NOTTINGHAM
Perry Road, Sherwood, Nottingham NG5 3AG
Tel: 0115 872 4000. Fax: 0115 872 4001
(M, L)

HMP OAKWOOD*
Oaks Drive, Featherstone, Wolverhampton WV10 7OD
Tel: 01902 799700. Fax: 01902 703001
(M, C)

HMP ONLEY
Willoughby, Rugby, Warwickshire CV23 8AP
Tel: 01788 523400. Fax: 01788 523401
(M, C, CL)

HMP/YOI PARC
Heol Hopcyn John, Bridgend, Mid Glamorgan CF35 6AP
Tel: 01656 300200. Fax: 01656 300201
(M, B, L, YOI(CL, RC))

HMP PENTONVILLE
Caledonian Road, London N7 8TT
Tel: 020 7023 7000. Fax: 020 7023 7001
(M, L)

HMP PETERBOROUGH*
Saville Road, Westfield, Peterborough PE3 7PD
Tel: 01733 217500. Fax: 01733 217501
(M, F, L, RC)

HMYOI PORTLAND
104 The Grove, Easton, Portland, Dorset DT5 1DL
Tel: 01305 715600. Fax: 01305 715601
(M, C, CL, YOI)

HMP/YOI PRESCOED
Coed-y-Paen, Pontypool, Gwent NP4 0TB
Tel: 01291 675000. Fax: 01291 675158
(M, C, CL, D, O, YOI(O))

HMP PRESTON
2 Ribbleton Lane, Preston, Lancashire PR1 5AB
Tel: 01772 444550. Fax: 01772 444551
(M, L)

HMP RANBY
Retford, Nottinghamshire DN22 8EU
Tel: 01777 862000. Fax: 01777 862001
(M, C, CL)

HMP RISLEY
Warrington Road, Risley, Warrington, Cheshire WA3 6BP
Tel: 01925 733000. Fax: 01925 733001
(M, C, CL)

HMP/YOI ROCHESTER
1 Fort Road, Rochester, Kent ME1 3QS
Tel: 01634 803100. Fax: 01634 803101
(YOI, C CL)

HMP RYE HILL*
Willoughby, Rugby, Warwickshire CV23 8SZ
Tel: 01788 523300. Fax: 01788 523311
(M, B)

HMP SEND
Ripley Road, Send, Woking, Surrey GU23 7LJ
Tel: 01483 471000. Fax: 01483 471001
(F, CL)

HMP SPRING HILL
Grendon Underwood, Aylesbury, Buckinghamshire HP18 OTL
Tel: 01296 445000. Fax: 01296 445001
(M, D, O)

HMP STAFFORD
54 Gaol Road, Stafford ST16 3AW
Tel: 01785 773000. Fax: 01785 773001
(M, C, CL)

HMP STANDFORD HILL (SHEPPEY CLUSTER)
Church Road, Eastchurch, Sheerness, Kent ME12 4AA
Tel: 01795 884500. Fax: 01795 884638
(M, D, O)

HMP STOCKEN
Stocken Hall Road, Stretton, Oakham, Rutland LE15 7RD
Tel: 01780 795100. Fax: 01780 410767
(M, C, CL)

HMYOI STOKE HEATH
Market Drayton, Shropshire TF9 2JL
Tel: 01630 636000. Fax: 01630 636001
(YOI, CL)

HMP/YOI STYAL
Styal Road, Wilmslow, Cheshire SK9 4HR
Tel: 01625 553000. Fax: 01625 553001
(F, CL, L)

HMP SUDBURY
Ashbourne, Derbyshire DE6 5HW
Tel: 01283 584000. Fax: 01283 584001
(M, D, O)

HMP SWALESIDE (SHEPPEY CLUSTER)
Brabazon Road, Eastchurch, Isle of Sheppey, Kent ME12 4AX
Tel: 01795 804100. Fax: 01795 804200
(M, B, CL)

HMP SWANSEA
200 Oystermouth Road, Swansea SA1 3SR
Tel: 01792 485300. Fax: 01792 485430
(M, L, RC(YOI))

HMYOI SWINFEN HALL
Swinfen, Lichfield, Staffs WS14 9QS
Tel: 01543 484000. Fax: 01543 484001
(YOI CL)

HMP THAMESIDE*
Griffin Manor Way, London SE28 0FJ
Tel: 020 8317 9777
(M, YOI, L)

HMYOI THORN CROSS
Arley Road, Appleton Thorn, Warrington, Cheshire WA4 4RL
Tel: 01925 805100. Fax: 01925 805101
(J, YOI, O)

HMP USK
47 Maryport Street, Usk, Monmouth NP15 1XP
Tel: 01291 671600. Fax: 01291 671752
(M, C, CL)

HMP THE VERNE
The Verne, Portland, Dorset DT5 1EQ
Tel: 01305 825000. Fax: 01305 825001
(M, C, CL)

HMP WAKEFIELD
5 Love Lane, Wakefield, West Yorkshire WF2 9AG
Tel: 01924 612000. Fax: 01924 612001
(M, A)

HMP WANDSWORTH
PO Box 757, Heathfield Road, Wandsworth, London SW18 3HS
Tel: 020 8588 4000. Fax: 020 8588 4001
(M, L)

HMYOI WARREN HILL
Grove Road, Hollesley, Woodbridge, Suffolk IP12 3BF
Tel: 01394 633400. Fax: 01394 633401
(CL, C, M)

HMP WAYLAND
Griston, Thetford, Norfolk IP25 6RL
Tel: 01953 804100. Fax: 01953 804220
(M, C, CL)

HMP WEALSTUN
Church Causeway, Thorp Arch, Wetherby, West Yorkshire LS23 7AZ
Tel: 01937 444400. Fax: 01937 444401
(M, C, CL, D, O)

HMYOI WERRINGTON
Ash Bank Road, Stoke-on-Trent, Staffordshire ST9 0DX
Tel: 01782 463300. Fax: 01782 463301
(J)

HMYOI WETHERBY
York Road, Wetherby, West Yorkshire LS22 5ED
Tel: 01937 544200. Fax: 01937 544201
(J, CL)

HMP WHATTON
New Lane, Whatton, Nottinghamshire NG13 9FQ
Tel: 01949 803200. Fax: 01949 803201
(M, C, CL)

HMP WHITEMOOR
Longhill Road, March, Cambridgeshire PE15 0PR
Tel: 01354 602350. Fax: 01354 602351
(M, A)

HMP WINCHESTER
Romsey Road, Winchester, Hampshire SO22 5DF
Tel: 01962 723000. Fax: 01962 723001
(M, B, L)

HMP WOODHILL
Tattenhoe Street, Milton Keynes, Buckinghamshire MK4 4DA
Tel: 01908 722000. Fax: 01908 867063
(M, A, L)

HMP WORMWOOD SCRUBS
PO Box 757, Du Cane Road, London W12 0AE
Tel: 020 8588 3200. Fax: 020 8588 3201
(M, L)

HMP WYMOTT
Ulnes Walton Lane, Leyland, Preston, Lancashire PR26 8LW
Tel: 01772 442000. Fax: 01772 442001

HIGH SECURITY PSYCHIATRIC HOSPITALS

ASHWORTH
Ashworth Hospital, Parkbourn, Maghull, Liverpool L31 1HW
Tel: 0151 473 0303

BROADMOOR
Broadmoor Hospital, Crowthorne, Berkshire RG11 7EG
Tel: 01344 773111

RAMPTON
Rampton Hospital, Retford, Nottinghamshire DN22 0PD
Tel: 01777 248321

NORTHERN IRELAND

HEADQUARTERS ESTABLISHMENTS

HEADQUARTERS
Prison Service Headquarters, Dundonald House, Upper Newtownards Road, Belfast BT4 3SU
Tel: 028 9186 3028/3063
Email: info@niprisonservice.gov.uk
Website: www.dojni.gov.uk/index/ni-prison-service.htm

PRISON SERVICE COLLEGE
Woburn House, Millisle, Co. Down BT22 2HS
Tel: 028 9186 3000. Fax: 028 9186 3022

PRISONS

MAGHABERRY
Old Road, Ballinderry Upper, Lisburn, Co. Antrim BT28 2PT
Tel: 028 9261 1888. Fax: 028 9261 9516

MAGILLIGAN
Point Road, Limavady, Co. Londonderry BT49 0LR
Tel: 028 7776 3311. Fax: 028 7772 0307

YOUNG OFFENDERS CENTRE AND PRISON

HYDEBANK WOOD
Hospital Road, Belfast BT8 8NA
Tel: 028 9025 3666. Fax: 028 9025 3668

SCOTLAND

SCOTTISH PRISON SERVICE HEADQUARTERS

HEADQUARTERS
Calton House, 5 Redheughs Rigg, Edinburgh EH12 9HW
Tel: 0131 244 8745
Email: gaolinfo@sps.pnn.gov.uk
Website: www.sps.gov.uk

PRISON SERVICE COLLEGE

SCOTTISH PRISON SERVICE COLLEGE
Head of College, Scottish Prison Service College, Newlands Road, Brightons, Falkirk, Stirlingshire
FK2 0DE
Tel: 01324 710400. Fax: 01324 710401

PRISONS

HMP ABERDEEN
Craiginches, 4 Grampian Place, Aberdeen AB11 8FN
Tel: 01224 238300. Fax: 01224 896209

HMP ADDIEWELL (SODEXO JUSTICE SERVICES)
9 Station Road, Addiewell, West Lothian EH55 8QF
Tel: 01506 874500. Fax: 01506 874501

HMP BARLINNIE
81 Lee Avenue, Glasgow G33 2QX
Tel: 0141 770 2000. Fax: 0141 770 2060

HMP OPEN ESTATE – CASTLE HUNTLY
Open Estate – Castle Huntly, Longforgan, Nr Dundee DD2 5HL
Tel: 01382 319333. Fax: 01382 319350

HMP/HMYOI CORNTON VALE
Cornton Road, Stirling FK9 5NU
Tel: 01786 832591. Fax: 01786 833597

HMP DUMFRIES
Terregles Street, Dumfries DG2 9AX
Tel: 01387 261218. Fax: 01387 264144

HMP EDINBURGH
33 Stenhouse Road, Edinburgh EH11 3LN
Tel: 0131 444 3000. Fax: 0131 444 3045

HMP GLENOCHIL
King O'Muir Road, Tullibody, Clackmannanshire FK10 3AD
Tel: 01259 760471. Fax: 01259 762003

HMP GREENOCK
Gateside, Greenock, Renfrewshire PA16 9AH
Tel: 01475 787801. Fax: 01475 783154

HMP INVERNESS
Duffy Drive, Inverness IV2 3HH
Tel: 01463 229000. Fax: 01463 229010

HMP KILMARNOCK (SERCO)
Mauchline Road, Kilmarnock KA1 5AA
Tel: 01563 548800. Fax: 01563 548845

HMP LOW MOSS
Crosshill Road, Bishopbriggs, Glasgow G64 2PZ
Tel: 0141 762 9500

HMP PERTH
3 Edinburgh Road, Perth PH2 8AT
Tel: 01738 458100. Fax: 01738 630545

HMP PETERHEAD
Peterhead, Aberdeenshire AB42 2YY
Tel: 01779 479101. Fax: 01779 470529

HMP SHOTTS
Shotts, Lanarkshire ML7 4LE
Tel: 01501 824000. Fax: 01501 824022

YOUNG OFFENDER INSTITUTIONS

HMYOI CORNTON VALE
Cornton Road, Stirling FK9 5NU
Tel: 01786 832591. Fax: 01786 833597

HMYOI POLMONT
Brightons, Falkirk, Stirlingshire FK2 0AB
Tel: 01324 711558. Fax: 01324 714919

STATE HOSPITAL

STATE HOSPITAL
Carstairs, Lanark ML11 8RP
Tel: 01555 840293
Fax: 01555 840024
Email: tsh.info@nhs.net
Website: www.tsh.scot.nhs.uk

INDEX TO PENAL ESTABLISHMENTS